UNLEASH HELL

The publishers would like to thank the team at IPC Media Ltd and DC Comics for their help in compiling this book, particularly David Abbott and Linda Lee.

Published in 2007 by Prion
An imprint of the Carlton Publishing Group
20 Mortimer Street
London W1T 3JW

A catalogue record for this book is available from the British Library.

ISBN 978-1-85375-629-0

Printed and bound in Slovenia
10 9 8 7 6 5 4 3 2 1

UNLEASH HELL

12 OF THE BEST WAR PICTURE LIBRARY COMIC BOOKS EVER!

GENERAL EDITOR:
STEVE HOLLAND

WAR PICTURE LIBRARY Nº 4
10D
FIGHT BACK TO DUNKIRK
DUNKERQUE
WAR PICTURE LIBRARY Nº 56
1/-
THE CROWDED SKY
WAR PICTURE LIBRARY Nº 3
10D
ACTION STATIONS
WAR PICTURE LIBRARY Nº 54
1/-
UMBRELLA IN THE SKY
WAR PICTURE LIBRARY Nº 53
1/-
CRASH CALL
WAR PICTURE LIBRARY Nº 25
1/-
THE IRON FIST
WAR PICTURE LIBRARY Nº 36
1/-
LONE COMMANDO
WAR PICTURE LIBRARY Nº 141
1/-
THE BLACK ACE
WAR PICTURE LIBRARY Nº 52
1/-
AIR COMMANDO
WAR PICTURE LIBRARY Nº 129
1/-
FIRE POWER
WAR PICTURE LIBRARY Nº 7
10D
The RED DEVILS
WAR PICTURE LIBRARY Nº 66
1/-
TASK FORCE

CONTENTS

INTRODUCTION

In 1958 Fleetway Publications let slip the dogs of war and unleashed a phenomenon. Britain's busiest comic-book publisher was looking for new ways to part youngsters from their pocket money. One of the best they had found was the pocket library – those 64-page, complete comic-strip stories that had first appeared in 1950 when an editor found that the only printing machine available to print his new comic was the one used to produce the romance and crime libraries. The result, *Cowboy Comics,* was a comic about the size of a paperback and slim enough to slip into your jacket pocket during school lessons, just waiting for the moment you ran into the playground for morning break. The new title in this format was *War Picture Library:* thrilling, complete adventures of daring from the battlefields of a war which the parents of most children had actually experienced.

And we loved them! When I was buying *War Picture Library* they cost a shilling (5p) each, which was a hefty chunk of my pocket money. But war libraries were like currency: once you'd finished the one you'd bought, you could swap it for one you hadn't read, then swap that one for another and so on. This was a practical necessity because at its peak *War Picture Library* was publishing 12 titles a month, and nobody I knew had *that* kind of pocket money.

There were several men behind the launch of *War Picture Library.* Editor, Alf Wallace, had been with the firm for around 20 years, rising from the ranks of sub-editor on titles like *Radio Fun* and *Comet.* Staff writer Val Holding, until 1957 to be found walking the floors of Gamages department store in London, added his first-hand knowledge of serving with the Parachute Regiment to the team, which also included ex-Fleet Air Arm pilot Trevor Newton who was responsible for the design of the new books. They were soon joined by sub-editor Ted Bensberg, a Sergeant with the Royal Signals during the war. Bensberg took over the editorial hot seat in 1961 and was to guide the success of *War Picture Library*, and its companion

Battle Picture Library, for a further 23 years.

The writers – ranging from Norman Worker, who spent his war years with the Royal Armoured Corps, to Colin Thomas, a colonel with the Ghurkha regiment in the Far East – brought their experiences to the page, which added a level of authenticity not often found in modern war stories. The artists were commissioned from across Europe, but particularly Italy, where Nevio Zeccara and Gino D'Antonio set the standard for the many artists who followed. And who can forget the extraordinary talents of artists like Giorgio De Gaspari, Nino Caroselli and Allessandro Biffignandi whose artwork graced the covers of *War Picture Library,* capturing, in a single image, the pain and the glory that every Tommy endured to bring victory to the Allies in those dark years.

These men, the editors, artists and writers, shaped the way generations of youngsters remembered the heroics of their fathers and grandfathers. We salute you!

Steve Holland

FIGHT BACK TO DUNKIRK
AT DAWN ON MAY 10TH., 1940, THE GREY-CLAD HORDES OF NAZI GERMANY SWARMED OVER THE FRONTIERS OF HOLLAND, BELGIUM AND LUXEMBOURG, AND THE FINAL BID FOR THE CONQUEST OF EUROPE BY THE POWER-CRAZED ADOLF HITLER HAD COMMENCED!
ONE HUNDRED HIGHLY-TRAINED GERMAN DIVISIONS WERE HURLED AT THE GALLANT DEFENDERS, AND IT NEEDED MORE THAN BRAVE HEARTS AND COURAGE TO WITHSTAND THE STEEL-CLAD MIGHT OF THE INVADERS...

Chapter 1. THE GRIM DEFENCE
THE GERMAN ARMY ROARED UNCHECKED THROUGH BELGIUM... AND THE BRITISH EXPEDITIONARY FORCE WAS HURRIEDLY ORDERED TO ADVANCE. A DESPERATE STRUGGLE ENSUED AGAINST THE OVERWHELMING MIGHT OF THE ENEMY AROUND THE TOWN OF LOUVAIN, ON THE RIVER DYLE....
NUMBER TWO AND THREE PLATOONS PREPARE TO WITHDRAW TO THE NEXT STREET. NUMBER ONE PLATOON WILL ACT AS REARGUARD. CEASE FIRE ON THE MORTAR!
IT'S ENOUGH TO MAKE YOU WEEP, NOBBY! WE'VE HIT ONE OF THOSE TANKS TWICE... AND THE BOMBS BOUNCED OFF LIKE PEAS!

TWO PLATOONS OF THE FORWARD COMPANY OF THE WESSEX REGIMENT PULLED BACK FROM THE BOMBED AND SHATTERED HOUSES. LEAVING LIEUTENANT HOWARD AND HIS MEN TO COVER THEIR WITHDRAWAL.
MY LEG! MY LEG! I'VE BEEN HIT!
OKAY, JIM... HANG ON TO ME. I'LL GET YOU OUT.

THE GERMANS HAD BROUGHT HEAVY GUNS INTO POSITION ON THE FAR SIDE OF THE RIVER AND A SAVAGE RAIN OF SHELLS WHINED AND EXPLODED AROUND THE COURAGEOUS PLATOON. LIEUTENANT HOWARD, A YOUNG FRESH-FACED OFFICER, CROUCHED BY THE FIELD TELEPHONE WITH HIS SERGEANT, DAVE GREEN, BESIDE HIM...
WE CAN'T HOLD OUT MUCH LONGER, SERGEANT. AS SOON AS CAPTAIN ANDERSON IS CLEAR, WE'LL HAVE TO PULL OUT!
IT'S DARNED TOUGH, SIR! ONCE THOSE HUNS GET ACROSS THE RIVER, THEY'LL BE ALL OVER US LIKE A SWARM OF HORNETS!

DAVE GREEN CREPT FORWARD WITH HIS BREN GUN TO GET A BETTER VIEW OF THE ENEMY. THEN A WHOLE SALVO OF SHELLS SMASHED INTO THE RUINS ... AND THE OFFICER AND SIX OF THE MEN COLLAPSED, WOUNDED.
AAAAGH!
BY GLORY! THE LIEUTENANT'S COPPED A PACKET. STRETCHER BEARERS!

SERGEANT GREEN INSTANTLY TOOK COMMAND AND ORGANISED A PARTY OF MEN TO TAKE THE WOUNDED BACK. WHEN HE PICKED UP THE TELEPHONE, HE SAW THAT IT WAS SMASHED... NO FURTHER ORDERS COULD REACH THEM BY THAT MEANS!
GET THOSE MEN BACK TO THE FIRST AID POST AND TELL CAPTAIN ANDERSON THE REST OF US WILL BE COMING BACK WITHIN HALF AN HOUR. I'LL HOLD ON AS LONG AS POSSIBLE.
RIGHT, SARGE. GOOD LUCK!
STUKAS! LOOK OUT! THEY'RE GOING TO DIVE BOMB US!

IN A FIENDISH CHORUS OF SCREAMING WHINES, THE GERMAN DIVE BOMBERS HURTLED DOWN ON THE EDGE OF THE TOWN ...... AND A SHOWER OF DEATH-DEALING BOMBS WAS UNLEASHED ON THE BATTERED BRITISH POSITIONS ...

DAVE GREEN SAW THE BOMBS FALLING AND YELLED TO HIS HANDFUL OF MEN TO TAKE WHAT COVER THEY COULD... THEN HE DIVED INTO THE NEAREST SHELL HOLE, STILL CLUTCHING HIS BREN GUN.
PHEW! THIS IS GETTING TOO HOT FOR COMFORT!

ONE OF THE BOMBS EXPLODED JUST BEYOND THE SHELL HOLE WITH A SHATTERING ROAR. DAVE WAS PICKED UP LIKE A RAG DOLL AND FLUNG BACK...

THEIR MISSION COMPLETED, THE STUKAS CLIMBED UP INTO THE SKY AND ROARED OFF EASTWARDS... TEN MINUTES PASSED BEFORE DAVE GREEN RAISED HIS ACHING HEAD AND GOT GROGGILY TO HIS FEET. AS HE PULLED HIMSELF OUT OF THE SHELL HOLE, HE SAW THE GERMANS WERE ADVANCING...
THEY'RE OVER! NOTHING CAN STOP THOSE HUNS TAKING LOUVAIN NOW NOTHING...

BITTER TEARS OF RAGE WELLED UP IN DAVE'S EYES. HE BRUSHED THEM ASIDE WITH A GRIMY HAND, THEN SEIZED HIS BREN GUN AND BEGAN FIRING STEADILY AT THE GERMANS CROSSING THE BRIDGE.

THIS IS THE LAST MAGAZINE ... BUT EVERY ROUND IS GOING TO FIND ITS MARK!

BUT TO HIS DISMAY, DAVE FOUND THAT THE ENEMY TROOPS HAD SENT ANOTHER SWIFT-MOVING COLUMN ROUND ON A FLANK... OF THE REGIMENT THERE WAS NO SIGN. THE WESSEX SERGEANT WAS CUT OFF! ALL THAT MORNING HE HID IN THE RUINS OF A BOMBED-OUT HOUSE, WATCHING THE GERMANS MOVING INTO LOUVAIN...

WEARY AND HUNGRY, DAVE LAY HIDDEN, WAITING HIS CHANCE TO ESCAPE.. IT WAS AROUND FOUR O'CLOCK WHEN A GERMAN DESPATCH RIDER SKIDDED TO A HALT OUTSIDE THE WRECKED BUILDING...
WHERE IS THE DIVISIONAL HEADQUARTERS? I CAN FIND NOBODY IN THIS MESS.
YOU'VE COME PAST IT. THEY'VE SET UP THEIR H.Q. IN THE UNIVERSITY, A MILE BACK DOWN THERE...
W.K. 3774

THE DESPATCH RIDER SPRAWLED IN THE MUD, GASPING. DAVE YANKED THE HEAVY BIKE ROUND, LEAPED ASTRIDE IT AND KICKED IT INTO GEAR. THE GERMAN PULLED OUT HIS MAUSER AND FIRED WILDLY AS THE BIKE WENT ROARING DOWN THE WRECKED STREET...

THANK HEAVENS THE JERRIES USE GOOD BIKES! WITH A BIT OF LUCK AND A FAIR WIND, I'LL GET RIGHT THROUGH THE TOWN AND OUT THE OTHER SIDE BEFORE ANYBODY CAN STOP ME!

THE BACK TYRE OF THE MOTOR BIKE WAS SHOT TO RIBBONS AND DAVE WAS CATAPULTED OVER THE HANDLEBARS...

THE BULLETS PINGED ON THE ROAD ALL ROUND THE HALF-WINDED SERGEANT. HE HEARD THE CLATTER OF BOOTS AND THE HARSH YELLS OF THE GERMANS ...WITH A MIGHTY EFFORT OF WILL-POWER, DAVE FORCED HIMSELF TO HIS FEET... AND RAN!
I...I'LL BEAT YOU YET, YOU SQUAREHEADED HUNS!

DODGING AND TWISTING LIKE A HARE, DAVE FINALLY GAVE THE GERMANS THE SLIP. HE CAME TO A THICK COPSE ON THE NORTH OF LOUVAIN AND FORCED HIS WAY THROUGH THE UNDERGROWTH. FOR THE TIME BEING HE WAS SAFE... HE SANK DOWN UNDER A BUSH.
BY GOLLY! I CAN'T RUN ANOTHER STEP. IT'LL BE DARK SOON... I'LL STAY HERE THE NIGHT AND PUSH ON EARLY TOMORROW. IT'S NO GOOD BLUNDERING AROUND IN THE DARK.

COMPLETELY EXHAUSTED AFTER HIS LONG RUN, DAVE SANK INTO A DEEP, DEEP SLEEP... HE WAS AWAKENED SOON AFTER DAWN BY A ROARING CRASH, FOLLOWED BY THREE MORE IN QUICK SUCCESSION. HE STAGGERED TO HIS FEET AS HE REALISED WHAT WAS HAPPENING..
THE WOODS BEING SHELLED...WHETHER BY THE JERRIES OR OUR BLOKES, I DON'T KNOW... EITHER WAY, IT'S SUICIDE TO STOP HERE!

HE RAN THROUGH THE WOOD AS MORE SHELLS EXPLODED AROUND HIM AND CAME OUT ON THE FAR SIDE TO SEE A SMALL VILLAGE IN A HOLLOW. ABOVE IT WAS A BRICK WORKS AND THE SERGEANT SAW THE FLASH OF A GUN AS IT FIRED...
MEDIUM GUNS... AND OURS! THEY MUST BE A REARGUARD OF GUNNERS. SO OUR CHAPS CAN'T BE FAR AWAY... I'M IN LUCK!

SUDDENLY, THERE WAS A RUSHING ROAR LIKE AN EXPRESS TRAIN IN THE AIR ABOVE THE SERGEANT...THEN THE EARTH SHOOK AND THE BRICKWORKS OPPOSITE WAS HIDDEN BEHIND A CURTAIN OF FLAME AND SMOKE...

A GERMAN HEAVY GUN HAD SCORED A DIRECT HIT ON THE BRITISH GUNNERS AND AS THE SMOKE AND DUST SWIRLED UP IN THE WARM SPRING SUNSHINE, THE EERIE SILENCE THAT FOLLOWED WAS BROKEN BY A BLACKBIRD SINGING HIS FULL-THROATED SONG IN A NEARBY TREE. DAVE SHIVERED . . .
I MUST GET UP THERE AND SEE WHAT I CAN DO TO HELP THOSE POOR CHAPS. THEY BOUGHT A REAL PACKET! THE JERRIES MUST HAVE GOT THEIR BIG GUNS UP ALREADY!

THE ARTILLERY POSITION WAS A SCENE OF TERRIBLE CONFUSION. ONLY ONE GUN APPEARED UNDAMAGED... BUT THERE WAS NOT A SIGN OF HUMAN LIFE TO BE SEEN ANYWHERE IN THE BRICKWORKS!
HEY! CAN ANYBODY HEAR ME?

THEN, FROM BENEATH A PILE OF STRAW AT ONE SIDE, A SMALL SCARED FACE EMERGED WITH TWO ROUND STARING EYES. THE FACE WAS TOPPED BY A MASS OF FAIR, CURLY HAIR...
I'M 'ERE! WHO'S CALLING?

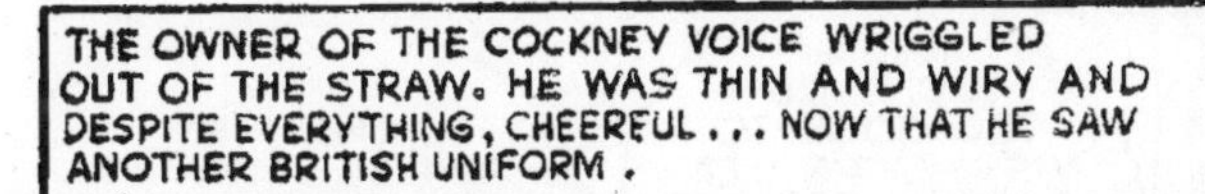
THE OWNER OF THE COCKNEY VOICE WRIGGLED OUT OF THE STRAW. HE WAS THIN AND WIRY AND DESPITE EVERYTHING, CHEERFUL ... NOW THAT HE SAW ANOTHER BRITISH UNIFORM.

WOTCHER, SARGE! LUMMY, I THOUGHT THE JERRIES WERE HERE FOR A SECOND! THEY CERTAINLY PASTED THE GUNS GOOD AND HARD JUST NOW. I'M STEVE CANNON, 512TH MEDIUM REGIMENT!
I'M DAVE GREEN, WESSEX REGIMENT... WHAT'S LEFT OF IT. THEY SEEM TO HAVE VANISHED INTO THIN AIR...THE ONLY SOLDIERS I'VE SEEN FOR THE PAST TWENTY-FOUR HOURS HAVE BEEN JERRIES. COME ON ....LET'S SEE IF ANY OF YOUR CHAPS SURVIVED THE SHELLING

THE COCKNEY GUNNER THREW BACK HIS HEAD AND LAUGHED...
I SHOULDN'T BOTHER...THERE'S NOBODY HERE BUT ME. I'M THE MAJOR'S BATMAN. I WAS OUT FORAGING FOR A CHICKEN LAST NIGHT; WHEN I CAME BACK, EVERYBODY HAD GONE. MOST OF THE GUNS WERE OUT OF ACTION. BUT I FOUND ONE OF THEM STILL WORKED, SO I THOUGHT I'D BETTER USE UP THE AMMO FIRST!

I JOINED THE ARTILLERY 'COS OF ME NAME... GUNNER CANNON, SEE? ALWAYS GOOD FOR A LAUGH! BUT I GOT MORE THAN I BARGAINED FOR WHEN THOSE JERRIES PLASTERED ME. LOOKS LIKE THE OLD GUN'S HAD IT!
YOU NEARLY BLEW ME TO BITS! ANYWAY, LET'S GET MOVING. THE SQUAREHEADS HAVE TAKEN LOUVAIN AND CAN'T BE FAR OFF. THE VILLAGE LOOKED AS IF IT WAS DESERTED. I SUPPOSE THOSE POOR FOLKS HAVE DONE A BUNK.

AS THE INFANTRY SERGEANT LOOKED DOWN THE HILL, HE SUDDENLY SAW A LINE OF LORRIES FILLED WITH GERMAN INFANTRYMEN SNAKING DOWN THE LANE TOWARDS THE BELGIAN VILLAGE.
HERE'S A CHANCE TOO GOOD TO MISS! LET'S GET THE GUN ON ITS WHEELS AND SEE IF IT WILL STILL FIRE.
OKAY! I OWE THEM JERRIES SOMETHING. THERE'S A FEW SHELLS LEFT AND THE GUN MAY NOT BE AS BAD AS IT LOOKS.

THEY STRAINED WITH ALL THEIR STRENGTH AND MANAGED TO GET THE GUN UPRIGHT. A QUICK EXAMINATION SHOWED IT WAS STILL IN WORKING ORDER. THEY SWUNG THE MUZZLE ROUND AND AIMED IT DOWN TOWARDS THE LANE. THE GUN WAS QUICKLY LOADED WITH SHELL AND CHARGE, AND THE LITTLE GUNNER PULLED THE LANYARD...
AND THE BEST OF BRITISH LUCK, JERRIES! FIRE!

AGAIN AND AGAIN THEY FIRED POURING SHELL AFTER SHELL INTO THE GERMANS, WHO PULLED UP IN CONFUSION. FOUR LORRIES BURST INTO FLAMES AND GREASY BLACK SMOKE CURLED UP INTO THE SKY ABOVE THE VALLEY...
ACHTUNG! THE GUNS IN THE BRICKWORKS ARE STILL FIRING! WE ARE PINNED DOWN AND CAN'T MOVE. RANGE ON THEM AGAIN WITH THE HEAVY GUNS. HURRY!

WITHIN A FEW MINUTES, HIGH EXPLOSIVE SHELLS BEGAN TO BURST WITH SAVAGE FURY AROUND THE BATTERY POSITION AND THE AIR WAS FILLED WITH JAGGED LUMPS OF LETHAL STEEL. SERGEANT GREEN AND THE LITTLE GUNNER KNEW THEY COULD NOT SURVIVE THAT CONCENTRATION OF FIRE FOR LONG...
QUICK... I SAW A BOX OF GRENADES BEHIND THE BIG BRICK STACK. GET ONE AND SHOVE IT DOWN THE BARREL. THIS IS THE LAST ROUND... AND WE'RE NOT GOING TO LEAVE THE GUN FOR THE JERRIES.
RIGHT, SARGE. HALF-A-TICK!

THEY LOADED THE GUN WITH THE LAST ROUND SLIPPED A GRENADE DOWN THE BARREL AND THEN BLOCKED IT WITH A HANDFUL OF MUD. DAVE TIED A LONG PIECE OF ROPE TO THE LANYARD, THEN THEY BOTH RACED BACK TO THE COVER OF THE NEAREST PILE OF BRICKS. STEVE HEAVED ON THE ROPE . . . .

AS THE ECHOES OF THE TREMENDOUS ROAR DIED AWAY, DAVE GREEN PULLED STEVE'S ARM AND THEY BOTH LEAPED UP AND RAN . . .
LET'S GO, PAL. WE'VE OUTSTAYED OUR WELCOME!
YEAH! BUT I RECKON WE'VE HELD UP THAT COLUMN FOR QUITE A WHILE. NICE GOING, SARGE!

Chapter 2. THE GERMAN PATROL
SERGEANT GREEN KNEW THE WAY TO THE COAST LAY TO THE WEST AND THEY WOULD HAVE TO CROSS FIVE RIVERS . . . EACH ONE A MAJOR OBSTACLE. THE SOUNDS OF DISTANT FIRING RUMBLED ALL ROUND THEM, BUT THEY REACHED THE RIVER SENNE WITHOUT MEETING ANY TROOPS, GERMAN OR BRITISH.
WE'RE LUCKY TO FIND THIS BRIDGE STILL STANDING. SOMETHING MUST HAVE PREVENTED OUR BOYS FROM BLOWING IT UP WHEN THEY PULLED BACK!
WELL, SOMEBODY'S HAD A GOOD GO AT BASHING IT! I WOULDN'T LIKE TO TRY AND DRIVE A TRUCK ACROSS!

THE ROAD ON THE OTHER SIDE WAS CHOKED BY A LONG COLUMN OF BURNED-OUT AND WRECKED LORRIES... SILENT EVIDENCE OF A RUTHLESS ATTACK BY GERMAN DIVE BOMBERS.
COR LUMMY! JUST LOOK AT THIS LOT! THE BLOKES IN THESE TRUCKS MUST HAVE HAD A ROUGH TIME, SARGE!
THE JERRIES CAUGHT THEM JUST AS THEY GOT OVER THE BRIDGE. POOR DEVILS! THE SURVIVORS MUST HAVE ABANDONED THE TRUCKS AND GONE ON FOOT.
27

TWICE THAT DAY THEY WERE FORCED TO TAKE COVER IN WOODS TO AVOID COLUMNS OF GERMAN TANKS WHICH CAME ROARING UP FROM BEHIND THEM. THE ENEMY TROOPS SEEMED TO BE EVERYWHERE. IT WAS EARLY EVENING WHEN SERGEANT GREEN AND STEVE CANNON CAME TO THE NEXT RIVER, THE DENDRE... AND FOUND THE BRIDGE BROKEN AND TWISTED...
WE'RE OUT OF LUCK HERE, STEVE. WE'LL HAVE TO TRY AND FIND SOMETHING TO MAKE A RAFT TO GET ACROSS.
LOOK... THERE'S A HUT IN THAT GARDEN. HOW ABOUT USING SOME OF ITS TIMBERS, SARGE?

QUICKLY THEY RIPPED THE WOODEN TOOLSHED APART PULLED A SECTION DOWN TO THE WATER'S EDGE AND STEPPED GINGERLY ON TO IT...
WHOOPS! STEADY, SARGE... OR YOU'LL MAKE ME SEASICK. I NEVER WAS MUCH OF A SAILOR. EVERY TIME I HEAR THE TUNE, A LIFE ON THE OCEAN WAVE, IT MAKES ME TURN GREEN!
YOU JUST STAY STILL AND BE QUIET! WE'LL GET ACROSS ... UNLESS ANY JERRIES SPOT US!

BUT THEY REACHED THE OTHER SIDE OF THE RIVER SAFELY. THE SMALL, SHELL-TORN VILLAGE A MILE FURTHER ON WAS DESERTED, SILENT AND EERIE. THE ONLY SOUND CAME FROM THE CRUNCHING OF THEIR BOOTS ON THE ROAD.
IT'S SURPRISED ME THAT WE COULD HAVE GOT SO FAR AND NOT MET ANYONE. EVERYBODY MUST HAVE FLED AS SOON AS OUR TROOPS STARTED MOVING BACK.
I ONLY HOPE THEY DIDN'T TAKE ALL THEIR GRUB WITH 'EM. I COULD EAT MY BOOTLACES, I'M SO HUNGRY. HOW ABOUT LOOKING FOR SOMETHING, SARGE?

THERE WAS A FARM AT THE END OF THE VILLAGE AND SEVERAL COWS WERE IN THE YARD. CHICKENS SCRATCHED IN THE HOT DUST, SEARCHING FOR GRAINS OF FOOD. THE COCKNEY GUNNER'S EYES LIT UP AND HE SMACKED HIS LIPS WHEN HE SAW THEM....
LOVELY GRUB! I DON'T KNOW WHICH CAME FIRST, THE CHICKEN OR THE EGG... BUT IF THEM HENS HAS LAID ANY, WE'RE GOING TO EAT, DAVE. COME ON!
ALL RIGHT... YOU SEARCH AROUND FOR EGGS. I KNOW SOMETHING ABOUT MILKING. AS LONG AS THOSE COWS AREN'T TOO FIERCE, WE'LL HAVE SOME MILK AS WELL!

TWENTY MINUTES LATER, THEY WERE BOTH SITTING DOWN IN THE FARMHOUSE TO A HUGE PLATE OF FRIED EGGS WASHED DOWN BY DRAUGHTS OF RICH, CREAMY MILK. STEVE CANNON SIGHED HAPPILY...
HEIGH-HO! MY MA ALWAYS TOLD ME THE MILK WE GOT IN BOTTLES AT HOME WAS NOTHING LIKE THE REAL STUFF. NOW I KNOW! BUT HOW DID YOU GET THEM GREAT BRUTES OF COWS TO PART WITH IT?
AH! THAT'S A TRADE SECRET, MY TOWNY FRIEND! BUT IT CERTAINLY IS GOOD!

THEY STAYED THE NIGHT IN THE FARMHOUSE AND SET OFF AGAIN NEXT MORNING. BY THIS TIME THE LITTLE GUNNER'S FEET WERE COVERED WITH BLISTERS AND HE LIMPED ALONG PAINFULLY. THEN ABRUPTLY, THEY HEARD THE RUMBLE OF HEAVY VEHICLES BEHIND THEM... IN A FLASH, THE SERGEANT PULLED STEVE OFF THE ROAD INTO A DITCH.....
DOWN! JERRIES!

THE LONG CONVOY OF GERMAN TRUCKS ROARED PAST THEM AS THEY CROUCHED IN THE DITCH, HOLDING THEIR BREATH.

THE LORRIES THUNDERED ON... THE TWO ENGLISHMEN LAY MOTIONLESS FOR A FEW MINUTES BEFORE GETTING TO THEIR FEET, CHOKING AND GASPING... BUT GRINNING THEIR RELIEF.
BLOOMIN' SQUAREHEADS! JUST LOOK AT MY BATTLE-DRESS. AND TO THINK I USED TO BE THE SMARTEST BLOKE IN THE BATTERY!

THEY LEFT THE ROAD THEN AND WENT ACROSS COUNTRY. THE NEXT RIVER THEY CAME TO WAS THE SHELDE, AND HERE AGAIN THE BRIDGES WERE DOWN. THEY SEARCHED IN VAIN FOR SOME MEANS OF CROSSING, BUT FINALLY THEY WERE FORCED TO SWIM, PUSHING THEIR CLOTHES AND EQUIPMENT IN FRONT OF THEM IN A BOX THEY HAD FOUND.
BRR! IT'S AS COLD AS THE ARCTIC!
SWIFT RUNNING RIVER WATER ALWAYS IS COLD, STEVE. BUT KEEP GOING, YOU'RE DOING FINE! AT LEAST WE'RE KEEPING OUR CLOTHES DRY... I HOPE!

THE WESSEX SERGEANT DRAGGED HIS SHIVERING COMRADE ASHORE. THEY DRIED THEMSELVES WITH HANDFULS OF GRASS, DONNED THEIR CLOTHES AND MOVED OFF AGAIN. AT ABOUT NOON, THEY FOUND A SMALL COTTAGE ON THE EDGE OF A WOOD AND APPROACHED IT CAUTIOUSLY...
WONDER IF WE CAN GET ANY GRUB HERE, DAVE? I'M STARVING AGAIN!
WE CAN TRY... BUT WATCH OUT FOR ANY HUNS. WE DON'T KNOW WHERE THEY ARE.

AS THEY DREW NEARER, THEY HEARD THE LOW MURMUR OF VOICES. DAVE GREEN LOOKED CAREFULLY ROUND THE WINDOW...
BY GLORY! A JERRY PATROL! THEY'RE WRECKING THE PLACE...

THERE WAS A RIFLE LEANING AGAINST THE WALL JUST UNDER THE WINDOW. SLOWLY, WITH EVERY NERVE TENSED, DAVE REACHED IN AND TOOK HOLD OF THE BARREL....
ACH! THESE PEASANTS FEED WELL, HANS. IT WAS A GOOD IDEA OF YOURS TO SEARCH THIS PLACE BEFORE WE JOINED UP WITH THE OTHERS.

A FEW MOMENTS LATER, THE FRONT DOOR OF THE COTTAGE BURST INWARDS... AND THE GRIM FIGURE OF SERGEANT DAVE GREEN STOOD THERE, RIFLE IN HAND....
GET YOUR HANDS UP, YOU SQUAREHEADS! QUICK!
AAH! A BRITISHER! AND HE'S GOT MY RIFLE!

THE FELDWEBEL IN CHARGE OF THE PATROL MADE A GRAB FOR THE PISTOL AT HIS WAIST... DAVE FIRED AND THE ENEMY SOLDIER FELL BACK WITH A YELL, A BULLET IN HIS ARM...
NO, YOU DON'T...
AAAAAGH!

AT A CRISP COMMAND FROM DAVE, THE LITTLE GUNNER DASHED INTO THE ROOM. HE COLLECTED THE GERMANS' WEAPONS WHILE DAVE KEPT THEM IN LINE AGAINST THE WALL.
PILE THEIR ARMS IN A HEAP, STEVE. THEN WE'LL TAKE OUR PICK. THERE'S A WELL OUTSIDE... THE THINGS WE DON'T WANT CAN GO IN THERE. NIP INTO THE BEDROOM AND SEE IF YOU CAN FIND A SHEET... WE'LL USE THAT TO TIE UP THIS BUNCH.
OKAY, SARGE. LEAVE IT TO ME!

THE GERMANS WERE SOON BOUND HAND AND FOOT .. DAVE BANDAGED THE FELDWEBEL'S WOUNDED ARM AND THEN THE TWO TOMMIES HELPED THEMSELVES TO THE FOOD.
IT'LL BE A LONG WHILE BEFORE THESE HUNS ARE FOUND. AT LEAST WE'VE MANAGED TO PUT A FEW OF THEM OUT OF ACTION!
YEP! AND I'M GOING TO TAKE THAT MACHINE-PISTOL. I'LL FEEL MUCH HAPPIER WITH SOMETHING TO FIGHT BACK WITH. COR! THIS SAUSAGE IS GOOD!

DAVE TOOK THE FELDWEBEL'S MAUSER AND STEVE THE DEADLY MACHINE-PISTOL. AFTER HURLING THE REST OF THE GUNS DOWN THE WELL OUTSIDE, THEY LEFT THE FURIOUS GERMANS HELPLESS AND RAN.
LET'S GO! AND WOE BETIDE ANY HUNS WE BUMP INTO NOW!
WITH THIS LITTLE BABY IN MY MITTS, I CAN EVEN STAND THE BLOOMIN' BLISTERS ON MY FEET!

SEVERAL HOURS LATER, THEY SAW ANOTHER RIVER GLEAMING IN THE HOT SUNLIGHT AHEAD OF THEM ... AND A NARROW BRIDGE SPANNING OVER THE WATER, APPARENTLY INTACT!
LOOK... A BRIDGE...AND ALL IN ONE LUVERLY PIECE! COME ON, SARGE... WE WON'T GET OUR FEET WET THIS TIME.
IT MUST BE THE RIVER LYS. THEN THERE'S ONLY THE RIVER YSER IN FRONT OF US BEFORE WE HIT THE COAST.

AS THEY RACED DOWN THE HILL TO THE BRIDGE, DAVE SUDDENLY SAW A LONE FIGURE IN BATTLEDRESS BENDING OVER A SMALL BOX ON THE FAR SIDE OF THE RIVER ... THE SERGEANT GAVE A SHOUT OF ALARM...
HE'S GOING TO BLOW UP THE BRIDGE! THAT'S A DETONATING BOX HE'S BENDING OVER. HI! HI!

THE FIGURE BENDING OVER THE DETONATOR WAS A CORPORAL IN THE ROYAL ENGINEERS. HE SWUNG ROUND AND LOOKED UP AS HE HEARD THE SHOUTS AND THE POUNDING FEET ON THE BRIDGE....
OCH! TWO MORE OF OUR LADS!

THE TALL, RAWBONED SCOT STOOD UP AND WAITED FOR STEVE AND DAVE TO COME PANTING UP TO HIM....
PHEW! I THOUGHT YOU WERE JUST GOING TO BLOW UP THE BRIDGE, CORPORAL. WE DIDN'T FANCY SWIMMING ANOTHER RIVER. ARE YOU ALL ALONE?
AYE. BUT YE DINNA HAVE TO WORRY. I'VE GOT ANOTHER HOUR AFORE I SET OFF THE CHARGES. MY ORDERS ARE TO STAY HERE UNTIL FIFTEEN HUNDRED HOURS, SO ANY ODD LADDIES LIKE YOURSELVES CAN GET ACROSS!

THE CORPORAL TOLD THEM THAT PARTIES OF BOTH THEIR UNITS HAD CROSSED THE BRIDGE THE DAY BEFORE.
THEN WE'RE SOME WAY BEHIND OUR BLOKES. THERE'S A LOT OF JERRIES SWARMING AROUND BEHIND US, JOCK. I RECKON YOU OUGHT TO BLOW THE BRIDGE AT ANY TIME.
I HAE ME ORDERS. FIFTEEN HUNDRED HOURS AND NOT BEFORE. THEN I'M TO MAKE MY WAY TO THE YSER AND JOIN UP WITH MY COMPANY.

THE DOUR SCOTS CORPORAL WAS OBVIOUSLY NOT GOING TO TAKE ADVICE FROM SERGEANT GREEN! BUT DAVE KNEW THE ENEMY ARMOURED COLUMNS WERE NOT FAR OFF AND HE CLIMBED TO THE UPPER FLOOR OF A NEARBY BUILDING AND LOOKED OVER THE RIVER.
PANZERS! A MOB OF HEAVY TANKS, TOO! WE **GOT** TO STOP 'EM CROSSING THE RIVER. I'LL HAVE TO USE MY RANK ON THAT CORPORAL!

DAVE DASHED DOWN AND WENT RACING BACK TO JOCK NORTH AND STEVE....
THERE'S A WHOLE PANZER DIVISION COMING THIS WAY, MAKING STRAIGHT FOR THE BRIDGE! BLOW IT UP NOW, BEFORE THEY GET ACROSS! *QUICK, MAN! THAT'S AN ORDER!*
TANKS, EH? WELL, I DINNA TAKE ORDERS FROM NO FOOT-SLOGGING SERGEANT. BUT MAYBE THIS IS THE TIME TO USE WHAT THE OFFICERS CALL... *INITIATIVE!*

Chapter 3. A TRAP FOR THE NAZIS

WITH THE HARSH RUMBLING OF STEEL TRACKS AND THE DEEP-THROATED ROAR OF THEIR MIGHTY ENGINES, THE SPEARHEADS OF THE PANZER DIVISION NOSED STEADILY FORWARD TOWARDS THE BRIDGE ...

THE LEADER HALTED AT THE EDGE OF THE RIVER AND AN OFFICER IN THE BLACK LEATHER UNIFORM OF THE PANZERS, STOOD IN THE TURRET AND SEARCHED THE LENGTH OF THE BRIDGE FOR ANY SIGN OF OBSTACLES OR MINES....
ADVANCE! THE BRIDGE IS CLEAR... RADIO BACK TO HEADQUARTERS!

THE THREE SOLDIERS ON THE FAR SIDE OF THE BRIDGE CROUCHED DOWN BEHIND AN OVERTURNED CAR AND WAITED BREATHLESSLY. JOCK CROUCHED WITH HIS HANDS ON THE PLUNGER OF THE DETONATOR, AS DAVE WATCHED THE TANKS MOVING FORWARD.
CAN YE SEE THEM, SERGEANT?
SURE! THE FIRST ONE IS JUST CRAWLING ON TO THE BRIDGE. I'LL WAIT TILL THREE OF 'EM ARE ON, THEN I'LL GIVE YOU THE WORD.

SLOWLY, CAUTIOUSLY, THE HUGE TANKS CLANKED ON TO THE BRIDGE. BUT JOCK NORTH HAD DONE HIS JOB WELL... ALL THE EXPLOSIVE WAS PACKED UNDER THE BRIDGE AND NOTHING COULD BE SEEN FROM ABOVE...

SUDDENLY, DAVE RIPPED OUT ONE WORD....
NOW!

WHOOPING WITH DELIGHT, THE THREE BRITISHERS DANCED WITH JOY BEHIND THE OVERTURNED CAR ...
YIPEEE! WE'VE DONE IT! COR! TALK ABOUT BONFIRE NIGHT.. I AIN'T NEVER SEEN A BLOW-UP LIKE THAT BEFORE!
THREE OF EM IN THE DRINK! AND THE OTHERS WON'T GET ACROSS WITHOUT BUILDING A PONTOON BRIDGE. WELL DONE, JOCK!
AYE! IT WAS A GUID WEE BANG!

BUT THE TRIO WERE SEEN BY THE FURIOUS GERMANS IN THE SURVIVING TANKS ON THE FAR BANK... NEXT INSTANT, A SAVAGE HAIL OF SMALL ARMS FIRE AND H.E SHELLS SCREAMED OVER THE RIVER. DAVE GREEN GAVE A MOAN... AND SANK TO THE GROUND, BLOOD OOZING FROM A WOUND ON THE SIDE OF HIS HEAD.
UUURGH!
SARGE! DAVEY BOY! HE'S WOUNDED... QUICK, HELP ME GET HIM UNDER COVER, JOCK.

CORPORAL NORTH PICKED UP THE WOUNDED SERGEANT AND WITH STEVE FOLLOWING, HE RAN TOWARDS THE WAREHOUSE BEHIND THEM...

THEY REACHED THE WAREHOUSE SAFELY, BUT THE SHELLS WERE RIPPING THROUGH THE WALLS AS IF THEY WERE MADE OF PAPER SO DAVE GREEN, JOCK NORTH AND STEVE CANNON STAGGERED OUT OF THE BACK AND ACROSS A TRAIN DEPOT. THERE, IN A SHED, JOCK TENDED TO DAVE'S WOUND...
JOCK, LOOK! I'VE FOUND A BREN GUN AND SOME AMMO! NOW WE'VE REALLY GOT SOMETHING TO FIGHT BACK WITH!

THE SERGEANT'S WOUND WAS NOT SERIOUS
WHAT HAPPENED? OUCH! MY HEAD!
YOU COLLECTED A HUNK O' JERRY CANNON SHELL ON YOUR NAPPER, SARGE. BUT YOU MUST HAVE A THICK SKULL, 'COS IT ONLY SHAVED A BIT OF HAIR OFF!
OCH! YOU BLATHERING SASSENACH! IF IT HAD BEEN YOUR HEAD, IT WOULD HAVE DAMAGED THE SHELL SPLINTER!

THE TOUGH SERGEANT SOON FELT WELL ENOUGH TO STAND AND HE EXAMINED THE BREN GUN STEVE HAD DISCOVERED...
THIS IS QUITE A FIND, LADS. IF THERE'S ONE THING I KNOW HOW TO USE, IT'S A BREN! ALL WE WANT NOW IS SOME TRANSPORT TO GET US ON OUR WAY. I DON'T THINK I COULD WALK VERY FAR... MY HEAD'S GOT A TRIP HAMMER INSIDE IT!
LET'S SCOUT AROUND. WE MAY FIND SOMETHING OUTSIDE!

IN A SIDE STREET NEAR THE RAILWAY DEPOT, THEY FOUND AN ABANDONED BAKER'S TRUCK. THE TANK WAS FULL OF PETROL, BUT THE ENGINE REFUSED TO FIRE... UNTIL STEVE BURROWED INSIDE AND FOUND ONE OF THE LEADS FLAPPING LOOSE...
GOT IT! THERE AIN'T MUCH WRONG WITH THIS... APART FROM OLD AGE.
NICE WORK, STEVE!

STEVE FIXED THE LEAD AND THE ENGINE HUMMED INTO LIFE. WITH JOCK DRIVING, THEY SCORCHED THROUGH THE DESERTED STREETS, ALL GNAWING AT THE STALE FRENCH BREAD THEY HAD FOUND IN THE TRUCK...
HOME, JAMES, AND DON'T SPARE THE HORSES! IF WE GO ON AT THIS RATE, I'LL BE BACK HOME TUCKED UP IN MY NICE LITTLE BED BY TOMORROW!
DINNA COUNT YE CHICKENS BEFORE THEY'RE HATCHED. WE'VE GOT A LONG WAY TO GO YET, LADDIE.

THEY SPED ON FOR MILE AFTER MILE, KEEPING AWAY FROM THE MAIN ROADS, BUT ALWAYS WITH THE DISTANT SOUNDS OF BATTLE RUMBLING AROUND THEM. SUDDENLY, THEY ROARED ROUND A BEND AND CAME TO A CROSS-ROADS... AND STEVE GULPED AND POINTED...
OH, CORKS...LOOK! JERRIES!
3718

THERE WAS NO ROOM TO TURN AND GO BACK . . . JOCK STAMPED ON THE ACCELERATOR AND THE ANCIENT TRUCK BOUNDED ACROSS THE ROAD AND SHOT UP THE SIDE ROAD OPPOSITE. HARSH YELLS CAME FROM THE GERMANS AS THEY SAW THE THREE SOLDIERS.
ACHTUNG! BRITISHERS! STOP! YOU ARE OUR PRISONERS! YOU CANNOT ESCAPE!
THAT'S WHAT YOU THINK, MATE! WE'LL HAVE A BLOOMIN' GOOD TRY!

THE HARSH CHATTER OF THE MACHINE GUN WAS FOLLOWED BY A SWIFT ANSWER FROM THE WESSEX SERGEANT... SWINGING THE BREN GUN ROUND, HE POURED A WITHERING FIRE INTO THE MOTOR CYCLE COMBINATION AS IT CAME ROARING AFTER THEM...
HOLD THAT, SQUAREHEADS!
YAAAH!

THE GERMAN HALF-TRACKS BEHIND WERE FORCED TO STOP AS THE FALLEN CYCLE COMBINATION BLOCKED THE NARROW ROAD. THE ENEMY SOLDIERS FIRED WILDLY AFTER THE OLD BAKER'S TRUCK, WHICH CLATTERED OFF TRIUMPHANTLY ROUND THE WINDING ROAD...
YOU FOOLS! PULL THAT BIKE OUT OF THE WAY SO WE CAN GET AFTER THEM!

BUT BY THE TIME THE ROAD WAS CLEARED, DAVE AND HIS PALS WERE WELL AWAY, TWISTING AND DODGING DOWN THE NARROW LANES. SUDDENLY STEVE STOOD UP IN THE FRONT AND WAVED EXCITEDLY TOWARDS A ROAD SNAKING OVER A HILL AHEAD OF THEM....
LOOK! ONE OF OUR CONVOYS! WE'VE CAUGHT UP WITH SOME OF OUR BLOKES. STEP ON IT, JOCK!

THE BAKER'S TRUCK RATTLED AND SHOOK AS THE SCOTS CORPORAL FORCED IT ALONG AT BREAKNECK SPEED....
HEY! HEEEY! WAIT FOR US! WAIT FOR US!
SAVE YOUR BREATH. THEY'LL NO'HEAR YOU FROM THIS DISTANCE. WE'LL SOON CATCH 'EM UP.

BUT SUDDENLY THERE WAS A SINISTER WHINE FROM THE SKY...
A STUKA! IT'S GOING TO DIVE-BOMB THE CONVOY!

IN A FLASH, THE SERGEANT LIFTED THE HEAVY BREN GUN TO HIS SHOULDER, TOOK AIM... AND FIRED.
I'LL STOP THAT HUN, CURSE HIM! SLOW DOWN, JOCK... YOU'RE SPOILING MY AIM!

THE BULLETS TORE INTO THE DIVING PLANE...

DAVE GREEN HELD THE PLANE IN HIS SIGHTS AND FIRED HIS REMAINING ROUNDS.. WITH DEADLY ACCURACY!
BINGO! YOU'VE GOT HIM! HE'S ON FIRE!
3718

THE STUKA SEEMED TO HANG IN THE AIR FOR A MOMENT...THEN IT PLUNGED TO EARTH...

THE MIGHTY BLAST OF THE UNRELEASED BOMBS EXPLODING ON THE GERMAN PLANE HURLED THE OLD TRUCK ON ITS SIDE AND THE THREE SOLDIERS WERE FLUNG OUT . . .
OOOWW!

FOR A FEW SECONDS, THEY LAY WHERE THEY HAD FALLEN, HALF STUNNED. THEN DAVE STAGGERED TO HIS FEET, HIS HEAD THROBBING WITH INTOLERABLE PAIN...
AAAH! MY...MY HEAD...

THEN, ABOVE THE FIERCE ROAR OF THE BURNING PLANE, DAVE HEARD ANOTHER SOUND ALONG THE LANE...
QUICK! LET'S GET OUT OF HERE... HERE COME THE JERRIES IN THEIR HALF-TRACKS!

Chapter 4. THE PANZERS POUNCE
CAUTIOUSLY, THE HEAVY GERMAN HALF-TRACKS AND ARMOURED VEHICLES LUMBERED ROUND THE BEND IN THE LANE. THE MOMENT THE THREE SOLDIERS WERE SEEN, A MACHINE GUN OPENED UP ON THEM, CHATTERING HARSHLY....

SERGEANT GREEN SNATCHED UP THE BREN GUN AND SHOUTED TO THE OTHER TWO...THEY BURST THROUGH THE HEDGE AND WENT RACING ACROSS THE FIELD ON THE FAR SIDE..
COME ON, RUN FOR IT... ONCE WE'RE IN THAT DIP IN THE GROUND AHEAD, THEY WON'T BE ABLE TO HIT US!
COR! WHAT A CAPER! IF I GET THROUGH THIS LOT ALIVE, I RECKON I'M GOING IN FOR THE NEXT OLYMPIC GAMES!

BULLETS WHINED AND ZIPPED ROUND THEM LIKE ANGRY HORNETS AS THEY ZIG-ZAGGED ACROSS THE FIELD ...BUT NONE OF THEM WAS HIT. THEY THREW THEMSELVES INTO THE FOLD IN THE GROUND, CHESTS HEAVING....
I DINNA THINK YON SCUM WILL GIVE CHASE. THEY'RE AFTER BIGGER FISH, YOU KNOW... THE CONVOY!
YOU'RE RIGHT, JOCK. AND IF WE CUT STRAIGHT ACROSS THIS DIP, WE SHOULD JUST CATCH UP WITH THE TAIL END OF THE TRUCKS!

BENDING LOW, THEY RAN FOR IT. AS THEY GOT NEAR TO THE SLOW MOVING CONVOY, THEY SAW THE LAST LORRY WAS SOME WAY BEHIND THE OTHERS. SUDDENLY, THE LITTLE COCKNEY GUNNER GAVE A YELL...
HEY, LOOK, MATES! THAT BACK TRUCK'S GOT AN ANTI-TANK GUN IN TOW.
IF THEY'VE GOT ANY AMMO, THEY OUGHT TO HAVE A SMACK AT THE JERRIES... OTHERWISE THEY'RE GOING TO BE IN TROUBLE *WITH A CAPITAL 'T'!*

PANTING AND GASPING, THEY DRAGGED THEMSELVES UP THE SIDE OF THE HILL ON TO THE ROAD AND WAVED FRANTICALLY AT THE LORRY. THE BEGRIMED R.A.S.C. DRIVER CLAPPED ON HIS BRAKES...
DRIVER! HAVE YOU GOT ANY SHELLS FOR THAT GUN? IF THOSE JERRIES DOWN THERE AREN'T MADE TO DUCK THEIR HEADS, EVERY TRUCK IN THIS CONVOY IS GOING TO GET PLASTERED.
THERE'S THREE SHELLS IN A BOX IN THE BACK, CHUM. THAT'S ALL! AND I'VE GOT A CARGO OF WOMEN AND KIDS AND TWO WOUNDED OFFICERS. ONE OF THEM MADE ME BRING THE GUN... BUT HE'S UNCONSCIOUS NOW. I HAVEN'T A CLUE HOW TO FIRE IT!

ALL AT ONCE, GERMAN SHELLS SCREAMED THROUGH THE AIR AND BURST WITH SAVAGE EXPLOSIONS ON THE SMALL HILL...

CALLING TO STEVE AND JOCK TO FOLLOW HIM, DAVE GREEN RAN TO THE BACK OF THE LORRY AND THEY QUICKLY SLASHED THE ROPES HOLDING THE GUN. JOCK PULLED THE AMMUNITION BOX OUT OF THE BACK OF THE LORRY.
THERE'S SOME CLIPS OF THREE-O-THREE AMMO HERE TOO, SERGEANT... I'LL HAVE 'EM AS WELL.
FINE! THEY'LL DO FOR THE BREN. I'VE ONLY GOT ONE FULL MAGAZINE LEFT.

DAVE SHOUTED TO THE DRIVER TO GET AWAY, THEN STEVE, AS THE GUNNER OF THE PARTY, SWIFTLY LOADED THE ANTI-TANK GUN. THEY SWUNG IT ROUND, SIGHTING IT ON THE APPROACHING GERMAN PANZERS....
WE'VE ONLY GOT THREE SHOTS, STEVE... NOW'S YOUR CHANCE TO GET THREE BULLSEYES!
I'LL DO MY BEST. NEVER FIRED ONE OF THESE THINGS BEFORE... STEADY NOW. I'LL JUST SET THE RANGE...

A LINE OF GERMAN TANKS HAD COME INTO VIEW NOW AND IT WAS AT ONE OF THESE THAT STEVE AIMED... THE GUN FIRED WITH A COUGHING ROAR OF FLAME AND SMOKE!
...BUT THE SHOT WENT WIDE AND PLOUGHED A FURROW BETWEEN TWO TANKS!

STEVE GRUNTED AND THEY QUICKLY RELOADED...AGAIN THEY FIRED... AND THE ARMOUR-PIERCING SHELL SMASHED THROUGH THE WEAKEST PART OF ONE OF THE TANKS... BETWEEN THE HULL AND THE TURRET... LIKE A KNIFE THROUGH BUTTER!

AS THE TANK SLITHERED TO A STANDSTILL, THEY SLAMMED THE LAST SHELL INTO THE BREECH AND JOCK AND DAVE HELD THEIR BREATH AS THE LITTLE GUNNER TOOK AIM AGAIN... WHOOMP!
HOOTS, MON! YOU'VE DONE IT AGAIN!
YAHOO! NICE GOING, STEVE! THAT'S TWO OF THE BLIGHTERS KNOCKED OUT!

UNSURE OF THE STRENGTH OF THE OPPOSITION AHEAD, THE GERMANS HALTED AND THE UNARMOURED VEHICLES SWUNG ROUND AND SPED FOR THE COVER OF THE LANE BEHIND THEM. ON THE HILLSIDE, JOCK TURNED TO SPEAK TO DAVE... JUST IN TIME TO SEE HIM FALL TO THE GROUND!
SERGEANT, WHAT... OCH! HE'S BEEN HIT!

BUT AS HE BENT OVER THE SERGEANT, THE SCOT REALISED THAT DAVE HAD ONLY FAINTED. JOCK YELLED TO STEVE TO COME AND HELP HIM.
THE WEE LADDIE'S OUT FOR THE COUNT... HIS HEAD, I DINNA DOUBT. QUICK... GIVE ME A HAND WITH HIM, STEVE. THIS PLACE ISNA A HEALTHY SPOT TO STAY IN.
POOR OLD SARGE! HANG ON, I'M COMING.

THEY STAGGERED ALONG THE ROAD WITH THEIR LIMP BURDEN AND IN THE DISTANCE THEY HEARD THE FURIOUS SOUNDS OF A HEAVY BATTLE. PLANES WHEELED ACROSS THE SKY AND ALL AT ONCE A NEW SOUND FILLED THEIR EARS... THE DRUMMING OF HOOVES ON THE ROAD AHEAD.
LOOK OUT, JOCK... THERE'S A NAG COMING DOWN THE ROAD TOWARDS US— QUICK... GET OUT OF THE WAY!

DRAGGING THE SHATTERED REMAINS OF TWO CART SHAFTS BEHIND HIM, THE TERRIFIED HORSE CAME THUNDERING TOWARDS THEM. IN A FLASH, JOCK SWUNG SIDEWAYS AND LOWERED THE UNCONSCIOUS SERGEANT TO THE GROUND. THEN THE TALL SCOT FLUNG HIMSELF AT THE HORSE'S HEAD!

JOCK NORTH'S OUTSTRETCHED HANDS CLOSED ROUND THE HORSE'S REINS ...... AND HE HUNG ON WITH HIS WEIGHT PULLING DOWN LIKE AN ANCHOR ... SLOWLY, THE GREAT ANIMAL'S HEADLONG CHARGE WAS STOPPED...
WHOAH, YOU HUCKLE-HEADED BIG BRUTE! WHOAH!

FOAM-FLECKED AND LATHERED, THE CART HORSE CAME TO A SLITHERING HALT. JOCK SPOKE SOOTHINGLY TO THE SCARED ANIMAL AS IT STOOD TREMBLING IN EVERY LIMB. THEN THE CORPORAL TURNED IT ROUND AND LED IT BACK TO STEVE, WHO WAS WATCHING WIDE-EYED!
LUMMY, CORP! DIDN'T KNOW YOU'D BEEN A COWBOY!
OCH, STOP YOUR BLATHERING! I DIDN'T DO THIS FOR FUN... SEE YON BURNED-OUT CAR? I'VE GOT AN IDEA ....

A WRECKED FRENCH STAFF CAR LAY AT THE SIDE OF THE ROAD AND JOCK LED THE HORSE ROUND TO THE FRONT AND STRAPPED THE BROKEN CART-SHAFTS TO THE REMAINS OF THE BONNET. WHEN DAVE GREEN CAME-TO TEN MINUTES LATER, HE LOOKED AROUND HIM IN STARTLED SURPRISE.
WHAT... WHAT...WHERE ARE WE?
HULLO, SARGE OLD CHUM! HOW'RE YOU FEELING? WE GOT FED UP WITH CARRYING YOU... SO WE'VE HIRED A ONE HORSE-POWER TAXI. NOT BAD, EH? ANY OLD IRON? ANY OLD IRON?

FOR MILE AFTER MILE THEY WENDED THEIR WAY THROUGH THE TRAGIC REMAINS OF THE WITHDRAWING BRITISH FORCES.... THEN AHEAD OF THEM THEY SAW A MIGHTY PALL OF GREASY BLACK SMOKE, RISING HIGH INTO THE BLUE HEAVENS...
LOOK AT THAT! WHAT'S GOING ON?
UNLESS I'M MISTAKEN, THAT'S DUNKIRK. OUR BLOKES MUST HAVE REACHED THERE AND THAT SMOKE'S FROM THE BURNING STUFF THEY'RE FORCED TO LEAVE BEHIND 'EM.
YOU MEAN THEY'RE PULLING-OUT, SERGEANT? AYE, I'M THINKING YOU'RE RIGHT. THEN IT'S DUNKIRK WE'LL HAVE TO MAKE FOR

SAVAGELY, THE THREE GERMAN FIGHTERS MACHINE-GUNNED THE ROAD AND THE HORSE GAVE A NEIGH OF TERROR... WITH A MIGHTY KICK, IT LASHED OUT AND TORE ITSELF FREE FROM THE SHAFTS...

Chapter 5. LAST BOAT TO SAFETY
THEY MOVED CAUTIOUSLY THROUGH THE DESERTED TOWN AND CAME TO THE LONG SANDY BEACH WHICH STRETCHED FOR MILES BEYOND THE DUNES... AND THERE, OUT AT SEA, THEY SAW A BRITISH DESTROYER STEAMING AT FULL SPEED TOWARDS DISTANT ENGLAND.
LOOK... A DESTROYER!... AND NOT A SOLDIER IN SIGHT. WELL, LADDIES ...I'M THINKING WE'RE TOO LATE. THE LAST BOAT'S GONE!
CRUMBS! DOES THAT MEAN WE'LL HAVE TO SWIM FOR IT? AND I'VE LEFT MY BLOOMIN' WATER WINGS AT HOME!

A TERRIBLE EMPTY FEELING GRIPPED THEIR HEARTS AS THE TRUTH DAWNED ON THEM... AFTER ALL THEY HAD BEEN THROUGH, THE WAY TO ESCAPE WAS CLOSED! THEY STOOD IN SILENCE...THEN SUDDENLY, SERGEANT GREEN GRIPPED HIS COMRADES' ARMS AND PULLED THEM DOWN...
GET DOWN!
PRISONERS! THE JERRIES MUST BE ROUNDING UP ALL THE POOR BLIGHTERS WHO ARE LEFT. THAT'S A NICE TURN UP FOR THE BOOK...TO SPEND THE REST OF THE DARNED WAR IN A CAGE!

PRISON IS NOT FOR THE LIKES OF US, MON... I DINNA RATE MY LIFE VERY HIGH, BUT I'LL SELL IT DEAR BEFORE I ROT BEHIND BARBED WIRE! HOW SAY YOU... DAVE...STEVE?
I'M WITH YOU, JOCK. ALL OR NOTHING. WE'RE NOT BEAT YET!
NOT 'ARF, BLOKES! WE'VE HAD A RIPE ROUGH DO SO FAR...BUT THIS AIN'T THE END, NOT BY A LONG CHALK!

THERE WAS A BOMBED CAFE JUST ALONG THE BEACH AND THE THREE COMRADES HID UNDER THE DEBRIS OF THE KITCHEN UNTIL THE GERMANS HAD FINISHED SEARCHING THE AREA... FOR TWO DAYS AND NIGHTS THE SOLDIERS HID THERE, WELL SUPPLIED WITH FOOD, BUT NOT DARING TO VENTURE OUT... THEN, JUST AFTER DAWN ON THE THIRD DAY...
HERE...LOOK, YOU TWO. THERE'S A MOTOR BOAT DOWN THERE. OBVIOUSLY HAD A BASHING... BUT IT'S STILL AFLOAT. I WONDER...?

IT WAS AROUND FOUR O'CLOCK WHEN THE SERGEANT, WHO WAS LYING ON DECK WATCHING THE BEACH, GAVE A SHARP WHISTLE AND HISSED DOWN TO THE LITTLE GUNNER AND JOCK NORTH.

QUICK...OVER THE SIDE AND INTO THE WATER! THERE'S A BOATLOAD OF ARMED JERRIES COMING THIS WAY FROM THE HARBOUR!

DESPITE HIS PROTESTS, STEVE WAS THE FIRST OVER THE SIDE... THE THREE OF THEM CROUCHED DOWN BY THE STERN OF THE BOAT, ONLY THEIR FACES ABOVE THE WARM LAPPING WATER...
EMPTY! NOBODY HERE. BUT MAKE A NOTE... THIS LAUNCH CAN BE SALVAGED. IT IS NOT TOO BADLY DAMAGED.
JA, HERR LEUTNANT, IT WILL BE DONE.

WITH HEARTS BEATING WILDLY, THE THREE BRITISH SOLDIERS HUGGED THE SIDE OF THEIR LAUNCH. THEN THE LONG LEAN SHAPE OF THE GERMAN BOAT SLID AWAY ...AND DAVE GREEN FELT LIKE CHEERING!
THEY'RE GOING... THANK HEAVENS! BUT DON'T MOVE YET... THERE'S A JERRY IN THE BACK WITH A MACHINE PISTOL, WHO LOOKS AS IF HE'S JUST WAITING FOR A TARGET TO FIRE AT!

THEY CROUCHED IN THE WATER FOR OVER AN HOUR, UNTIL THE GERMANS HAD VANISHED FROM SIGHT. THEN THE THREE OF THEM CLIMBED INBOARD AGAIN AND STEVE WRESTLED AFRESH WITH THE BOAT'S ENGINE. NIGHT WAS CLOSING IN WHEN HE LOOKED UP AND GRINNED...
HOLD TIGHT, GENTS... KEEP YOUR FINGERS CROSSED... THERE! GOT IT! IT'S GOING!
WELL DONE, STEVE... THAT'S MORE THAN I COULD HAVE MANAGED.
YOU'RE A GUID WEE SASSENACH, STEVIE! AYE, YOU ARE THAT!

STEVE AND THE SCOTS CORPORAL WERE ALL FOR SETTING COURSE FOR ENGLAND RIGHT AWAY. BUT SERGEANT GREEN STOPPED THEM.
OKAY, SO THE BOAT'S FIXED AND THE ENGINE'S FINE... BUT WHAT ABOUT ALL THE WRECKS OUT THERE? AND FLOATING MINES AND OTHER JUNK? WE'D BE HOLED BEFORE WE'D GONE A MILE IN THE DARK. NO! SWITCH HER OFF, STEVE... WE'LL SAIL AT DAWN... AND THAT'S AN ORDER, WHETHER YOU LIKE IT OR NOT!

THEY REALISED DAVE WAS RIGHT. SO, WITH ONE ON GUARD ALL NIGHT, THEY TOOK IT IN TURNS TO SLEEP. AND AS THE SUN ROSE ON ANOTHER BRILLIANT, CLOUDLESS DAY, THE LITTLE GUNNER STARTED THE ENGINE WITH TREMBLING HANDS... THE NOISE ALMOST DROWNED JOCK'S CRY OF WARNING!
FULL SPEED AHEAD! THE JERRIES ARE AFTER US!

A FUSILLADE OF SHOTS WHINED AROUND THE BOAT, SOME SMASHING THROUGH THE THIN SIDES. LUCKILY, DAVE HAD SLIPPED ASHORE DURING THE NIGHT AND FOUND SIX FULL BREN MAGAZINES FROM THE LITTER ON THE BEACH. JOCK USED THEM WITH DEADLY EFFECT!
LET 'EM HAVE THE LOT, MATE! NICE SHOOTIN'!
DON'T WASTE THE AMMO THOUGH, JOCK... WE MAY NEED TO DEFEND OURSELVES ON THE WAY HOME.

BEFORE JOCK NORTH COULD REPLY, HE GAVE A GROAN AND ROLLED SIDEWAYS...
AAAGH!
STEVE! HE'S BEEN SHOT... GRAB HIM!

STEVE THREW HIMSELF FORWARD AND GRABBED JOCK'S LEGS . . . JUST AS THE TALL SCOT WAS ABOUT TO SLIDE OVER THE SIDE OF THE BOAT .
COME BACK, STOOPID... IT AIN'T BARF NIGHT!

STEVE CANNON'S PROMPT ACTION SAVED JOCK FROM A WATERY GRAVE. HE DRAGGED THE CORPORAL BACK INTO THE COCKPIT OF THE BOAT AND TOOK THE HELM, WHILST DAVE TENDED THE WOUND IN JOCK'S SHOULDER... WAVES OF SEARING PAIN SWEPT OVER THE WEARY SOLDIER, BUT HE GRITTED HIS TEETH AND SAT THERE WHITE-FACED.
SORRY IF I'VE HURT YOU, JOCK... BUT I RECKON THAT'LL BE ALL RIGHT UNTIL YOU SEE A DOC. THE BULLET WENT RIGHT THROUGH. HOW'S THAT?
FINE, DAVE. OCH, YOU OUGHT TO HAVE BEEN A MEDICO YESELF!

IT WAS NOON WHEN THE WELCOMING WHITE CLIFFS OF DOVER LOOMED AHEAD OF THE BATTERED LITTLE LAUNCH. THE THREE TIRED AND GRIMY SOLDIERS DID NOT CHEER... THEIR THROATS WERE TOO CHOKED WITH THE EMOTION OF SEEING ENGLAND AGAIN...
WELL, THERE'S HOME, BOYS. ANOTHER HALF AN HOUR AND WE'LL BE STEPPING OUT ON DRY LAND.

DAVE GREEN BROUGHT THE LAUNCH SMARTLY INTO HARBOUR, PULLING IN ALONGSIDE A MOTLEY COLLECTION OF SHIPPING WHICH HAD ALREADY BROUGHT THOUSANDS OF TROOPS BACK FROM DUNKIRK. WILLING HANDS HELPED THE SOLDIERS ASHORE.
THE POOR DEAR BOYS... I EXPECT THEY CAN DO WITH A NICE HOT CUP OF TEA.
CATCH HOLD, MATE...HERE...
YOU BETCHA, MISSUS...AND IF YOU'VE GOT ANY FAGS ON YOU, I'LL KISS YOU ON BOTH CHEEKS! GEE! AIN'T IT GOOD TO HEAR THE KING'S ENGLISH SPOKE PROPER AGAIN!

AS SOON AS A DOCTOR HAD ATTENDED TO THEM AND THEY HAD BEEN GIVEN A GOOD MEAL, A TALL GUARDS SERGEANT MAJOR WITH A FIERCE MOUSTACHE STALKED INTO THE HUT WHERE THEY WERE SITTING AND BARKED AT THEM IN A VOICE OF THUNDER.
HURRY UP THERE! TWO WALKING WOUNDED AND ONE FIT MAN... FALL IN OUTSIDE AT ONCE! TRANSPORT WILL TAKE YOU TO THE STATION. ON YOUR FEET!
AW, NO! SERGEANT MAJORS... I'D FORGOTTEN ALL ABOUT 'EM! LUMMY! 'ERE WE GO AGAIN!

The CROWDED SKY
THIS IS THE STORY OF RUDOLPH WEYMANN, LATER KNOWN IN THE BLENHEIM SQUADRONS OF THE ROYAL AIR FORCE AS JOE ARKWRIGHT. IT TELLS OF THE ODDS HE FOUGHT AGAINST AND THE BRIEF MOMENT OF GLORY HE FOUND IN THE CROWDED SKY.

Chapter 1. THE HATED GESTAPO
RUDOLPH WEYMANN WAS A YOUNG GERMAN FREIGHT PILOT — AND ON THE EVE OF WAR, IN AUGUST 1939, HIS JOB WAS FERRYING SPECIAL MACHINERY PARTS FROM SWITZERLAND.
WHAT A SLUG OF AN AIRCRAFT. IF ONLY THEY WOULD RELEASE ME TO THE LUFTWAFFE - I MIGHT NOW BE AT THE CONTROLS OF A MESSERSCHMITT LIKE HANS METTERLING.

WEYMANN WAS NOT A NAZI, BUT HE WAS A PATRIOTIC YOUNG GERMAN — AND THE DULL FERRYING FLIGHTS IN A HEAVY JUNKERS TRANSPORT BETWEEN BERLIN AND BERNE WERE IRKSOME TO HIM.
SCHMITT! THE PORT ENGINE RESPONSE IS POSITIVELY FOUL. HOW CAN YOU EXPECT ME TO CLEAR THE MOUNTAINS WITH A HEAVY LOAD WHEN I HAVEN'T GOT POWER? YOU'D BETTER SEE TO IT — NOW!
VERY GOOD, HERR WEYMANN - WE'LL STRIP THE ENGINE.

NORMALLY, WEYMANN WOULD CHAT WITH PILOTS FROM OTHER AIRLINES–FOR HIS ENGLISH AND FRENCH WERE GOOD. BUT THE THREAT OF THE COMING WAR HAD STRAINED RELATIONS BETWEEN THE CIVILIAN FLYERS.
THAT'S HIM – HIS NAME IS WEYMANN. HE CAME IN WITH THE JUNKERS AN HOUR AGO.
YOU STAY HERE. I'LL APPROACH HIM AND DO THE TALKING. I KNOW IT'S RISKY– BUT WE'VE GOT TO TAKE A CHANCE.
AIR
FLY

THE PILOT LOOKED UP FROM HIS NEWSPAPER TO SEE A PORTLY LITTLE BUSINESS MAN STANDING TIMIDLY BY HIS TABLE...
MISTER WEYMANN?
THAT'S ME– SO..?
EXCUSE ME SPEAKING ENGLISH, MISTER WEYMANN– I AM A GERMAN LIKE YOURSELF– BUT I AM GOING TO ASK YOU SOMETHING IMPORTANT, AND IT MIGHT BE DANGEROUS FOR BOTH OF US IF ANOTHER GERMAN WERE TO OVERHEAR.

WEYMANN WAS NOT NORMALLY RUTHLESS OR ARROGANT. BUT THE FRUSTRATION OF FLYING A CLUMSY TRANSPORT CRAFT HAD EMBITTERED HIM.

YOU MISERABLE - LITTLE TRAITOR! NO DOUBT THE GESTAPO HAD GOOD REASONS FOR BEING ON YOUR TRAIL. NOW YOU WANT ME TO VIOLATE MY COUNTRY'S BORDERS - BREAK HER LAWS - JUST TO SNATCH MORE CRIMINALS FROM JUSTICE.

MISTER WEYMANN - PLEASE, *PLEASE* KEEP YOUR VOICE DOWN.

THE ENGLISHMAN WAS NOT TO BE SILENCED . . .
LOOK, FRIEND, I'LL PILOT YOUR PLANE FOR YOU. I KNOW AUSTRIA PRETTY WELL AND I'D DO ANYTHING TO SOCK THE GESTAPO IN THE EYE. AS FOR WEYMANN HERE, HE CAN CRAWL BACK INTO HIS HOLE!
SIR, IF YOU WOULD —
I WON'T STAY HERE AND BE INSULTED!

AS WEYMANN WALKED AWAY, SHAKING WITH FURY . . .
NO, JERRY — YOU STICK AROUND WHEN YOU THINK YOU CAN GIVE THE INSULTS WITHOUT TAKING THEM. GET YOURSELF PROMOTED INTO THE LUFTWAFFE – THEY'LL BE NEEDING YOU SOON . . .

FOR THE NEXT TWO DAYS WEYMANN WAS IN A COLD RAGE. HE AVOIDED THE AIRPORT LOUNGE, AND SPENT HIS TIME HARASSING THE GROUND CREW UNTIL HIS CARGO ARRIVED.
. . . I KNOW I WAS IN A FOUL MOOD — BUT HOW COULD THAT REFUGEE EXPECT ANY GERMAN PILOT TO DO HIS DIRTY WORK FOR HIM? WOULD THE ENGLISHMAN HAVE FERRIED CRIMINALS OUT OF ENGLAND, I WONDER?

WEYMANN WAS STILL BROODING OVER HIS THOUGHTS AS HE BROUGHT THE CLUMSY, LADEN JUNKERS EXPERTLY INTO TEMPLEHOF AIRPORT, IN BERLIN.
I'VE HEARD A LOT ABOUT THE GESTAPO FROM FOREIGN PILOTS IN SWITZERLAND — AND DON'T BELIEVE HALF OF IT. THEY USUALLY GET THEIR INFORMATION FROM BIASED REFUGEES. THE GESTAPO HAS NEVER DONE ME ANY HARM . . .
LUFTHANSA

AT TEMPLEHOF, WEYMANN FOUND EVERYONE AGOG WITH STARTLING NEWS. THAT MORNING, THE WEHRMACHT HAD INVADED POLAND, AND THE ALLIES HAD DELIVERED AN ULTIMATUM. WEYMANN'S PULSE POUNDED — NOW HE WAS BOUND TO BE CALLED UP FOR LUFTWAFFE SERVICE. AS HE WAS LEAVING THE TRANSIT OFFICE A CLERK CALLED HIM OVER . . .
HERR WEYMANN! YOUR MOTHER HAS PHONED THE OFFICE SEVERAL TIMES. SHE SAYS SHE MUST SEE YOU — URGENTLY.
I WONDER WHAT IT'S ALL ABOUT?

TAKING A TAXI FROM THE AIRPORT, WEYMANN WAS HOME IN TEN MINUTES...
RUDOLPH — THANK HEAVEN YOU'VE ARRIVED! THE GESTAPO — THEY HAVE TAKEN YOUR FATHER AND BROTHER. THEY CAME YESTERDAY...
THEY... WHAT!

WEYMANN'S FATHER WAS A PROMINENT BERLIN BUSINESS MAN, AND ALTHOUGH HE WAS NOT A NAZI HIMSELF, HE HAD DONE NOTHING TO ANTAGONISE THE PARTY AT ANY STAGE OF HIS CAREER. WEYMANN'S YOUNGER BROTHER GUNTHER WAS A STUDENT OF TWENTY...
IT WAS AT DAWN — WE WERE IN BED — THEY BROKE DOWN THE DOOR, AND SEIZED YOUR FATHER. GUNTHER TRIED TO FIGHT THEM OFF. THEY BEAT HIM, AND TOOK HIM AWAY ALSO...
BUT... BUT WHAT HAD THEY DONE?

WEYMANN STOOD, STUNNED, THEN WITH GRIM SET FACE, TURNED TOWARDS THE DOOR...
WHERE ARE YOU GOING?
GESTAPO HEADQUARTERS!
YOU MUST NOT — IT IS OF NO USE — THEY WILL TAKE YOU, AS WELL...

BUT WEYMANN WAS DEAF TO HIS MOTHER'S ENTREATIES. NEITHER HE NOR HIS FAMILY HAD DONE ANY WRONG — THEREFORE THEY WOULD HAVE TO LISTEN TO HIM. IT WAS IN THIS FRAME OF MIND THAT HE CONFRONTED THE GESTAPO . . .
MY NAME IS WEYMANN: YOU ARE HOLDING MY FATHER AND BROTHER – I WANT TO SEE THEM!
YOU ARE OUT OF DATE, WEYMANN. WE *WERE* HOLDING THEM. *THEY WERE SHOT THIS MORNING!*

SHOT . . . MY FATHER AND BROTHER SHOT!
THAT IS WHAT I SAID. THEY WERE DENOUNCED BY A BUSINESS FRIEND OF YOUR FATHER'S. WE HAD GOOD REASON TO BELIEVE THEY WERE PLOTTING AGAINST THE REGIME; I PRESUME *YOU* ARE RUDOLPH WEYMANN . . .

WE HAVE A WARRANT HERE FOR *YOUR* ARREST, AS WELL – AND NOW THAT YOU HAVE TURNED UP, IT WILL SAVE US THE TROUBLE OF FINDING YOU. SIT DOWN, HERR WEYMANN – YOU ARE NOT GOING ANYWHERE.
YOU CURS – YOU COLD-BLOODED MURDERING CURS . . !

SUDDENLY BERSERK, WEYMANN LASHED OUT...
YOU VILE RAT...!
GUARD!

A BURLY BLACK-UNIFORMED TOUGH BLUNDERED THROUGH THE DOORWAY, TUGGING A MAUSER FROM HIS HOLSTER, AND A SLUG SLAMMED INTO THE PILOT'S ARM.
MURDERERS, ALL OF YOU—AAGH!
KILL HIM! KILL HIM!

BUT WEYMANN'S UNINJURED RIGHT ARM FASTENED ON THE BACK OF A CHAIR ... AND WITH DESPERATE FORCE HE HURLED IT AT THE MIDRIFF OF THE ONCOMING GUARD ...
GET OUT OF MY WAY!
UUUGH!

THEN WEYMANN BURST FROM THE HEADQUARTERS, AND RAN FRANTICALLY ALONG THE STREET, CLUTCHING HIS WOUNDED ARM ...
THERE HE GOES!
THEY'RE AFTER ME – GOT TO FIND SOMEWHERE TO HIDE – MUSTN'T GO NEAR MOTHER'S HOUSE – THEY'LL LOOK THERE!

FOR WEYMANN THE NEXT HOUR WAS A NIGHTMARE. DIZZY WITH PAIN, HE STAGGERED FROM ALLEY TO ALLEY, FRANTICALLY RACKING HIS MIND FOR SOMEWHERE TO GO. THEN HE REMEMBERED THAT AN OLD SCHOOL FRIEND, HANS OLENDORFF, HAD TAKEN A FLAT IN THE AREA WHILE STUDYING MEDICINE AT THE UNIVERSITY...
I NEED HELP – THE GESTAPO ..!
GOOD GRIEF! WEYMANN! COME IN – QUICKLY!

OLENDORFF WAS A HOUSE SURGEON IN A SMALL CITY HOSPITAL - AND AS WEYMANN GASPED OUT HIS STORY, OLENDORFF BEGAN TO DRESS HIS WOUND...
I'VE NO ANAESTHETICS - THIS IS GOING TO HURT!
I DON'T CARE - GET THE BULLET OUT...

WHEN THE ORDEAL WAS OVER, WEYMANN SLEPT. HE WOKE JUST BEFORE DUSK AT THE SOUND OF OLENDORFF COMING BACK INTO THE FLAT.
THERE WERE BLOODSTAINS LEADING TO THE DOOR! I SCRUBBED THEM AWAY, AS FAR ALONG THE ALLEY AS I DARED - BUT THERE'S STILL SOME BEYOND THAT, AND THEY'LL LEAD TO THIS AREA! THE GESTAPO WILL SEARCH EVERY HOUSE...
YOU'VE SAVED MY LIFE AND THE BEST WAY I CAN REPAY YOU IS TO GET OUT OF HERE.

IT WAS NEAR TO MIDNIGHT WHEN WEYMANN SLIPPED AWAY FROM OLENDORFF'S FLAT. EYES WARY FOR SIGNS OF PATROLLING GESTAPO, HE HAILED A TAXI AND DROVE TO TEMPLEHOF AIRPORT...
THIS IS THE ONLY WAY I'LL GET OUT OF THE COUNTRY – BUT IT'S DEVILISH RISKY! THE GESTAPO KNOW I'M A PILOT – THEY'RE BOUND TO BE WATCHING THE AIRPORT. WAIT! I KNOW THAT FACE..!

WEYMANN HAD SEEN A MAN HE HAD ONCE MET IN SWITZERLAND – AN AMERICAN CALLED ARKWRIGHT, WHO FLEW HIS OWN PRIVATE PLANE...
SAY, I REMEMBER YOU! YOU'RE..!
DON'T MENTION MY NAME! LISTEN, ARKWRIGHT – THE GESTAPO ARE AFTER ME AND I MUST GET OUT OF GERMANY! IF I CAN'T MANAGE IT TONIGHT, I'M FINISHED. CAN YOU HELP ME?

SUCH WAS THE COURAGE AND SPIRIT OF THE AMERICAN THAT HE ASKED FOR NO FURTHER EXPLANATION. IN A FEW MOMENTS THEY WERE STEALING ACROSS THE AIRFIELD ITSELF...
OKAY – NOW LET'S MAKE FOR MY CRATE NICE AND EASY! WE'LL TAKE OFF WITHOUT BENEFIT OF CONTROL – AND IF ANYTHING IS COMING IN TO LAND, THAT'S JUST TOO BAD...
THANKS, ARKWRIGHT! I'M MAKING YOU TAKE AN APPALLING RISK! THEY'D SHOOT BOTH OF US..!

BOTH MEN'S HEARTS WERE POUNDING AS THEY CROSSED THE EXPOSED AIRFIELD TO THE AMERICAN'S LITTLE TWO-SEATER CABIN PLANE...
WELL, WE MADE IT SO FAR...
I NEVER THOUGHT I COULD BE SO SCARED!

THE AMERICAN CLAMBERED INTO THE CABIN, AND TOOK THE STICK. WARY EYES PEERING AHEAD INTO THE DARKNESS, HE OPENED THE THROTTLE WIDE...
CAN'T SEE ANY OTHER LANDING LIGHTS – SO HERE GOES!

THE PLANE WAS AIRBORNE IN FIFTY YARDS. BANKING AWAY FROM THE CONTROL BUILDINGS, THEY CLIMBED INTO THE NIGHT...
MY TANKS ARE FULL— SO WE OUGHT TO MAKE SWITZERLAND.

AND SO WEYMANN LEFT BERLIN FOR EVER—A LUCKY MAN, FORTUNATE IN HIS FRIENDS...
...YES, THE TABLES HAVE BEEN TURNED ON ME, ALL RIGHT! IT'S ONLY THREE DAYS SINCE I WAS REVILING THAT REFUGEE BECAUSE HE WANTED ME TO HELP HIS RELATIVES— AND NOW IT'S ME THAT'S RUNNING FROM THE GESTAPO!

FOR THE NEXT THREE HOURS THEY SPED SOUTHWARDS. THEN ARKWRIGHT PUT THE STICK FORWARD, AND THEY DROPPED STEEPLY DOWN THROUGH THE CLOUD LAYER...
BAD WEATHER!
YES — BUT WE'VE GOT TO ROUGH IT! WE'RE NEAR THE MOUNTAINS, AND WITH A FULL LOAD I CAN'T GO OVER THEM! WE MUST FIND A PASS THAT WILL TAKE US THROUGH!

BUFFETED BY WIND AND RAIN, THE TINY MACHINE PITCHED VIOLENTLY UNDER ARKWRIGHT'S RESTRAINING HANDS.
DO YOU KNOW WHERE YOU'RE GOING?
I THINK I DO– IF MY BEARINGS ARE RIGHT, WE OUGHT TO BE IN LINE WITH A GOOD PASS THAT WILL TAKE US THROUGH WITH ROOM TO SPARE! BUT IF WE'VE BEEN DRIFTING . . .

...AND THEN SUDDENLY, DEAD AHEAD, WEYMANN SAW GIGANTIC, REARING MASSES OF CLOUD-WREATHED ROCK . . .
MOUNTAIN!
WE CAN'T CLIMB– WE'VE GOT TO GO ROUND...

WORKING STICK AND RUDDER FORCIBLY, THE AMERICAN THREW THE MACHINE INTO A STEEP BANKING TURN.
HARDER TO PORT... HARDER! THERE'S MOUNTAIN EVERYWHERE!
CAN'T DO IT! SHE'S TURNING FULL CIRCLE NOW!

WITHOUT WARNING, THE PLANE HIT THE ROCK-FACE AND SPUN ROUND. THEN THEY WERE SKIDDING HELPLESSLY FROM IMPACT TO IMPACT...
WE'VE STRUCK...!
SWITCH OFF, ARKWRIGHT— SWITCH OFF!

WEYMANN REMEMBERED NOTHING MORE ... UNTIL HE CAME TO HIS SENSES, TO FIND HIMSELF HANGING UPSIDE DOWN IN HIS STRAPS IN A DARK SILENCE, THE STENCH OF PETROL AND BURNT OIL IN HIS NOSTRILS ...
MY ARM ... IT HURTS LIKE THE DEVIL! GOT TO GET OUT OF HERE!

PAINFULLY AND WITH GREAT DIFFICULTY, WEYMANN UNDID THE TAUT STRAPS, AND TUMBLED FORWARD, KICKING HIS WAY OUT THROUGH THE TORN SIDE-PANELS.
WHAT A MESS! GOOD THING THAT ARKWRIGHT SWITCHED OFF THE IGNITION OR WE'D BE BURNING — ARKWRIGHT! — HE'S STILL IN THERE..!

BUT ARKWRIGHT'S SIDE OF THE CABIN HAD TAKEN THE FULL FORCE OF THE IMPACT . . .
ARKWRIGHT! HE'S . . .

THE AMERICAN WOULD NEVER FLY AGAIN. WITH INFINITE CARE, WEYMANN EASED THE BODY OUT OF THE WRECKAGE, AND ON TO THE RAIN-SOAKED GRASS. THEN HE REACHED INTO ARKWRIGHT'S JACKET — AND TOOK OUT A WALLET AND PASSPORT . . .
BY RIGHTS, IT SHOULD BE ME WHO IS LYING THERE, ARKWRIGHT! I'VE GOT NOTHING LEFT TO LOSE EXCEPT MY LIFE! YET IT HASN'T WORKED OUT THAT WAY! SO I'M TAKING YOUR PAPERS AND MONEY — YOU WON'T NEED THEM ANY MORE, AND THEY'LL MAKE ALL THE DIFFERENCE TO ME!

TWO HOURS LATER, WEYMANN STAGGERED INTO A LITTLE HAMLET FAR DOWN THE MOUNTAINSIDE . . . HE WAS IN SWITZERLAND.
I'M AN AMERICAN — MY NAME IS ARKWRIGHT! I'VE BEEN IN A PLANE CRASH — MY CO-PILOT HAS LOST HIS LIFE . . !

Chapter 2 FIRST CREW

IT WAS AS JOE ARKWRIGHT, THAT WEYMANN FINALLY REACHED ENGLAND. HE CARRIED IN HIS HEART A BURNING HATRED OF EVERYTHING NAZI.
SORRY, SIR, GOT TO CHECK YOUR BAG! CUSTOMS FORMALITIES, YOU KNOW — AND NOW THAT THERE'S A WAR ON, THINGS ARE RATHER STRICT!
SWISS
SO THIS IS ENGLAND, WHERE EVEN THE OFFICIALS ARE POLITE! IN NAZI GERMANY, THIS MAN WOULD BE SUSPICIOUS AND THREATENING!

THE URGE TO FLY WAS DEEP IN THE MARROW OF WEYMANN'S BONES, AND THERE WAS ONLY ONE WAY HE COULD FLY IN WARTIME BRITAIN. HE HAD A FIERCE DESIRE TO STRIKE BACK AT THE VILE REGIME WHICH HAD OUTLAWED HIM. AND ONE DAY, AFTER SIX MONTHS IN LONDON, HE WENT TO THE AIR MINISTRY...
MY NAME IS ARKWRIGHT, AND I'M AN AMERICAN. EXCUSE THE ACCENT, BUT MY MOTHER WAS SWISS, AND I SPENT QUITE A LOT OF MY LIFE IN BERNE! YOU NEED PILOTS URGENTLY — WELL, I'M A TRAINED COMMERCIAL PILOT, AND I'D LIKE TO VOLUNTEER!
I SEE, YOU'LL HAVE TO GO THROUGH CERTAIN FORMALITIES, OF COURSE...

THE WHEELS TURNED SWIFTLY. THREE DAYS LATER, 'ARKWRIGHT' WAS BEING INTERVIEWED BY AN INTELLIGENCE OFFICER ...
ARKWRIGHT, WE'VE BEEN CHECKING UP ON YOU IN BERNE! ACCORDING TO OUR INFORMATION, YOU CRASHED A PRIVATE AIRCRAFT SIX MONTHS AGO IN THE ALPS! THAT SAME DAY, *BERLIN*, OF ALL PLACES, COMPLAINED THAT A SWISS-REGISTERED LIGHT AIRCRAFT HAD VIOLATED TAKE-OFF PROCEDURES AT TEMPLEHOF! NOW WHAT DO YOU KNOW ABOUT THAT?

ARKWRIGHT'S MOUTH WENT DRY– BUT HE FACED UP TO THE INTELLIGENCE OFFICER WITH A TENSE SMILE ...
I'D RATHER NOT TALK ABOUT IT...
WELL, *I'LL* TALK ABOUT IT, ARKWRIGHT! OUR SOURCES REPORT THAT YOU FERRIED A HUNTED GERMAN OUT FROM UNDER THE NOSES OF THE GESTAPO. A MAN CALLED WEYMANN, WHO WAS, UNFORTUNATELY, KILLED IN THE CRASH!

TO HIS UTTER ASTONISHMENT, THE GERMAN FOUND HIMSELF SHAKEN BY THE HAND ...
WE *NEED* MEN LIKE YOU, ARKWRIGHT – TOUGH, DARING, AND COURAGEOUS – AND WE'RE PREPARED TO CUT A LOT OF RED TAPE TO GET THEM! SO IF YOU WANT TO FLY IN THE R.A.F. WE CAN ARRANGE IT!
TH-THANK YOU!..

WITHIN THREE WEEKS, ARKWRIGHT WAS GRANTED A COMMISSION IN THE ROYAL AIR FORCE AND POSTED TO A NEWLY-FORMED BLENHEIM SQUADRON IN CAMBRIDGESHIRE . . .
REPORTING FOR DUTY, SIR - THE NAME IS ARKWRIGHT!
AH, YES - YOU'RE THE AMERICAN WE HAD A MEMO ABOUT FROM THE AIR MINISTRY! THINGS ARE A BIT HAYWIRE HERE AT THE MOMENT. AIRCRAFT ARE IN DARNED SHORT SUPPLY, BUT WE'VE GOT ENOUGH TO TRAIN WITH!

PILOT OFFICER ARKWRIGHT SOON FOUND THAT MOST OF THE NEW PILOTS WERE MEN WHO, LIKE HIMSELF, HAD HELD CIVIL LICENCES AND HAD FLOWN TWIN-ENGINED AIRCRAFT . . .
AS YOU KNOW, GENTLEMEN, WE'RE TAKING ALL THE SHORT-CUTS! EVERY MAN IN THE ROOM HAS PASSED A FORMAL TEST ON TRAINERS AND NOW WE'RE GOING STRAIGHT ON TO BOMBERS! NOW, HERE IS THE BLENHEIM FOUR!
BLENHEIM IV

ARKWRIGHT WON HIS WINGS AS A BLENHEIM PILOT AFTER LESS FLYING HOURS THAN ANY OTHER MAN ON THE SQUADRON. HE WAS PROMOTED TO FLYING OFFICER, AND GIVEN HIS OWN CREW . . .
WELL, ARKWRIGHT, THESE ARE THE MEN YOU'LL SKIPPER TO DEATH OR GLORY! STOWELL, HERE, IS YOUR NAVIGATOR-BOMB-AIMER, AND THOMAS YOUR GUNNER! JOHNNIE STOWELL HAS A BROTHER WHO WAS AN OPPO OF MINE ON HAWKER HARTS JUST BEFORE HOSTILITIES – SO IF YOU PRANG WITH *HIM* ABOARD, I'LL NEVER LIVE IT DOWN!
PLEASED TO MEET YOU, SIR!

LATER, IN THE AIRCREW MESS, ARKWRIGHT TURNED TO JOHNNIE STOWELL . . .
WELL, JOHNNIE, SO THE C.O. IS A PAL OF YOUR BROTHER! WITH THOSE CONNECTIONS, YOU SHOULD'VE PUT IN FOR PILOT DUTIES...
LOOK, ARKWRIGHT, LET'S CUT THE PERSONAL STUFF RIGHT NOW. I DON'T LIKE AMERICANS – AND THE BARE FLYING ROUTINE IS AS FAR AS I GO WITH YOU – NO FURTHER!

STOWELL WALKED INSOLENTLY AWAY, LEAVING ARKWRIGHT STARING AFTER HIM WITH NARROWED EYES. IT WAS ANOTHER PILOT NEARBY WHO SUPPLIED THE ANSWERS...
NOW WHAT'S THE MATTER WITH HIM?
YOU BOOBED THERE, ARKWRIGHT! STOWELL'S BEEN MAD ABOUT FLYING SINCE HE WAS A KID, BUT HE FAILED ON FIGHTERS — THEN HE FAILED ON BOMBERS! WHAT RUBS IT IN IS THAT HIS ELDER BROTHER IS A BIG SUCCESS ON HURRICANES..!

IN THE WEEKS OF AIRCREW TRAINING THAT FOLLOWED, ARKWRIGHT WAS TO FIND THAT LACK OF TEAM-SPIRIT IN A SMALL BOMBER LIKE A BLENHEIM COULD BE A DANGEROUS LIABILITY...
THIS IS OUR FIFTH ROUTE FLIGHT, NAVIGATOR, SO IT WON'T BE LONG BEFORE WE'RE READY FOR OPS! WE'RE ON OUR OWN THIS TIME - SO LET'S MAKE IT A GOOD ONE!
YOU GIVE THE ORDERS — I'LL GIVE THE COURSE!

THE TARGET AREA WAS A DESOLATE STRETCH OF CORNWALL, FITTED OUT AS A BOMBING RANGE WITH GREAT YELLOW MARKERS. DURING THE MONOTONOUS FLIGHT SOUTHWARD, THE USUAL AIRCREW SMALLTALK WAS ABSENT. AS THEY CAME IN FOR THEIR BOMBING RUN, TENSION WAS HIGH ...
STEADY... STEADY... STEADY, CURSE YOU!
I'M DOING MY BEST, STOWELL–THERE'S A STRONG CROSS-WIND!

THE BOMBS FELL WIDE!
NOT TOO GOOD!
YOU DIDN'T GIVE ME MUCH CHANCE, SKIPPER! WE WERE ROLLING LIKE A HIPPO IN A MUD-BATH...

AS THEY CLIMBED ABOVE CLOUD CEILING FOR THE LONG HAUL BACK TO BASE . . .
LOOK, STOWELL, I'M NOT HAPPY ABOUT THIS SET-UP. THIS IS OUR SECOND DUFF RUN IN TWO DAYS! I'LL HAVE TO PUT A REPORT IN TO THE C.O. ABOUT YOUR INCOMPETENCE!
MY INCOMPETENCE! LISTEN TO HIM! HE FLIES THIS KITE AS IF IT WERE A JUNKERS, TALKS LIKE A GERMAN, AND ACTS LIKE A NAZI! DID YOU HEAR THAT, TAFFY-

BUT THE SITUATION WAS TOO MUCH EVEN FOR THE PLACID WELSH GUNNER —
STOW IT, JOHNNIE — STOW IT! ARKWRIGHT IS THE SKIPPER, AND HE'S TAKEN TOO MUCH FROM YOU ALREADY BY MY WAY OF THINKING! THIS IS NO PICNIC FOR ME, EITHER!
THE FLIGHT CONTINUED IN SILENCE WITH ARKWRIGHT SITTING TENSE AND TIGHT-LIPPED, FOR STOWELL'S REMARKS HAD UNWITTINGLY BEEN TOO NEAR THE TRUTH.
BY DUSK, THE BLENHEIM WAS OVER THE HOME COUNTIES...
CHECK OUR COURSE, NAVIGATOR — GIVE ME A POSITION FIX!
HE'S TRYING TO IMPLY THAT MY LAST CALCULATIONS MIGHT BE WRONG — I DON'T SEE WHY I SHOULD TAKE THAT FROM HIM . . .
COURSE, O-EIGHT-FIVE AS BEFORE — I MAKE US OVER STAINES.

BUT HAD JOHNNIE STOWELL CHECKED UP, HE WOULD HAVE FOUND THAT THE CROSS-WIND HAD FRESHENED CONSIDERABLY—AND THE BLENHEIM WAS DRIFTING WELL OFF COURSE TO THE EAST. FIFTEEN MINUTES LATER IT NOSED DOWNWARDS...
I RECKON WE'RE JUST ABOUT THERE—CORRECT ME IF I'M WRONG, NAVIGATOR!
YOU'RE THERE, ALL RIGHT—YOU'RE THERE!

BUT THE LONE BOMBER WAS NOWHERE NEAR BASE—IT WAS ALMOST DIRECTLY ABOVE A SPITFIRE SQUADRON AIRFIELD IN LINCOLNSHIRE, AND WAS DROPPING DOWN STRAIGHT INTO THE PATH OF A FIGHTER LANDING CIRCUIT...
RED APPLE TO CONTROL—CIRCLING BASE AT ANGELS FOUR—MAY I COME IN—MAY I COME IN?
YOU MAY COME IN, RED APPLE.

THE SPITFIRE STREAKED ROUND IN THE GATHERING DUSK . . .
GOOD GRIEF!

IN THE SPLIT-SECOND BEFORE COLLISION, ARKWRIGHT SAW THE ONCOMING MACHINE . . .
FIGHTER . . !

ARKWRIGHT JAMMED WIDE THE THROTTLE AND HURLED THE BLENHEIM OVER AND UP – BUT WITH A BRIEF, FIENDISH SNARL THE FIGHTER ROCKETED IN UPON THEM . . .
BALE OUT . . . EVERYBODY! BALE OUT — WE'VE HAD IT!
. . . AND SUDDENLY THE BLENHEIM, TAILLESS, WAS YAWING DRUNKENLY THROUGH THE SKY.

GALVANISED BY URGENCY, ARKWRIGHT PRACTICALLY HURLED HIS DAZED CREW OUT OF THE HATCH – AND WAS THE LAST MAN TO JUMP FROM THE SPINNING WRECK.
THERE'S JUST GOT TO BE HEIGHT FOR MY CHUTE TO OPEN.

THERE WAS ENOUGH HEIGHT – JUST –
I MADE IT – SO THE OTHERS MUST HAVE!

GRIMLY, ARKWRIGHT WALKED TOWARDS THE PILLAR OF FLAME AND SMOKE ON THE SKYLINE, AND FOUND THAT A DETACHMENT FROM THE NEARBY FIGHTER STATION HAD GOT THERE FIRST.
I'M THE PILOT OF *THAT*!
THEN THERE'S TROUBLE AHEAD FOR *YOU*, BOY! YOU WANDERED INTO OUR FIGHTER LANDING CIRCUIT, AND ALMOST PRANGED A SPITFIRE — AND THAT, LADDIE, IS HIGH TREASON! THEY WON'T HANG YOU — BUT THEY'LL KEEP YOU SO CLOSE TO TERRA FIRMA FROM NOW ON THAT YOU'LL SPROUT ROOTS!

IN THE NEXT HOUR, ARKWRIGHT'S NAVIGATOR AND GUNNER WERE PICKED UP BY PATROLS FROM THE FIGHTER STATION — AND AFTER A TOUGH SESSION WITH THE FIGHTER C.O., THE BLENHEIM CREW WERE GIVEN TEMPORARY QUARTERS ...
I'VE SAID NOTHING SO FAR, STOWELL — BUT THERE'LL BE AN ENQUIRY, AND THEN I'LL *HAVE* TO SPEAK! WE WERE WELL OFF COURSE — YET I STUCK STRICTLY TO YOUR DIRECTIONS!
I KNOW, ARKWRIGHT, I ADMIT IT! I THOUGHT I WAS A CLEVER JOHNNIE, SO I DIDN'T CHECK THE COURSE AT STAINES — *I DIDN'T CHECK IT!*

TO THE BLENHEIM SQUADRON, THE NEW BOMBERS WERE WORTH THEIR WEIGHT IN GOLD – AND WHEN THE ENQUIRY WAS HELD, NO PUNCHES WERE PULLED . . .
WE'RE LIKE THE ANCIENT SPARTANS HERE, ARKWRIGHT – YOU EITHER COME BACK *WITH* YOUR SHIELD, OR *ON* IT – THE SHIELD IN THIS CASE BEING A VALUABLE BOMBER! SO YOU'D BETTER HAVE A GOOD EXCUSE FOR BEING OVER THAT FIGHTER DROME!
WELL, SIR . . .
SIR! I'D LIKE TO SPEAK FIRST – I FEEL IT OUGHT TO COME FROM ME –

BUT ARKWRIGHT STEPPED FORWARD AND SPOKE DECISIVELY . . .
AS THE SKIPPER, IT'S *MY* RIGHT TO SPEAK FIRST, SIR! THE FACTS ARE SIMPLY THESE – I DELIBERATELY DEVIATED FROM COURSE AS A TEST ROUTINE. WE WERE AT TWELVE THOUSAND FEET – WELL OUT OF THE WAY OF ANY FIGHTER CIRCUIT –
THEN HOW THE DEUCE DID YOU COME TO COLLIDE WITH A SPIT AT ANGELS FOUR?

ARKWRIGHT WAS CONCOCTING A 'STORY' AND A PLAUSIBLE STORY AT THAT . . .
ENGINE TROUBLE, SIR! THE PORT ENGINE PACKED UP UNEXPECTEDLY, AND WE HAD TO GO DOWN! IT WAS AN UNLUCKY SHOW WE HAPPENED TO BE SITTING ON TOP OF A FIGHTER CIRCUIT.
'UNLUCKY SHOW' – IT WAS A *DISASTER!* STOWELL – WHAT HAVE *YOU* GOT TO SAY?
THE SKIPPER HAS SAID ALL THERE IS TO SAY, SIR!

...AND THAT WAS THAT! ARKWRIGHT GOT A BLISTERING REPRIMAND — BUT IF THE ACCIDENT HAD BEEN PINNED ON THE NAVIGATOR'S NEGLECT OF DUTY, STOWELL WOULD HAVE BEEN TAKEN OFF AIRCREW FOR EVER. AND NOBODY KNEW THIS BETTER THAN JOHNNIE STOWELL...
ARKWRIGHT — I — I'VE BEHAVED BADLY TOWARDS YOU EVER SINCE WE TEAMED UP! YET YOU TOOK THE BLAME IN THERE, AND PULLED ME OUT OF THE HOTTEST SPOT IN MY CAREER!
IN MY SCHEME OF THINGS THE SKIPPER IS RESPONSIBLE FOR *EVERYTHING* ON HIS AIRCRAFT — EVEN HIS NAVIGATOR!

THERE WAS A SILENCE — AND THEN STOWELL GRINNED, AND IMPULSIVELY HELD OUT HIS HAND...
SKIPPER, YOU'VE JUST GOT YOURSELF A NAVIGATOR WHO *WON'T* MAKE MISTAKES — EVEN IF HE HAS TO CALCULATE HIS COURSES TEN TIMES OVER!
I'LL KEEP YOU TO THAT, JOHNNIE!

Chapter 3. SELF-BETRAYAL
FROM THEN ON, ARKWRIGHT AND HIS NAVIGATOR WERE FIRM FRIENDS AND THEY THREW THEMSELVES WHOLEHEARTEDLY INTO PERFECTING THEIR FLYING AND BOMBING TECHNIQUE. IT WAS NOT UNTIL MAY, 1940, THAT THE WAR BECAME A REAL THING FOR ARKWRIGHT, ALIAS RUDOLPH WEYMANN. THEN HE, AND OTHERS OF HIS SQUADRON, FOUND THEMSELVES RANGING OVER BELGIUM ON PERILOUS DAYLIGHT MISSIONS ...
WE'VE GOT TO BUST THAT BRIDGE, SO LET'S GET IN THERE AND FOR HEAVEN'S SAKE, DON'T SCATTER! IF MESSERSCHMITTS JUMP US, WE CAN HANDLE THEM ONLY IF WE STICK IN CLOSE FORMATION!

IT WAS WAR AT ITS MOST RUTHLESS – AND ARKWRIGHT AND HIS CREW BECAME A SINGLE POWERFUL UNIT, WORKING TOGETHER WITH UNERRING SKILL .
HOLD IT, SKIPPER . . . HOLD IT . . . *BOMBS AWAY!*

BUT EVEN THIS KIND OF BOMBING, AT THE DANGEROUS LEVEL OF 500 FEET, WAS TO ARKWRIGHT AN IMPERSONAL THING . . .
RATHER AN EERIE FEELING, SKIPPER, TO BE SITTING WITHIN A QUARTER OF A MILE OF THE WHOLE GERMAN ARMY!
JUDGING FROM THE STUFF THAT'S HITTING OUR WINGS, THEY'RE ALL SHOOTING AT US AT ONCE!

SOON THE AREA OF THE BRIDGE WAS A BILLOWING INFERNO OF FLYING STEEL AND EARTH! THEN THE BLENHEIMS CLIMBED INTO FORMATION AGAIN, AND THUNDERED AWAY TOWARDS THE NORTH . . .
EVERYBODY WITH US?
G FOR GEORGE IS LIMPING A BIT – SOMETHING THE MATTER WITH HIS STARBOARD WHIRLER.
FIGHTER, FIGHTER!

IT WAS TAFFY THOMAS, ALERT AND WARY IN HIS TURRET, WHO HAD SEEN THE BRIEF FLASH OF LIGHT TO SUNWARD!
MESSERSCHMITTS! I COUNT SIX...

BLENHEIMS! IF WE CAN BREAK THEIR FORMATION, THEY'RE HIGHLY VULNERABLE FROM ABOVE... THE TURRETS HAVE ONLY TWO GUNS...

A MERCILESS DOOM STRUCK 'G FOR GEORGE' LIMPING ON ONE ENGINE BEHIND THE OTHERS...
GEORGE HAS BOUGHT IT!
LIKE VULTURES; THEY PICK ON THE STRAGGLERS!

THE VALUE OF CLOSE FORMATION FLYING WAS REVEALED AS THE FIRE FROM THE UPPER TURRETS OF THE SQUADRON CONVERGED INTO A LETHAL FUNNEL — AND THE FIGHTERS, SWEEPING HEAD-ON INTO THE TORRENT OF BULLETS, PULLED UP AND BROKE AWAY...
THEY CAN'T TAKE IT! THEY'VE GOT TO OVERSHOOT! WE'LL RAKE THEM AS THEY FLIP OVER!

ARKWRIGHT GLANCED UP AS A FIGHTER STREAKED OVERHEAD. THERE, ON THE MESSERSCHMITT'S SLATE-GREY BODY, WERE SPECIAL MARKINGS HE HAD KNOWN WELL IN THE DAYS WHEN HE HAD FLOWN FOR ANOTHER COUNTRY UNDER ANOTHER NAME — AND THE REALISATION STRUCK HIM LIKE A HAMMERBLOW...
IT'S METTERLING! HANS METTERLING! THAT'S HIS MESSERSCHMITT! I'VE EVEN SAT IN ITS COCKPIT! I TRAINED THE MAN, GAVE HIM HIS FIRST FLIGHTS IN A BIPLANE! HOW CAN METTERLING BE ATTACKING ME?

IT WAS ONLY THEN THAT THE FULL HORROR OF WAR CAME HOME TO ARKWRIGHT — FOR EVEN AS HE RECOGNISED THE YELLOW LETTERS, A MURDEROUS CONE OF FIRE FROM THREE BRITISH TURRETS CLOSED ON THE ENEMY FIGHTER . . .
DONNER! IT'S *METTERLING* IN THERE — LET HIM GET OUT! STOP FIRING, GUNNER — GIVE THE MAN A CHANCE — GIVE HIM A *CHANCE* . . !

BUT AS ARKWRIGHT'S INCREDIBLE SHOUT CRACKLED OVER THE INTERCOM, THE ME-109 EXPLODED! FRAGMENTS OF WHIRLING METAL RAINED BACK THROUGH THE THUNDERING BOMBERS . . .
ONE UP FOR CHARLIE! HOW DO YOU LIKE *THAT*, SKIPPER?

THE WELSH GUNNER HAD HEARD NOTHING ABOVE THE CHATTER OF HIS BROWNINGS. BUT JOHNNIE STOWELL HAD HEARD HIS SKIPPER'S SHOUT. HE SWUNG ROUND TO LOOK AT ARKWRIGHT CURIOUSLY — BUT THE OTHER HAD RECOVERED HIS COMPOSURE AGAIN . . .
SKIPPER — DID I HEAR YOU SAY YOU *KNEW* THAT HUN?
JOHNNIE — WE'RE IN THE MIDDLE OF A BATTLE! THE TALKING CAN COME LATER.

THE SUDDEN AGONY OF MIND THAT HAD CAUSED ARKWRIGHT TO BETRAY HIMSELF HAD PASSED — AND THE MAN WHO WAS PILOTING THE BLENHEIM WAS ONCE AGAIN THE COOL ROYAL AIR FORCE OFFICER. AGAIN THE FIGHTERS RETURNED TO THE ATTACK — AND THIS TIME, WAR STRUCK CLOSE TO ARKWRIGHT HIMSELF . . .
HE'S HIT OUR STARBOARD!
BELT BACK, TAFFY - GIVE HIM ALL YOU'VE GOT!
I'LL NAIL THE BLIGHTER, SKIPPER, IF IT TAKES EVERY BULLET!

THEN, AS RAPIDLY AS THEY HAD COME, THE FIGHTERS WERE GONE — AND THE BOMBERS CONTINUED ON THEIR WAY TOWARDS BASE. ARKWRIGHT, WITH ONLY ONE GOOD ENGINE, HAD FALLEN BEHIND AND BELOW THE FORMATION . . .
I JUST DON'T GET IT, SKIP! THAT MESSERSCHMITT – IT WAS THE LATEST VERSION OF THE ONE-O-NINE, WITH SPECIAL MARKINGS — YET YOU KNEW IT AT ONCE, AND EVEN CALLED OUT THE NAME OF THE PILOT — METTERLING, YOU SAID HE WAS . . .
FORGET IT, JOHNNIE!

BUT JOHNNIE STOWELL KNEW THAT ARKWRIGHT COULD NEVER HAVE LEARNED THESE THINGS IN SWITZERLAND . . .
YOU *TALK* LIKE A GERMAN – YOU SEEM TO KNOW A LOT ABOUT THE LUFTWAFFE – AND YOU WERE A SKILLED PILOT BEFORE YOU JOINED THIS LOT! NOW JUST *WHAT* DOES THAT ADD UP TO . . !
THE PAST DOESN'T MATTER ANY MORE, JOHNNIE! SOMEDAY I'LL TELL YOU A FEW THINGS – BUT NOT NOW . . .

THEY CAME IN TO A TRICKY LANDING, THEIR MINDS ONCE AGAIN ON THE BUSINESS OF WAR, PERSONAL MATTERS FORGOTTEN . . .
THE STARBOARD WHEEL IS DOWN, ALL RIGHT — BUT WILL IT HOLD!
CONTROL ARE TAKING THE PESSIMISTIC VIEW! I SEE THE FIRE BUGGY AND THE BONE WAGON STANDING BY.

FOR THE REST OF THAT GRIM, EVENTFUL MONTH OF 1940, THE SQUADRON HARASSED THE ENEMY IN FRANCE — AND THEIR BLENHEIMS WERE ON PATROL NEAR THE BEACHES OF DUNKIRK DURING THE GREAT EVACUATION . . .
STUKAS!
LET'S GET AMONGST THEM!

FRANCE FELL AND THE LUFTWAFFE LAUNCHED ITS OWN BOMBERS AGAINST BRITAIN! IT WAS THE TURN OF MEN LIKE JOHNNIE STOWELL'S BROTHER FRANK, IN EIGHT-GUNNED HURRICANES AND SPITFIRES, TO ATTACK THE ENEMY . . .

BUT IN BOMBER COMMAND, THE SPIRIT WAS — RETALIATE! IN EARLY 1941, A DARING DAYLIGHT RAID ON COLOGNE WAS PLANNED AND ARKWRIGHT'S BLENHEIM SQUADRON WAS ONE OF THE THREE THAT COMBINED FOR THE OPERATION...
I KNOW THAT DAYLIGHT MISSIONS ARE DICEY — BUT WE'VE BEEN GIVEN A STRONG FIGHTER COVER — AND I CAN REVEAL THAT THE AIRCRAFT WILL BE WHIRLWINDS — NEW, TWIN-ENGINED JOBS WITH A LONG RANGE AND COLOSSAL ARMAMENT — SO WE'LL BE WELL LOOKED AFTER.

THE NEWS WAS OF SPECIAL INTEREST TO JOHNNIE STOWELL – AND LATER, HE DISCUSSED IT ENTHUSIASTICALLY WITH ARKWRIGHT . . .
MY BROTHER'S ON WHIRLWINDS, SKIPPER! HE WAS TRANSFERRED TO THEM FROM HURRICANES A COUPLE OF MONTHS AGO, BUT ASKED ME TO KEEP THE NEWS UNDER MY HAT!
THEN IT LOOKS AS IF THIS IS GOING TO BE A FAMILY TRIP, JOHNNIE!

PREPARATIONS FOR THE COLOGNE RAID PROGRESSED AND AT A MASS BRIEFING SESSION, PILOTS AND AIRCREW OF ALL THE FIGHTER AND BOMBER SQUADRONS INVOLVED WERE PRESENT . . .
AS LONG AS WE DON'T HIT SOLID FIGHTER OPPOSITION, WE SHOULDN'T HAVE TOO MUCH TROUBLE! THE BOMBERS WILL GO IN AS THREE WAVES WITH THE WHIRLWINDS COVERING US HIGH UP. ALTITUDES AS FOLLOWS . . .
EUROPE

THE GROUP CAPTAIN COVERED HIS SUBJECT THOROUGHLY — AND WHEN HE WAS FINISHED...
JUST A POINT, SIR! IF NO ENEMY FIGHTERS TURN UP, ARE WE PERMITTED TO TAKE THE WHIRLWINDS DOWN INTO THE ACTION!
YOU STAY WHERE WE PUT YOU, STOWELL! DON'T WORRY ABOUT JERRY — HE'LL TURN UP, ALL RIGHT! YOUR JOB IS PROTECT THE BOMBERS!

IT WAS FRANK STOWELL, COMMANDING A WHIRLWIND FLIGHT. WHEN THE BRIEFING WAS OVER, JOHNNIE LED ARKWRIGHT FORWARD TO MEET HIS BROTHER ...
JOHNNIE, YOU SON OF A GUN — HAVEN'T SEEN YOU IN MONTHS! SO THIS IS WHERE YOU'VE DUG YOURSELF IN..!
STILL THE SAME OLD FRANK! MEET MY SKIPPER, JOE ARKWRIGHT, BEST BOMBER PILOT THIS SIDE OF PARADISE!

ARKWRIGHT HELD OUT HIS HAND AS FRANK STOWELL SWUNG TO GREET HIM – *AND THE TWO MEN FROZE*. FOR ARKWRIGHT FOUND HIMSELF FACING THE TALL, LEAN ENGLISHMAN WHO HAD CONFRONTED HIM SO LONG AGO, IN BERNE!
.YOU..!
YOU KNOW EACH OTHER?
YES...WE KNOW EACH OTHER!

FRANK STOWELL, IGNORING THE PROFFERED HAND, WAS STANDING WITH NARROWED EYES – AND ARKWRIGHT, IN SUDDEN PANIC, SPUN ON HIS HEEL, AND WALKED HURRIEDLY AWAY...
WHAT'S UP WITH ARKWRIGHT?
ARKWRIGHT! THAT MAN'S NAME IS WEYMANN – AND HE'S A GERMAN! I MET HIM IN BERNE AT THE OUTBREAK OF WAR – HE WAS FLYING A JUNKERS, THEN! I NEVER FORGET A FACE, AND I CERTAINLY WOULDN'T FORGET *THAT* FACE!

BUT HE CLAIMS TO BE AN AMERICAN!
THEN THERE'S A ROTTEN APPLE IN THE BARREL SOMEWHERE! COME ON — WE'RE GOING TO LOOK INTO THIS!

THEY FOUND ARKWRIGHT IN THE SHADOW OF THE BLENHEIMS...
WEYMANN — I WANT A WORD WITH YOU!
SAY YOUR PIECE — I'M LISTENING!

FRANK STOWELL WAS FAMOUS FOR HIS BOLDNESS AND RUTHLESSNESS AS A FIGHTER ACE — AND NOW ARKWRIGHT GOT A TASTE OF HIS FORCEFUL METHODS...
OKAY, WEYMANN — LET'S COMPARE NOTES! THE LAST TIME WE MET, YOU WERE THREATENING A HARMLESS LITTLE REFUGEE — AND IT MAY INTEREST YOU TO KNOW THAT I GOT HIS FAMILY OUT OF AUSTRIA! YOU WERE QUITE A LAD FOR DEFENDING THE GESTAPO, THEN — SO, WHAT ARE YOU DOING IN BRITISH UNIFORM?
I'M GLAD YOU GOT THEM OUT OF AUSTRIA, STOWELL — AND I'M NOT POSING AS A BRITISH OFFICER!

DON'T GIVE ME THAT–*YOU'RE GERMAN!*
I'VE GOT BRITISH NATURALISATION PAPERS — YOU CAN SEE THEM —
NOW WAIT A MINUTE! WHAT'S GOING *ON*, HERE?

YES, STOWELL – I *WAS* A GERMAN ONCE, *AND* A LOYAL GERMAN! THEN THE GESTAPO STRUCK AT *ME* – AND I FOUND OUT FOR THE FIRST TIME WHAT THEY WERE LIKE! THEY SHOT MY FATHER AND BROTHER WITHOUT REASON OR TRIAL!
A LIKELY STORY, WEYMANN!

JOHNNIE STOWELL COULD SEE THAT ARKWRIGHT PASSIONATELY MEANT EVERY WORD HE SAID...
WOULD YOU LIKE TO SEE WHAT THE GESTAPO DID TO ME — TO SHOW YOU THE WOUND! YOU HAVE NO IDEA HERE WHAT THE GESTAPO ARE LIKE!
SO NOW YOU'RE TRYING TO TELL *ME* ALL THAT! THE SHOE WAS ON THE OTHER FOOT IN SWITZERLAND! HOWEVER, WE'LL SEE WHAT THE AUTHORITIES HAVE TO SAY..!

JOHNNIE SUDDENLY INTERRUPTED, GLARING FIERCELY AT HIS BROTHER...
FRANK, *LISTEN TO ME!* ARKWRIGHT'S ON THE SQUARE — *I'LL* VOUCH FOR HIM! WHY BUST UP A GOOD AIRCREW! IF ARKWRIGHT IS TAKEN OFF BOMBERS AND I'M SWITCHED TO ANOTHER CREW, WE'D BE FINISHED, YOU AND I, *FINISHED!*
OKAY, JOHNNIE! IF THAT'S THE WAY YOU WANT IT — THAT'S THE WAY IT'LL BE!

FRANK STOWELL STARED GRIMLY AT HIS BROTHER FOR A MOMENT — AND THEN STRODE AWAY...
WHERE'S HE GOING? WHAT WILL HE DO?
IT'S ALL RIGHT, ARKWRIGHT! I KNOW MY BROTHER — HE'LL HOLD HIS TONGUE! BUT THINGS WILL BE A BIT STRAINED BETWEEN US FROM NOW ON! LET'S DROP THE SUBJECT!

A WEEK LATER, THE RAID WAS ON. WITHIN THIRTY MINUTES OF TAKE-OFF, THREE SQUADRONS OF BLENHEIMS WERE THUNDERING EAST IN CLOSE FORMATION, HIGH ABOVE THE ENGLISH COAST...
CAN YOU SEE THE FIGHTER COVER YET, TAFFY?
I'M NOT SURE, SKIPPER — PERHAPS IT'S EARLY MORNING SPECKS BEFORE THE EYES...

BUT THE FIGHTER COVER WAS THERE, ALL RIGHT, AT SIXTEEN THOUSAND FEET.

IT WAS AN UNEVENTFUL SEA CROSSING, WITH THE RISING SUN FLARING DEAD AHEAD, AND GLEAMING ON THE PERSPEX WINDOWS OF THE MASSED RANKS OF GENTLY DIPPING AND SWAYING MACHINES. ARKWRIGHT, HIS MIND ON THE MISSION, GAZED CALMLY AHEAD, THE TENSION OF THE PAST WEEK FORGOTTEN — AND NEAR TO HIM, JOHNNIE STOWELL WAS GAZING UP AT THE HUGE, VAULTING SKY...
I SUPPOSE FRANK IS SOMEWHERE UP THERE, KEEPING AN EYE ON THINGS...

BUT THE WHIRLWINDS HAD ALREADY SEEN THE MESSERSCHMITT PACK — AND WITH ENGINES HOWLING AT SUPERCHARGED PITCH, THEY PEELED OFF TO INTERCEPT — EACH CARRYING A BATTERY OF FOUR OERLIKON CANNON IN ITS NOSE, THE DEADLIEST ARMAMENT IN THE SKY . . .

STAY PUT AT ANGELS SIXTEEN, YELLOW LEADER – WE CAN HANDLE THIS! THERE MAY BE OTHERS, HIGHER UP . . !

Chapter 4. BALE OUT!

THE BOMBERS FLEW STEADILY ONWARDS, IGNORING THE PITCHED BATTLE BEING WAGED ABOVE THEM . . .

COLOGNE AHEAD, JOHNNIE.

ARKWRIGHT LEVELLED OFF ON HIS BOMBING RUN. JOHNNIE WAS LYING IN THE TRANSPARENT NOSE, HIS EYE TO THE BOMB-SIGHT — AND TAFFY, IN THE TURRET AMIDSHIPS, WAS SWIVELLING HIS TWIN GUNS AND WATCHING THE HURTLING FIGHTERS WARILY . . .
STEADY— STEADY— BOMBS AWAY!

THEN CAME DISASTER! AS THE BLENHEIM, LIGHTER BY A THOUSAND POUNDS WEIGHT, BUCKED UP THROUGH THE SKY, THERE WAS A VIVID FLASH TO ONE SIDE OF THE CABIN . . .
FLAK! WE'VE BEEN HIT!

AT THE SAME INSTANT, ARKWRIGHT FELT A SEARING BLOW ACROSS HIS LEGS — AND AS HE WRESTLED WITH THE VIBRATING CONTROL-COLUMN, HE SAW, THROUGH THE SHATTERED SIDE-PANELS OF THE CABIN, THAT THE PORT ENGINE WAS A REEKING SCRAP-HEAP . . .
WE'RE IN TROUBLE, JOHNNIE —BIG TROUBLE..!

THEN HE SAW THAT JOHNNIE WAS HANGING IN HIS STRAPS, HIS FLYING-SUIT TERRIBLY LACERATED . . .
FIGHTER! FIGHTER!
JOHNNIE..!
I'VE COPPED IT, SKIPPER, THAT LAST LOT BELTED ME IN THE CHEST!

AS THE CANNON SHELLS FROM THE DIVING ME-109 SLAMMED INTO FUSELAGE AND WINGS, ARKWRIGHT DRAGGED THE CRIPPLED BOMBER INTO A LABOURING TURN, AND DESPERATELY FLICKED OVER HIS R.T. SWITCH . . .
MAYDAY, MAYDAY! Z-ZEBRA CALLING WHIRLWINDS! FIGHTER ON MY TAIL — Z-ZEBRA —

. . . AND A WHIRLWIND, ROCKETING OUT OF A TIGHT ENGAGEMENT WITH ANOTHER OF THE GERMAN FIGHTER PACK, PICKED UP THE CRACKLING MESSAGE . . .
— FIGHTER ON MY TAIL — Z-ZEBRA..!
I SEE YOU, Z-ZEBRA! HOLD TIGHT — I'M COMING!

HOWLING DOWN AT FULL VELOCITY, THE TWIN-ENGINED FIGHTER STREAKED ACROSS THE SKIES TOWARDS THE MESSERSCHMITT ON ARKWRIGHT'S TAIL. ITS FOUR DEADLY CANNON FLARED ALL THE WAY IN FROM MAXIMUM RANGE...
GET A LOAD OF THESE AND LEAVE A LAME DUCK ALONE!

THE WHIRLWIND PILOT'S VOICE CAME CRACKLING OVER THE BLENHEIM'S R.T. AND JOHNNIE WAS ROUSED FROM A PAIN-FILLED COMA...
SKIPPER! THAT'S MY BROTHER'S VOICE! IT'S FRANK!

IN THAT LIGHTNING SWOOP, THE WHIRLWIND BLASTED THE MESSERSCHMITT INTO A SPINNING SHELL-TORN WRECK . . .
THANKS, STOWELL—YOU'VE SAVED JOHNNIE'S LIFE—AND MINE—THOUGH JOHNNIE'S BEEN BADLY KNOCKED ABOUT BY FLAK!
WEYMANN! IT'S YOU!

IT WAS TAKING ARKWRIGHT ALL HIS TIME TO HOLD THE STRICKEN BLENHEIM IN LEVEL FLIGHT . . .
LISTEN, STOWELL! WE'RE IN A BAD WAY! OUR PORT ENGINE'S HAD IT, AND JOHNNIE AND MYSELF ARE BOTH WOUNDED—JOHNNIE BADLY! IF WE BALE OUT, THERE'S A CHANCE THAT JOHNNIE MIGHT GET HELP DOWN THERE IN TIME—BUT THEY'LL SHOOT ME . . .!
IT'S NO MORE THAN YOU DESERVE, WEYMANN!

AS THE BLENHEIM DRAGGED ITSELF NORTHWARD, THE WHIRLWIND CIRCLED ABOVE WITH FRANK STOWELL KEEPING A WARY EYE ON THE AIR BATTLE STILL RAGING TO THE SOUTH-EAST . . .
LET'S DROP OUR PERSONAL DIFFERENCES, STOWELL - I'M DEADLY SERIOUS! WITHOUT FIGHTER COVER, WE'VE NO CHANCE OF GETTING BACK IN THIS STATE. SO I'M ASKING YOU TO STICK AROUND - *FOR JOHNNIE'S SAKE!*
ALL RIGHT, WEYMANN . . .

. . . BUT ONLY FOR JOHNNIE'S SAKE! IF IT WAS YOU ALONE DOWN THERE, WEYMANN, YOU COULD *FRY*, FOR ALL I CARED! THERE'S A DOZEN GOOD BRITISH PILOTS BACK IN THAT INFERNO WHO NEED MY CANNON RIGHT NOW!
THAT'S ALWAYS BEEN THE TROUBLE WITH MY BROTHER FRANK. HE NEVER CHANGES HIS MIND ABOUT ANYTHING, ONCE HE'S MADE IT UP!

THE STRANGE SITUATION HAD RELAXED FRANK STOWELL'S FIGHTER INSTINCTS BY JUST THAT VITAL SPLIT-SECOND – AND IT WAS TAFFY THOMAS, EVER WARY IN HIS TURRET, WHO SUDDENLY SAW THE ENEMY FIGHTER DIVING OUT OF THE SUN . . .
FIGHTER, FIGHTER – HIGH IN THE SUN!
LOOK OUT, STOWELL!

THE WHIRLWIND ACCELERATED DESPERATELY. . .
DIVE TOWARDS US, STOWELL – DIVE!
DON'T TELL ME MY BUSINESS, WEYMANN –

BUT THE SPLIT-SECOND DELAY HAD BEEN FATAL. RAKED AND TORN BY CANNON SHELLS, THE WHIRLWIND WAILED ACROSS THE SKY IN A STREAM OF SMOKE AND WRECKAGE —AND IT WAS TAFFY THOMAS WHO GOT THE ME-109 SQUARE IN THE SIGHTS OF HIS TWIN BROWNINGS.
GOT HIM! GOT HIM!
FRANK...IT CAN'T HAPPEN TO FRANK—
STOWELL..!
THE WHIRLWIND WAS PLUNGING DOWN TO ITS DOOM...
JUMP, STOWELL!
GET JOHNNIE BACK, WEYMANN— GET HIM BACK! IF IT'S THE LAST THING YOU DO!

THEY SAW HIM JUMP CLEAR, AND THE PARACHUTE OPEN...
HE'S MADE IT!
THANK HEAVENS, SKIPPER ... THANK HEAVENS!

THE DAMAGED BLENHEIM WAS ALONE IN THE SKIES — THE SLATE-GREY COASTLINE WAS BENEATH AND COLOGNE LAY FAR BEHIND. AS ARKWRIGHT'S MIND TURNED ONCE AGAIN TO HIS OWN CONDITION, HE REALISED THAT HIS LEFT LEG WAS SHRAPNEL-TORN AND USELESS!
I'D COME FORWARD AND GIVE A HAND WITH JOHNNIE, BUT I DAREN'T LEAVE THE GUNS!
YOU STAY WHERE YOU ARE, TAFF — WE'VE MANAGED THIS FAR, SO WE'LL STICK IT OUT THE REST!
I'M ALL RIGHT... ALL RIGHT...

FOR TWO, GRIM, PAIN-RACKED HOURS, ARKWRIGHT FOUGHT TO HOLD THE SHELL-PIERCED BOMBER STEADY ON ITS COURSE. THEY WERE AT TWO THOUSAND FEET, AND STILL DROPPING, WHEN AT LAST THE ENGLISH COAST CREPT IN TOWARDS THEM – AND ARKWRIGHT THANKFULLY PUMPED DOWN THE WHEELS. BUT ONLY THE STARBOARD WHEEL CAME DOWN!
THE SET-UP GETS DICIER EVERY MINUTE, TAFFY! NOW WE'VE GOT ONLY ONE WHEEL AS WELL AS ONE ENGINE!
YOU'LL MAKE IT, SKIPPER – YOU'VE PULLED US OUT OF WORSE JAMS!
BUT ARKWRIGHT KNEW THAT HE COULD NEVER TAKE THE RISK OF BRINGING THE MACHINE IN WITH JOHNNIE AND TAFFY ON BOARD. CALLING TAFFY FORWARD, HE GOT HIM TO LASH A CORD FROM JOHNNIE'S CHUTE RELEASE HANDLE TO ONE OF THE FITTINGS IN THE CABIN – AND AS THEY CAME IN TOWARDS BASE AT 1,500 FEET, HE GAVE THE ORDER TO BALE OUT.
THIS IS IT, TAFFY – PUSH JOHNNIE OUT FIRST – THEN OUT YOU GO AFTER HIM!
OKAY, SKIPPER – BUT WHAT ABOUT YOURSELF?
I'LL SEE IT THROUGH, TAFF –

AN ORDER WAS AN ORDER— AND JOHNNIE WENT OUT FIRST, FOLLOWED BY THE WELSHMAN...
Z-ZEBRA TO BASE — HAVE ORDERED CREW TO BALE OUT — BUT CAN'T BALE OUT MYSELF. I'M BRINGING Z-ZEBRA IN ON ONE WHEEL AND ONE ENGINE — STAND BY — STAND BY..!

DIPPING THE SHATTERED NOSE, ARKWRIGHT CAME IN TOWARDS THE AIRFIELD, HIS HEAD SWIMMING WITH PAIN, HIS EYES BLURRED AND MISTY...
...NOW THE ONLY LIFE AT STAKE IS MY OWN! YOU ONCE SAID, MY KOMMANDANT, THAT YOUR PILOTS WERE LIKE THE ANCIENT SPARTANS — THEY CAME BACK WITH THEIR SHIELDS OR ON THEM! WELL, I'M COMING BACK WITH MY SHIELD AND ON IT!

THE LONE BOMBER STAGGERED IN LOW, AND THE WATCHERS IN THE CONTROL TOWER KNEW AT ONCE IT COULD NEVER MAKE IT! AS THEY WAITED TENSELY FOR THE PILE-UP, THEY SUDDENLY HEARD OVER THE R.T. AN INCREDIBLE THING — A SAD GERMAN FOLK-SONG, A TALE OF PLACES THAT WOULD NEVER BE SEEN AGAIN, SUNG SOFTLY AND BITTERLY . . . AND WEYMANN WAS SINGING IT, ALMOST TO THE END . . .
. . . I'VE FOUGHT THE GOOD FIGHT. THERE WILL BE NO TOMORROW . . .

WEYMANN WAS KILLED IN THE CRASH – BUT JOHNNIE AND THE WELSH GUNNER HAD BALED OUT SAFELY. WHEN JOHNNIE HAD RECOVERED SUFFICIENTLY TO SEE VISITORS — THE FIRST PERSON TO VISIT HIM WAS HIS C.O.
WELL, JOHNNIE, I'VE GOT NEWS FOR YOU ON TWO SCORES! FIRST, YOUR BROTHER FRANK IS ALIVE – IN A GERMAN LUFTSTALAG! AND SECOND, YOUR LATE SKIPPER, ARKWRIGHT, HAS BEEN AWARDED A POSTHUMOUS D.F.C.! THE VERY FACT THAT HE GOT HIS BLENHEIM HOME AT ALL WAS A SIGN OF BRAVERY AND DEVOTION TO DUTY OF A VERY HIGH ORDER. YOU OWE YOUR LIFE TO HIM, LADDIE!
I KNOW, SIR – AND I'LL NEVER FORGET IT!

...AND JOHNNIE STOWELL NEVER DID FORGET IT. IT WAS THREE MONTHS BEFORE HE WAS FINALLY RETURNED TO HIS OLD SQUADRON. ON HIS FIRST DAY BACK, HE STOOD ALONE FOR A WHILE IN A FAR CORNER OF THE AIRFIELD, AT A PLACE WHERE A LONE BLENHEIM, AFTER A HEROIC AND HOPELESS LANDING, HAD CRASHED.
...I'VE KEPT YOUR SECRET, OLD FRIEND — AND I'LL KEEP IT UNTIL THE END OF THE WAR! FOR WE WERE A GREAT TEAM, AND I'LL STAND BY YOU, AS YOU STOOD BY ME! SOME THINGS WILL NEVER DIE, NOT AS LONG AS MEN KEEP THEM FRESH IN THEIR MEMORY! ARKWRIGHT OR WEYMANN, IT DOESN'T MATTER NOW — YOU FOLLOWED YOUR STAR TO THE END!

ACTION STATIONS
1941 AND THE STEEL TALONS OF THE GERMAN WAR EAGLE WERE THROTTLING THE LIBERTIES AND LIVES OF THE CONQUERED PEOPLES IN EUROPE. YET ONE COUNTRY STILL REMAINED FREE. ON THE ISLAND FORTRESS OF BELEAGUERED BRITAIN, A GALLANT NATION STOOD IN PROUD DEFIANCE OF THE NAZIS. WITH EACH DAY BRITAIN GREW STRONGER, FED BY THE LIFE BLOOD OF GUNS, AMMUNITION, TANKS AND PLANES WHICH THE CONVOYS BROUGHT FROM AMERICA. DAUNTLESSLY THE SHIPS BRAVED THE DANGERS OF THE ATLANTIC-AND THE PERIL LURKING BELOW THE WAVES... THE SEA WOLVES... THE U-BOATS!

Chapter 1. ATTACK FROM BELOW
WITH MANY SHIPS OF WAR KEEPING AN UNCEASING BLOCKADE ON THE GERMAN BATTLE FLEETS, THE ROYAL NAVY WAS STRAINED TO THE LIMIT— AND EACH CONVOY WAS DEFENDED BY ALL TOO FEW WARSHIPS.
SIXTY THREE MERCHANT SHIPS... GUARDED BY ONE LIGHT CRUISER, FOUR DESTROYERS AND TWO CORVETTES! IT'S LIKE A BOY TAKING A HERD OF FAT CATTLE THROUGH A JUNGLE FULL OF TIGERS!
AND WE'VE GOT AS MUCH CHANCE! IF WE GET THROUGH, SIR, WE'LL BE LUCKY!

THE DESTROYERS TWISTED AND TURNED UNENDINGLY THROUGH THE LINES OF LADEN, WALLOWING MERCHANT SHIPS, EVER WATCHFUL FOR THE OMINOUS EYES OF THE SEA WOLVES . . . THE PERISCOPES!
WUNDERBAR! WE ARE IN A PERFECT ATTACK POSITION— LOAD ALL BOW TORPEDO TUBES!
BEARING OF ENEMY SHIPS — ONE-EIGHT — ONE DEGREES!

THIRTY SECONDS LATER A SHATTERING ROAR LIFTED A COLUMN OF WATER MASTHEAD HIGH BESIDE A LUMBERING FREIGHTER.
WHAT'S HAPPENED?— LUMME, SHE'S BEEN TORPEDOED!
SOUND THE ALARM— TORPEDO TRACK AMIDSHIPS!

THE SECOND TORPEDO STRUCK WITH A TREMENDOUS EXPLOSION — AND WATER POURED INTO THE GAPING HOLE . . .
ENGINE ROOM — EMERGENCY SPEED!
PERISCOPE DEAD AHEAD — FOUR HUNDRED YARDS — NOW IT'S GONE!

OVER THE SPOT RACED THE DESTROYER AND FROM HER STERN ROLLED FOUR SINISTER BLACK DRUMS — THE WEAPONS MOST DREADED BY SUBMARINE CREWS — DEPTH CHARGES!
IF WE DON'T GET THE BRUTE, THOSE BRICKS WILL KEEP HIM DEEP UNTIL THE SURVIVORS CAN BE PICKED UP!
WELL, NUMBER ONE, THAT JERRY SUB IS THE FIRST THIS TRIP — BUT NOT THE LAST! FROM HERE ON THEY HUNT IN PACKS!

THE MOMENT THE CONVOY HAD PASSED ON ITS EASTWARD PATH, THE U-BOAT'S RADIO SPARKED INTO LIFE – SUMMONING IT'S DESTRUCTION-HUNGRY BROTHERS . . .
U ONE-O-ONE REPORTING LARGS CONVOY ON COURSE EIGHTY FIVE DEGREES TEN KNOTS — GOOD HUNTING!

THEN THE NIGHTMARE BEGAN FOR THE CONVOY. AGAIN AND AGAIN THE GERMAN SEA WOLVES LAY IN WAIT— AND TIME AFTER TIME THEIR FANGS RIPPED THE SHIPS INTO SHATTERED, SINKING HULKS.
SIGNAL TO ALL SHIPS— TAKE IMMEDIATE ACTION TO KEEP CLEAR OF BURNING SHIPS OR THEY WILL MAKE FINE TARGETS! THEN REFORM CONVOY POSITIONS! IF THEY START STRAGGLING THEY HAVEN'T GOT A CHANCE!
AYE, AYE, SIR!

FOR FIVE DAYS AND NIGHTS THE MEN OF THE ESCORT SHIPS FOUGHT BACK DOGGEDLY AGAINST THE UNDERWATER MENACE — AND REAPED A GRIM REWARD.
GOOD TEAM WORK! ORION BRINGS UP THE SARDINE TINS AND WE OPEN 'EM!
FORRARD TURRETS — FIRE AS YOUR GUNS BEAR!
K 15

STAND BY TO SLIP THE STARBOARD WHALER TO PICK UP SUBMARINE SURVIVORS!
U-251

TWO DAYS LATER THE SAVAGELY MAULED CONVOY REACHED A WEST COAST PORT IN ENGLAND . . .
FORTY ONE – FORTY TWO! THAT'S ALL, SIR, NOT INCLUDING THE ESCORT VESSELS!
GREAT SCOTT! TWENTY ONE SHIPS LOST! AND EVERY ONE OF 'EM FULL OF FOOD OR WEAPONS! WE CAN'T AFFORD THESE LOSSES FOR LONG – AND WHEN WE CAN'T ANY MORE WE'VE LOST THE WAR!

SOON AFTERWARDS THOSE WORDS WERE ECHOED AT A CONFERENCE OF SENIOR NAVAL OFFICERS IN LONDON.
GENTLEMEN – OUR LOSSES IN SHIPPING ARE LEAPING TO A DISASTROUS PEAK! THE U-BOATS ARE BUILDING A BARRIER OF HIGH EXPLOSIVE ACROSS THE ATLANTIC. IF THAT WALL IS COMPLETED – WE MAY NEVER BE ABLE TO TEAR IT DOWN!

OUR SHIPS ARE SINKING A FEW U-BOATS – BUT NOT ENOUGH! I'M SURE THAT IF THE GERMAN SUBMARINE CASUALTIES GO UP, THEY'LL HAVE TO BECOME MORE CAUTIOUS – AND THAT'LL GIVE US TIME WHILE WE BUILD ENOUGH ESCORT CRAFT TO CRACK THAT WALL WIDE OPEN!

SO OUR PLAN MUST BE TO GIVE THE NEXT BIG CONVOY THE MAXIMUM POSSIBLE ESCORT WITH ORDERS TO CRACK DOWN ON THE U-BOATS, SIR!
THAT'S IT – AND IF IT FAILS WE WILL HAVE TO WITHDRAW OUR BLOCKADING SHIPS TO GET THE CONVOYS THROUGH – ALLOWING THE GERMAN FLEET TO SAIL OUT AND CAUSE CHAOS!

BY A STRANGE JEST OF TIME AND FATE. AT THAT VERY MOMENT A GROUP OF GERMAN NAVAL OFFICERS MET IN HIGH SPIRITS IN A ROOM IN WILHELMSHAVEN.

EVERY U-BOAT COMMANDER LEAPED EAGERLY TO HIS FEET WITH SHOUTS OF APPROVAL. THEN VON KLAUSMAN'S LIFTED HAND SILENCED THEM.

MEANWHILE, ON THE OTHER SIDE OF THE ATLANTIC, A WEEK LATER, TWO TOUGH AMERICAN MARINES STOOD GUARDING THE GATES OF THE U.S. NAVY YARD AT BOSTON.
WHAT D' YOU WANT, KIDDO?
I'M JOINING A BRITISH DESTROYER UNDER REPAIR HERE, ~ THE EXCALIBUR. I'VE COME DOWN FROM NEW YORK BY TRAIN I'VE GOT MY PAPERS UNDER MY CAP!

HIS PASS CHECKED, THE YOUNG BRITISH SAILOR STRODE EAGERLY THROUGH THE GATES.
HECK, SAM– THAT LIMEY IS HARDLY DRY BEHIND THE EARS! NOBODY CAN TELL ME THAT THE BRITISH WILL WIN THE WAR WITH SCHOOL KIDS! LIKE THAT!
YEAH~ GUESS WE'LL JUST HAVE TO STEP IN AND SAVE 'EM SOONER OR LATER!

UNAWARE OF THE YANKS' COMMENTS, ABLE-SEAMAN KEN HOLT WENT ON LOOKING FOR HIS SHIP.
E47
WHAT A BEAUTY! AT LAST I'M REALLY IN THE NAVY!

JUST THEN A JEEP PULLED UP BEHIND KEN...
MORNING, SEAMAN! IF YOU'VE GOT A FREE HAND, TAKE THAT SMALL CASE ABOARD FOR ME, WILL YOU?
AYE, AYE, SIR!

THE OFFICER LED THE WAY UP THE GANGWAY.
LIEUTENANT ROBERT MEADOWS, ROYAL NAVAL RESERVE, REPORTING FOR DUTY AS FIRST LIEUTENANT IN EXCALIBUR!
WELCOME ABOARD, SIR. I'LL HAVE YOU TAKEN TO YOUR CABIN ~ AND WE WOULD HAVE COLLECTED YOUR LUGGAGE FROM THE WHARFSIDE FOR YOU, SIR!

FOR A MOMENT BOB MEADOWS THOUGHT THE YOUNG OFFICER'S VOICE CARRIED A REBUKE. BUT THERE WAS NO SIGN OF IT IN HIS BLANKLY CHEERFUL FACE.
ABLE-SEAMAN KENNETH HOLT REPORTING FOR DUTY IN EXCALIBUR, SIR!
NOW, WAS THAT BEANPOLE TRYING TO HINT THAT BECAUSE I CARRIED MY OWN SUITCASES ABOARD, I'D NEVER DO FOR THE REGULAR NAVY?

BOB WENT ON AND WAS SHOWN TO THE SHIP CAPTAIN'S CABIN.
I'M GLAD YOU'RE ABOARD AT LAST, MISTER MEADOWS~ I'VE BEEN EXPECTING YOU FOR OVER A WEEK!
I'M SORRY, SIR~ MY TRANSFER TO EXCALIBUR WAS DATED A WEEK AGO. BUT I ASKED FOR A POSTPONEMENT BECAUSE THE SKIPPER OF MY MERCHANT SHIP WAS SUDDENLY TAKEN ILL!

LIEUTENANT~COMMANDER JAMES BAKER, D.S.C., R.N., STARED AT HIS NEW FIRST LIEUTENANT IN AMAZEMENT.
DO YOU MEAN YOU'VE JUST COME FROM A MERCHANT VESSEL, AND NOT FROM A WARSHIP?
YES, SIR~ I UNDERSTOOD THAT I WAS THE ONLY OFFICER AVAILABLE. UP TO LAST WEEK I WAS FIRST MATE ON THE TANKER~ GLENCARROW!

BAKER'S BROWS KNITTED IN A FROWN..
MY LAST NUMBER ONE WAS INJURED WHEN WE RAMMED A JERRY SUB — HENCE THE REPAIRS WE HAD DONE! THEY'RE FINISHED NOW BUT I WAS ALSO EXPECTING A RATING AS REPLACEMENT BEFORE WE SAILED!
ONE CAME ABOARD WITH ME, SIR — IT'S PROBABLY HIM!

KEN HOLT HAD BEEN DETAILED OFF TO A MESS DECK, WHERE HE FOUND A VARIED WELCOME.
COR, NOW THE FLIPPING NAVY IS RAIDING THE NURSERY! WHAT SHIP YOU FROM, SONNY BOY?
WELL — UH — I HAVEN'T BEEN IN ONE BEFORE — YOU SEE THIS IS MY FIRST POSTING! MY NAME'S KEN HOLT!
GLAD TO KNOW YOU, KEN I'M SWEDE JOHNSON!

A GLEAM OF SLYNESS CREPT INTO "TICKER" GRIMES' LITTLE EYES AS KEN'S WORDS TUMBLED OUT...
WELL, GOLDILOCKS, YOU'RE IN THE SAME DUTY WATCH AS ME – "TICKER" GRIMES – AND I RECKON YOU AND ME ARE GOING TO HAVE SOME FUN!
I'M GLAD TO HAVE ONE FRIEND ALREADY! ON THE MERCHANT SHIP FROM ENGLAND TO NEW YORK I DIDN'T HAVE A CHANCE TO MAKE ANY FRIENDS AT ALL!

GRIMES NOTICED KEN'S FACE PALE SLIGHTLY AS HE SPOKE, BUT SUDDENLY THERE WAS NO TIME TO WONDER AT THIS...
ATTENTION! ALL HANDS TO STATIONS FOR LEAVING HARBOUR!
JUST FOLLOW ME, YOUNGSTER – I'LL SHOW YOU WHERE TO GO!

FOR WITH THE ARRIVAL OF THE TWO NEW CREW MEMBERS, EXCALIBUR WAS READY FOR ACTION —— AND LIEUTENANT-COMMANDER BAKER WAS WASTING NO TIME . . .
CAST OFF FORRARD. STAND BY TO CAST OFF AFT ! SLOW AHEAD BOTH ENGINES !
SLOW AHEAD BOTH !

HER WHITE ENSIGN STREAMING IN THE BREEZE, EXCALIBUR WAS A MAGNIFICENT SPECTACLE OF POWER AND GRACE AS SHE GLIDED THROUGH THE CROWDED HARBOUR TOWARDS THE OPEN SEA.
GEE—JUST WATCH THAT BABY GO ! I KINDA FEEL SORRY FOR ANY KRAUT SUB SHE STARTS CHASING !
THEM GUNS LOOK PURTY NICE FROM HERE— BUT I BET WHEN THEY OPEN UP SOMEONE'S FOR TROUBLE !

AS THE WATCH OFF DUTY WERE DISMISSED TO GO BELOW AGAIN. JOHNSON TURNED TO KEN BESIDE HIM ON THE AFT DECK.
YOU DON'T LOOK SO GOOD. WHAT'S UP, YOUNGSTER?
FEEL ALL SORT OF GIDDY — I'LL BE OKAY!
YOU'D BETTER GO DOWN TO THE SICKBAY AND SEE IF THE PILL PEDLAR CAN FIX YOU UP!

BUT A FEW MINUTES BEFORE KEN REACHED THE TINY SICKBAY, THE CHIEF PETTY OFFICER IN CHARGE HAD ANOTHER PATIENT — TICKER GRIMES!
HONEST, CHIEF, THIS EAR-ACHE'S AGONY — YOU GOT TO HELP ME!
DODGING WORK AGAIN, GRIMES, BY REPORTING SICK, EH? WELL, YOU CAN'T SWING THE LEAD WITH ME, YOU SKIVER!

BARELY A MINUTE LATER THE SICKBAY HAD ITS NEXT PATIENT — AND THE CHIEF'S JAW DROPPED!

COR LOVE OLD RILEY! I HAVEN'T SEEN THIS FOR THE LAST TWENTY YEARS OF PILL PUSHING — A *SAILOR — SEASICK!*

ALL MY LIFE I'VE WANTED TO BE IN THE NAVY—AND I TURN OUT TO BE USELESS AS A SAILOR!
TAKE THIS, BOY—AND STOP WORRYING! I WILL FIND SOMETHING TO CURE YOU!

THE C.P.O. WATCHED IN SILENT SYMPATHY AS KEN STAGGERED TO HIS FEET AND STUMBLED OUT. A MOMENT LATER, TICKER GRIMES POKED HIS FACE AROUND THE CURTAIN!
HEY, CHIEF—MY EAR'S MUCH BETTER—SO I'LL SHOVE OFF NOW!

TICKER HURRIED BACK TO THE MESS-DECK, GRINNING TO HIMSELF AT HAVING FOUND SOMETHING EVEN MORE AMUSING THAN DUTY DODGING.
YOU SHOULD HAVE STUCK TO SAILING YOUR BOAT ON THE PARK POND, HOLT—OR DID THE BIG WAVES THERE MAKE YOU FEEL FUNNY, TOO, YOU DUMB LANDLUBBER!

I'LL KNOCK THOSE WORDS DOWN YOUR THROAT, GRIMES!
YOU ARE WELCOME TO TRY— IF YOU CAN WALK THIS FAR!

HAVEN'T YOU GOT YOUR SEA-LEGS YET, SAILOR-BOY? WELL GET THIS— NOBODY FALLS AT TICKER GRIMES' FEET UNLESS MY FISTS PUT 'EM THERE—— LIKE THIS!

TICKER'S CLUBBING FIST HAMMERED DOWN — AND STOPPED AN INCH FROM KEN'S JAW AS SWEDE'S GREAT HAND CLOSED AROUND THE BULLY'S WRIST!
HEY LEGGO! YOU'RE BREAKING MY WRIST! AWW!
LIFT THE BOY UP NICE AND EASY, YOU BILGE RAT, OR YOU'LL BE SEARCHING THE SCUPPERS FOR YOUR TEETH!

HASTILY TICKER OBEYED. . . AND AS KEN STOOD UP, SWEDE'S MILD EYES BECAME STEEL DRILLS BORING INTO GRIMES' FLINCHING FACE.
LISTEN YOU DOZY HALF-BAKED APOLOGY FOR A MATELOT — YOU TRY ANY TRICKS ON YOUNG HOLT AGAIN — AND YOU'LL THINK A GUN TURRET FELL ON YOU! . . .
YEAH OKAY, SWEDE I WAS ONLY KIDDING ANYWAY!

Chapter 2. THE WOLF PACK

THE FOLLOWING MORNING, ***EXCALIBUR*** JOINED UP WITH HER CONVOY IN NEW YORK HARBOUR.

AS BOB LOWERED THE BINOCULARS, HE TURNED TO MEET THE NARROWED GAZE OF THE DESTROYER CAPTAIN.
TAKE HER UP ALONGSIDE THE HECTOR, NUMBER ONE. I'M GOING TO MY CABIN TO GET THE CODE BOOKS READY TO READ OUT ORDERS!
AYE AYE, SIR!

AS LIEUTENANT-COMMANDER BAKER DISAPPEARED DOWN THE BRIDGE LADDER, BOB GRINNED TO HIMSELF.
HALF AHEAD BOTH! ALTER COURSE THREE POINTS TO PORT!
SO THE SKIPPER WANTS TO SEE HOW I CAN HANDLE HIS SHIP EH? WELL, I WON'T KEEP HIM IN DOUBT FOR LONG!

SMOOTHLY THE R.N.R. OFFICER BROUGHT EXCALIBUR GLIDING GENTLY IN TOWARDS HECTOR'S SIDE. AT EXACTLY THE RIGHT MOMENT BOB ORDERED SLOW ASTERN, ON THE ENGINES . . . AND THEN SUDDENLY IT HAPPENED!
LOOK OUT, SIR! SHE'S GOING TO HIT US!
HARD ASTERN BOTH!

THE SEA BOILED UNDER EXCALIBUR'S STERN AS HER TURBINES DESPERATELY DRAGGED HER AWAY FROM THE CRUISER'S SWINGING BULK. WITH A GENTLE CRUNCH THE SHIPS TOUCHED — AND PARTED.
WHEW! THAT WAS TOO CLOSE FOR COMFORT! LUCKY IT COST US ONLY A COAT OF PAINT!
IF YOU'D HAD A MAN ON THE FOC'SLE, NUMBER ONE, HE'D HAVE WARNED YOU OF THAT MERCHANTMAN'S WAKE, PUSHING HECTOR'S STERN OVER!

THERE WAS NOTHING BOB COULD SAY— THE CAPTAIN WAS RIGHT— AND IN THE ROYAL NAVY THERE WAS NO ROOM FOR BAD LUCK EXCUSES.
I'LL TAKE OVER, MISTER MEADOWS— WHEN HECTOR'S CAPTAIN COMES OVER, WILL YOU CONVEY THE ORDER CASE TO MY CABIN, WITHOUT DAMAGING IT, OF COURSE!
AYE AYE, SIR!
COAST GUARD

WHEN THE CONVOY SAILED SHORTLY BEFORE SUNSET THAT DAY, EXCALIBUR FELL IN ON THE STARBOARD FLANK AS DETAILED BY THE SECRET ORDERS.
THIS IS THE TIME TO CLEAN THESE BEAUTIES, KEN. WHEN WE REACH U-BOAT ALLEY IN A COUPLE OF DAYS, WE'LL BE DARNED PLEASED WE DID! HEY— YOU STILL FEELING ROUGH?
JUST A BIT FRAGILE, SWEDE— CAN'T SEEM TO GET MY SEA LEGS!

FOR TWO DAYS THE LUMBERING, ILL-ASSORTED CONVOY PLOUGHED THROUGH THE GREY ATLANTIC WASTES, DEFYING THE PERILS OF THE SEA — AND HEADING FOR THE DANGER WHICH LURKED AHEAD.
THE NEWS WE WAIT FOR, HERR KAPITAN?
JA! U.232 IS SHADOWING A LARGE BRITISH CONVOY. WE WILL KNOW EVERY MOVE IT MAKES — UNTIL WE CLOSE IN FOR THE KILL!

LICKING HIS THIN LIPS AS IF IN ANTICIPATION, VON GROST SNAPPED OUT HARSH ORDERS TO THE RADIO OPERATOR.
ALL U-BOATS GATHER POSITION APFEL AT X.K.R. TIME! PRIORITY ONE. AND WHEN THE WOLF PACK STRIKES — THAT CONVOY WILL BE TORN TO PIECES!

TWENTY HOURS LATER, THE FIRST DISMAL LIGHT OF AN ATLANTIC DAWN TIPPED THE TOSSING WAVES WITH SILVER — AND OUTLINED THE BLACK SINISTER SHAPES SLINKING AMONGST THEM.
WUNDERBAR! ALL HERE — AND IMPATIENT TO SHOW THEIR FANGS! SIGNAL FOR ATTACK PLAN TO COMMENCE!

LIKE TEN GREAT SEA SLUGS, THE U-BOATS SLID BELOW THE SURFACE — EACH ONE A CARRIER OF DEATH AND DESTRUCTION — — AIMED FOR THE HEART OF THE BRITISH CONVOY!
U220

IN THE EYE-STRAINED VAGUENESS OF THAT SAME DAWN, H.M.S. EXCALIBUR PATROLLED CEASELESSLY HER STATION TO THE STARBOARD OF THE CONVOY.
I'LL BE STAYING ON THE BRIDGE, NUMBER ONE. I'M EXPECTING AN ORDER FROM HECTOR TO CLOSE UP ALL WATCHES TO BATTLE STATIONS — SO WE'LL DO IT NOW!
THAT MEANS WE'RE IN JERRY'S FAVOURITE HUNTING GROUNDS! AND A CONVOY OF THIS SIZE WILL MAKE THE U-BOAT CAPTAIN'S MOUTH WATER!

BOB COULD NEVER KNOW HOW TRUE HIS WORDS WERE — FOR AT THAT VERY MOMENT...

EYES GLUED TO THE PERISCOPE, VON GROST WAITED. HE SNAPPED A COMMAND... THEN A SECOND... AND TWO SLIM TORPEDOES LEAPED FROM THE U-BOAT BOWS.

TWENTY SECONDS LATER, A SHATTERING ROAR LIFTED A COLUMN OF YELLOW TINGED, BOILING WATER HIGH OVER THE SEA WOLF'S FIRST VICTIM . . .
ANOTHER HIT BEYOND FIRST TARGET, SIR!
TORPEDOES CAME FROM OUR STARBOARD, SIR!
FULL AHEAD, EMERGENCY SPEED! ALTER COURSE TWENTY DEGREES TO STARBOARD!

EXCALIBUR LEAPED FORWARD LIKE AN UNLEASHED GREYHOUND ~ AND SQUAT BLACK DRUMS ROLLED OVER HER STERN AS SHE RACED ACROSS THE SUSPECT AREA . . .
NO CONTACT ON ASDIC, SIR!
HE'S PROBABLY CUT HIS MOTORS AND IS SLIDING SLOWLY DOWN! WE'LL GIVE HIM ANOTHER DOSE WITH DEEPER SETTING ON THE DEPTH CHARGES!

THE SECOND PATTERN OF DEADLY DEPTH CHARGES EXPLODED ALL AROUND THE POWERLESS U-BOATS. DEEP BENEATH THE SURFACE . . .

SHOCK WAVES SHUDDERED THROUGH THE WATER AND BEAT ON U-121'S HULL LIKE GREAT HAMMER BLOWS. SHE SLID DEEPER, DESPERATELY SEARCHING FOR SAFETY— AND IN VAIN!
U-121

ON THE NORTH SIDE OF THE WIDE-SPREAD GATHERING OF MERCHANT SHIPS A TANKER EXPLODED IN A VIVID FLASH OF EYE SEARING FLAME— AND WAS GONE, COMPLETELY DISINTEGRATED.
PERISCOPE GREEN ZERO FIVE, SIR!
ENGINE ROOM— MAXIMUM REVS! SOUND ALARM SIGNAL FOR CREW TO STAND BY TO RAM!

AT THIRTY KNOTS THE DESTROYER KNIFED THROUGH THE WAVES TOWARDS THE TELL-TALE PERISCOPE. IT SEEMED TO TURN ITS EVIL EYE AND VANISH AS IF IN PANIC — BUT TOO LATE . . .
HARD ASTERN! IF WE DON'T DISENGAGE, THE SUB WILL DRAG OUR BOWS UNDER!

WITH THE GRINDING GROANS AND SHRILL SHRIEKS OF TORTURED METAL, THE DESTROYER DRAGGED HERSELF FREE OF THE SHATTERED SUBMARINE — LEAVING THE U-BOAT TO SLIDE SILENTLY BENEATH THE WATER FOR THE LAST TIME . . .
NO SERIOUS DAMAGE IN THE BOWS, SIR — THE PUMPS CAN CONTROL THE LEAKING!
GET THE FORRARD BULKHEADS SHEARED UP, NUMBER ONE — I DON'T WANT 'EM GIVING WAY UNDER THE PRESSURE WHEN WE START MOVING AT SPEED AGAIN!

MEANWHILE, *EXCALIBUR* WAS TWIRLING AND TURNING ON A RELENTLESS PATROL OF HER SECTION OF THE CONVOY. DOWN ON THE AFTER DECK, TICKER GRIMES WAS SUDDENLY A POPULAR MAN.
HOT COCOA AND CORNED BEEF SANDWICHES, ME LUCKY LADS. IF YOU DON'T WANT IT, I'LL FEED IT TO THE FISHES!
TRUST YOU, TICKER, TO GET DETAILED OFF FOR THAT CUSHY JOB! ANYWAY, YOU'RE FINISHED NOW — HAND 'EM OVER!

AS KEN FILLED HIS MUG WITH STEAMING HOT COCOA, TICKER'S HATCHET FACE SPLIT IN A SLY GRIN . . .
WELL, WELL — OUR HAPPY LITTLE LAD'S GETTING ALL DARING — AND HAVING SOMETHING TO EAT!
OPEN YOUR MOUTH AGAIN, TICKER, AND I'LL MAKE YOU EAT THE BUCKET — HANDLE AND ALL!

TICKER'S SMIRK DIED AS HE STARED AT KEN — AND FOR THE FIRST TIME HE SAW THAT THE YOUNG SAILOR WAS ANYTHING BUT SICK! PICKING UP THE HALF-EMPTY BUCKET, HE SLOUCHED OFF TO THE NEXT GUN TEAM.
THAT SHOOK HIM RIGID, KEN — GLAD YOU'RE FEELING OKAY NOW!
FUNNY THING IS, SWEDE, I HAVEN'T HAD A CHANCE TO THINK ABOUT BEING SICK — SO I HAVEN'T BEEN! THE EXCITEMENT'S MADE ME FORGET ALL ABOUT IT!

THEN SUDDENLY A MUFFLED ROAR SWUNG ALL EYES FORWARD AND NECKS CRANED TO SEE AHEAD OF THE RACING DESTROYER . . .
THE SCIMITAR'S GOT A TIN FISH IN THE RIBS!
SHE'S HAD IT, SWEDE!

ON THE BRIDGE, LIEUTENANT-COMMANDER BAKER GAVE THE STRICKEN SHIP AHEAD ONE GLANCE AND RAPPED OUT AN ORDER...
SCIMITAR WILL GO DOWN IN FIVE MINUTES, NUMBER ONE — WE'RE GOING TO PICK UP SURVIVORS. RIG THE NETS OVER THE SIDES IMMEDIATELY. WE'VE GOT TO BE FAST — EVERY SECOND WE'RE THERE WE'LL BE A SITTING DUCK TO A U-BOAT!

AND THAT VERY THOUGHT WAS ALSO BURNING IN ANOTHER MAN'S MIND — KAPITAN VON GROST IN U.220!
DOWN PERISCOPE! OUR TORPEDO HIT ON THE STARBOARD SIDE — THEREFORE THE SECOND DESTROYER WILL COME UP ON THE PORT SIDE! AND WE WILL ALSO BE ON THAT SIDE — WAITING! FULL AHEAD BOTH ENGINES, FOR HALF A MINUTE!
RELOAD BOW TUBES AND STAND BY TO FIRE!

AS *EXCALIBUR* LEAPED TO THE AID OF HER STRICKEN SISTER SHIP, AN OBSTINATE SUSPICION NAGGED IN BOB MEADOW'S MIND.
WHAT IF THAT SUB CAPTAIN WORKS OUT OUR NEXT MOVE, SIR ?
FOR ONCE WE THINK ALIKE, MISTER MEADOWS!
STOP ALL ENGINES! ASDIC OPERATOR ~ TURN ON YOUR BOX OF TRICKS!

AND IN A TINY CRAMPED COMPARTMENT BEHIND THE BRIDGE, A TAUT-FACED LEADING-SEAMAN SAT OVER HIS ASDIC APPARATUS . . . EVERY SENSE FOCUSSED ON THE DIALS BEFORE HIM.
NO CONTACT ~ NO CONTACT ~ NO ~ *WAIT A MINUTE! YES ~ LOUD AND CLEAR ECHO ~ READING RED ONE ZERO!*

Chapter 3. THE SURFACE RAIDER

ON THE BRIDGE, LIEUTENANT-COMMANDER BAKER WAITED FOR NO MORE.

ENGINE ROOM—FULL AHEAD BOTH! ALTER COURSE PORT TEN DEGREES!

THE U-BOAT COMMANDER TURNED THE PERISCOPE — AND FROZE WITH A STUNNING FEAR FOR A SECOND.

THEN, IN THE FLICKER OF A SINGLE PULSE BEAT, VON GROST SCREAMED A DESPERATE COMMAND.
DOWN PERISCOPE! DIVE—DIVE—DIVE! THE ENGLISHER IS GOING TO RAM US!

U.220 LURCHED TO A FRIGHTENING ANGLE OF DIVE AND PLUNGED DOWN TOWARDS THE BLACKNESS OF THE DEEP. SUDDENLY— THERE WAS A RENDING CRUNCH— A THUDDING JAR— AND WATER SPURTED INTO THE DAMAGED U-BOAT.
GET THE DAMAGE CONTROL PARTY TO PLUG THOSE FRACTURES. HIMMEL— WE'RE LUCKY WE'VE ONLY LOST THE PERISCOPE.

ON THE SEA ABOVE, EXCALIBUR MADE A SWEEPING, SLIDING TURN AND CAME IN AGAIN TOWARDS THE SCIMITAR'S SWIMMING CREW.
WE HIT THAT SUB FOR SURE, SIR – BUT IT DIDN'T EVEN SLOW US DOWN!
WE ONLY GOT A TOUCH, MISTER MEADOWS – BUT IT WAS ENOUGH TO SEND HER SCUTTLING DEEP! UNFORTUNATELY WE CAN'T DEPTH CHARGE HER WITH ALL THOSE CHAPS IN THE WATER!

THE WOUNDED AND EXHAUSTED SURVIVORS FROM SCIMITAR WERE QUICKLY LIFTED ABOARD EXCALIBUR, WHERE THEY HUDDLED TOGETHER ON THE DECKS – TO WATCH THE END OF THEIR GREAT HEARTED SHIP.
DOUBLE UP, TICKER – THOSE SCIMITAR BLOKES NEED ALL THE COCOA THE COOK'S GOT – BUCKETS OF IT!
RN
RIGHT, SWEDE!

WITH A FINAL GUSH OF ESCAPING AIR, SCIMITAF SLID BENEATH THE GREEDY GREY WAVES ~ AND LIPS GREW THIN AMONGST THE WATCHING SURVIVORS.
SHE WAS A FINE SHIP — AND SOME FINE LADS HAVE GONE DOWN WITH HER! IF ONLY I COULD GET MY HANDS ON THOSE JERRIES, I'D . . .
WE ALL HAD MATES ON SCIMITAR ~ I SURE HOPE WE GET A CHANCE AT THAT SUB!

LATER THAT DAY, THE SCIMITAR'S CREW WERE TRANSFERRED TO A MERCHANTMAN. AND TO THE CRUISER JASON, WHICH HAD FIRST CLASS MEDICAL FACILITIES FOR THE WOUNDED . . .
MESSAGE FROM JASON, SIR ~ COMPLETE TRANSFER WITH MAXIMUM SPEED!
LIKE NELSON, WE HAVEN'T SEEN THAT SIGNAL! I'M NOT GOING TO RISK THOSE POOR LADS' LIVES BY MAKING 'EM JUMP FOR IT. HUH ~ ANYWAY, LAST ONE'S COMING ABOARD NOW!

FOR TWO MORE DREAD FILLED DAYS THAT MERCILESS BATTLE WENT ON BETWEEN THE CONVOY AND THE RAVAGING SEA WOLVES AGAIN AND AGAIN THE U-BOAT PACK STRUCK, CLAIMING MORE VICTIMS~ BUT EACH TIME THEY PAID A HEAVY PRICE. ON THE THIRD DAY . . .
GENTLEMEN~ I THINK WE WILL WIN YET! WE'VE LOST TWENTY NINE SHIPS ~ AND WE CAN CLAIM EIGHT CONFIRMED U-BOATS SUNK! THE ESCORTS HAVE DONE MAGNIFICENTLY~ ONLY THROUGH THEM HAVE WE MANAGED TO BREAK THROUGH!

EVERYTHING ABOUT THE GERMAN TACTICS POINT TO THEM BEING ONE FLOTILLA~ TEN SUBS IN ALL — WE'VE BAGGED EIGHT, THERE ARE ONLY TWO LEFT ~ AND THEY MUST BE NEAR THE END OF THEIR TETHER!

THE CONVOY COMMANDER SWEPT THE TIREO FACES OF THE OFFICERS IN FRONT OF HIM ~ SEEING IN EACH ONE THE STRAIN OF JAGGED NERVES...
BUT WE'RE NOT OUT OF TROUBLE YET! THE SIX SHIPS MARKED WITH A STAR ARE HAVING DIFFICULTY IN KEEPING UP WITH THE REST OF THE CONVOY. I PROPOSE TO LEAVE THEM BEHIND ~ OUT AS A SMALL SEPARATE CONVOY! EXCALIBUR WILL ALSO BE LEFT AS THEIR ESCORT!

AN HOUR LATER, EXCALIBUR PULLED OUT OF HER MAIN ESCORT STATION AND HEADED FOR A SMALL KNOT OF SHIPS AT THE REAR OF THE MERCHANT VESSELS.
HEARD THE LATEST BUZZ? WE'VE BEEN LEFT BEHIND WITH SIX LAME DUCKS TO ACT AS THEIR FLIPPING ESCORT, WHILE THE REST GO ON! COR, OF ALL THE STONEY LUCK!
STOP GROUSING, TICKER~ WITHOUT US THOSE CIVVY SHIPS WOULDN'T STAND AN EARTHLY OF GETTING HOME!

A MILE AWAY, HIDDEN AMONG THE TOSSING, WHITE TIPPED WAVES, THE EMERGENCY PERISCOPE OF U-220 WATCHED THE *EXCALIBUR*'S MEN MOVE WITH A BALEFUL STARE . . .
DONNER WETTER! AS I HOPED, THAT CURSED CONVOY IS LEAVING ITS STRAGGLERS~ BUT ALSO THE DESTROYER WHICH NEARLY GOT US!

WE HAVE ONE TORPEDO ~ AND WE ARE THE ONLY U-BOAT LEFT. NO REPLY FROM ANY OF THE OTHERS EXCEPT 226 ~ AND SHE IS LIMPING BACK TO BASE. TOO BADLY DAMAGED TO FIGHT ON!

EYES GLITTERING WITH DRIVING FURY, VON GROST PACED THE TINY CONTROL ROOM LIKE A CAGED ANIMAL. THEN HE WAS FORCED TO STOP AS A RADIO OPERATOR STEPPED UP TO HIM . . .
WUNDERBAR! GREAT NEWS INDEED! THE PRINZ WILHELM IS AT SEA AS A RAIDER ~ AND HEADING FOR THIS AREA ~ ~ THOSE STRAGGLERS ARE OURS!

TWENTY SECONDS LATER A CODED WIRELESS MESSAGE FLASHED FROM THE U 220 . . .
U 220 TO PRINZ WILHELM ~ SMALL ENEMY CONVOY POSITON . MAKE TOP SPEED ~ WE WILL DELAY ENEMY IF POSSIBLE!

Chapter 4: Enemy Defeated

THE SLEEK GREY WARSHIP SURGED FORWARD ~ YET ALREADY THERE WAS AN OMINOUS BLACK PLUME OF SMOKE BURSTING OUT OF THE STRICKEN TANKER'S BOWS . . .
MESSAGE FROM TANKER, SIR! READS FORWARD . . . WATER-TIGHT . . . DOORS . . . HOLDING. STOP. FIRE . . CONFINED . . . TO . . . NUMBER ONE . . . TANK. STOP. MUST . . . HAVE . . . MORE . . . MEN . . TO . . FIGHT . . . IT. STOP. CAN . . . YOU . . . SPARE . . . SOME?
BY HEAVENS! THEY'RE SITTING ON TWO THOUSAND TONS OF LIQUID DYNAMITE AND THEY'RE NOT GIVING IN!

MISTER MEADOWS ~ WE MUST TRY TO SAVE THAT TANKER! I CAN'T ORDER ANYBODY TO GO, BUT WILL YOU LEAD A PARTY OVER TO HER TO FIGHT THAT BLAZE?
GIVE ME FIVE MINUTES TO MUSTER SOME VOLUNTEERS, SIR ~ THEN TAKE US ALONGSIDE!

MEADOWS SOON FOUND HIS VOLUNTEERS — ON THE GUN DECK AFT. AND STRANGELY ENOUGH, TICKER GRIMES WAS CLOSE BEHIND KEN AND SWEDE . . .
WE'LL HAVE TO JUMP FOR IT AS EXCALIBUR TOUCHES THE TANKER — AND THERE'LL ONLY BE ONE CHANCE!
SOMEHOW I THOUGHT YOU'D BE COMING, TICKER!
NOW I'VE BEEN KICKED OUT OF THE GALLEY, I'VE GOT TO FIND SOMEWHERE WARM TO GO!

THE DESTROYER KNIFED IN TOWARDS THE TANKER. FOR A BRIEF MOMENT THEY TOUCHED — AND THEN EXCALIBUR SKIDDED AWAY . . .
FOLLOW ME — AT THE DOUBLE!
OOW! LEGGO — NO DON'T!
MAKE UP YOUR MIND, CHUM!

CLOSE BEHIND MEADOWS THE NAVAL PARTY RACED ON TO THE BRIDGE...
HOW CAN MY BOYS HELP, SKIPPER?
WE'LL FIND 'EM FIRE FIGHTING GEAR AND SEND 'EM FORRARD TO TACKLE NUMBER ONE TANK. MY ENGINES ARE OKAY, BUT I DAREN'T USE 'EM — ANY MOVEMENT WILL FAN THE FIRE OUT OF CONTROL. SO WE HAVE TO STAY HERE UNTIL WE BEAT IT— — OR BLOW UP!

JUST THEN, KEN'S SEARCHING EYES NARROWED ON A SMUDGE OF SMOKE ON THE HORIZON...
SMOKE ON PORT BEAM HORIZON, SIR!
HMM! PROBABLY ONE OF OURS— BUT WE'LL MAKE SURE!

AS THE POWERFUL BINOCULARS FOCUSSED, BOB MEADOWS' BREATH CAUGHT HARSHLY IN HIS THROAT . . .
GREAT GLORY! I KNOW THAT OUTLINE, EVEN HEAD ON — IT'S THE PRINZ WILHELM, JERRY'S NUMBER ONE SURFACE RAIDER SINCE THE GRAF SPEE WAS SCUTTLED!
A LIGHT CRUISER AGAINST A DESTROYER! CRIPES ~ WHAT A FIGHT EXCALIBUR'S LANDED IN!

AND BY THEN EVERY MEMBER OF THE DESTROYER'S CREW KNEW THE ODDS WHICH FACED THEM . . .
THIS IS THE CAPTAIN SPEAKING. THERE'S A JERRY LIGHT CRUISER OUT THERE AND IT'S AFTER THE MERCHANTMEN. WHILE EXCALIBUR IS AFLOAT WE'RE GOING TO STOP HIM. WE'RE OUTGUNNED AND OUTMANNED ~ BUT WE CAN DO IT. WE WILL DO IT! PREPARE FOR SURFACE ACTION!

THEN, DECK PLATES TREMBLING WITH STRAIN OVER THE THROBBING ENGINES, EXCALIBUR'S SHARP BOW LIFTED OUT OF THE WATER AS SHE LEAPED TOWARDS THE PRINZ WILHELM . . .
PUH! A PUNY DESTROYER CHALLENGES US! IT WILL NEVER GET NEAR ENOUGH TO SHOOT. OPEN FIRE!

LEAVING THE MERCHANT SHIPS TO SCATTER LIKE FRIGHTENED QUAIL, EXCALIBUR SPED PAST THE TANKER. FROM MEADOWS' PARTY A THIN CHEER LIFTED AND DIED AS A GROAN . . .
JERRY NEARLY GOT HER FIRST TIME!
STONE THE CROWS! SHE'LL BE BLOWN OUT OF THE WATER BEFORE SHE CAN GET MORE THAN HER FORWARD GUNS TO BEAR!

ON THE BRIDGE OF THE DESTROYER, LIEUTENANT-COMMANDER BAKER TASTED THE BITTER SOURNESS OF COMING DEFEAT. EXCALIBUR, WITH ONLY HER FORWARD GUNS AGAINST THE CRUISER'S BROADSIDES, DIDN'T STAND A CHANCE. THEN SUDDENLY — DISASTER!
GOT TO GET HER OUT OF THIS FAST — OR WE'LL BE POUNDED TO SCRAP. NOW THE JERRY GUNNERS HAVE FIXED SIGHTS!

ON THE BRIDGE OF THE TANKER, BOB MEADOWS GROANED AS A SHELL STRUCK *EXCALIBUR* — AND THEN HE SAW THE DESTROYER HEEL OVER IN AN EMERGENCY TURN . . .
SHE DOESN'T STAND A CHANCE OF GETTING IN CLOSE. BY THUNDER — WHAT SHE NEEDS IS A SMOKE SCREEN!

SUDDENLY, BOB'S EYES WIDENED — THEN HE LEAPED INTO THE WHEELHOUSE, REACHING FOR THE ENGINE ROOM TELEGRAPH . . .
WHAT THE HECK ARE YOU DOING, MAN?
I'VE GOT JUST THE ANSWER! *FULL SPEED AHEAD* — QUARTERMASTER, ALTER COURSE TWENTY DEGREES TO PORT!

OUR SPEED WILL FAN THAT FIRE INTO AN INFERNO — THE OTHER TANKS WILL CATCH FIRE AND WE'LL BE BLOWN OUT OF THE WATER!
EXCALIBUR NEEDS A SMOKE SCREEN — WE CAN GIVE IT TO HER! WE'VE GOT TO TAKE THAT RISK — OR JERRY WILL BLOW US APART ANYWAY!

AS IF IN A DREAM, THE TANKER CAPTAIN NODDED TO THE HELMSMAN. GUSHING GREAT SPOUTS OF BLACK SMOKE, THE SHIP SURGED FORWARD AND THEN BEGAN TO TURN . . .
LOOK, SIR — THE TANKER — SHE'S TURNING TOWARDS THE PRINZ WILHELM! THEY MUST BE CRAZY!
YES — CRAZY BUT BRAVE MEN, LADDIE — THEY'RE TRYING TO LAY A SMOKE SCREEN FOR US! AND WE'LL USE IT!

WHIPPED BY THE WIND, THE FLAMES OF THE BURNING OIL LEAPED VICIOUSLY HIGHER AND A GREAT PALL OF SMOKE POURED OUT BEHIND THE TANKER . . .
EXCALIBUR IS TURNING TO COME AROUND BEHIND OUR SMOKE! SHE'S CAUGHT ON FAST!
AND MAYBE THE JERRY SKIPPER THINKS SHE'S ON THE RUN~BECAUSE HE'S OPENING UP ON US NOW!

WITH A SCREAM LIKE A DOZEN EXPRESS TRAINS, A HAIL OF SIX INCH SHELLS BRACKETED THE TANKER AND THE SEAS ERUPTED INTO YELLOW TINGED COLUMNS OF BOILING WATER!
STEER A ZIG-ZAG COURSE, HELMSMAN! WE'VE GOT TO SHAKE THE JERRY GUN LAYERS OFF FOR THE NEXT LITTLE LOT THEY THROW!

BUT ALREADY THE PRINZ WILHELM'S GUNS WERE SWINGING AWAY TO SEARCH FOR OTHER PREY . . .
CEASE FIRING! SHE WILL BE DESTROYED BY HER OWN FIRE WHILE WE SEND THOSE FAT MERCHANTMEN TO THE BOTTOM! DESERTED BY THEIR PUNY ESCORT, THEY WILL GIVE US EXCELLENT TARGET PRACTICE!

AND WHILE THE GERMAN CRUISER CAPTAIN GAVE HIS ORDERS SMUGLY, VON GROST OF THE U-220 SNARLED WITH SAVAGE FURY . . .
SO THAT IS THE BRITISHER'S PLAN! THAT TANKER MUST BE STOPPED—AND WE HAVE NO TORPEDOES LEFT! WE WILL USE THE DECK GUN— STAND BY TO SURFACE!

U-220 CAME UP OUT OF THE SEA LIKE A WALLOWING PORPOISE . . .
U-BOAT! A COUPLE OF SHELLS FROM HER AND WE'LL BE PLASTERED ALL OVER THE ATLANTIC!

HIS EYES RED AND BURNING WITH STABBING PAIN FROM THE BITING BLACK SMOKE, KEN HOLT LEAPED TO THE FOC'SLE . . .
SWEDE-TICKER-COME ON! THE FOC'SLE GUN~ WE'LL GIVE THAT SEA SLUG A BEATING YET!

THE STEEL PLATES OF THE CATWALK WERE RED HOT AND THE BOOTS OF THE THREE SAILORS BEGAN TO SINGE AS THEY SPED TOWARDS THE GUN. THEN THE U-BOAT'S GUN ROARED . . .
SIR ~ THE U-BOAT'S CLOUTING THE TANKER ~ SHALL WE ENGAGE IT?
NO TIME FOR IT! THE CRUISER WILL BE WARNED BY THE GUNFIRE ~ SO WE'VE GOT TO ATTACK NOW! HARD A STARBOARD ~ STAND BY TORPEDO!

AND AS EXCALIBUR TURNED WITH HER DECKS AWASH AND SLICED THROUGH THE OILY CLOUD OF SMOKE, HER CAPTAIN KNEW THAT HE LEFT THE TANKER'S CREW TO ALMOST CERTAIN DEATH . . .

EVERY NERVE BURNED AND JARRED AND BLOOD FROM A SCALP WOUND STREAKING HIS WHITE FACE, KEN LURCHED TO HIS FEET . . .
AT. . THE. . . DOUBLE. TICKER. MUST . . . GET. . THE . . GUN . . FIRING !
GLUTTON FOR . . . PUNISHMENT . THAT'S. . WHAT . . . YOU ARE !

THE MISTS OF PULSING PAIN CLEARED FROM SWEDE'S BRAIN, HE SIGHTED THE GUN AGAIN . . . NODDED, AND KEN JERKED THE FIRING BAR . . .
RAUS . . . RAUS . . . QUICK, YOU COWERING DUMPKOFS - GET THAT GUN LOADED AND FIRING !

BUT BATTERED AND EXHAUSTED AS THEY WERE, THE SUPERB GUNNERY TRAINING OF THE BRITISH SAILORS TOLD. A SECOND SHELL SLAMMED INTO THE BREECH ~ A FRACTIONAL ALTERATION IN ELEVATION ~ AND IT ROARED AGAIN . . .
WE'VE GOT HER! RIGHT ON THE WATER LINE ~ SHE'LL GO DOWN LIKE A STONE!

AS THE RELENTLESS GREY WATERS FOAMED INTO THE STRICKEN SUBMARINE, VON GROST KNEW HIS U-BOAT HAD ONLY MOMENTS TO LIVE. THERE WAS ONLY ONE ORDER LEFT TO HIM ~ ABANDON SHIP!
WE'LL HAVE TO GO AND PICK 'EM UP, SKIPPER ~ ANYWAY, WE CAN'T HELP EXCALIBUR ANY MORE -IT'S UP TO HER, NOW!

THE FIGHT HAD ONLY TAKEN SECONDS - LITTLE LONGER THAN IT TOOK EXCALIBUR TO BURST THROUGH THE WIDE BARRIER OF BLACKNESS . . .

ALREADY ALERTED BY THE GUNFIRE, THE *PRINZ WILHELM*'S MAIN GUN TURRET'S SWUNG ROUND — LASHING A FURY OF STEEL AND EXPLOSIVE AROUND *EXCALIBUR* . . .
RANGE 700 . . . 650 . . . 600 . . .
HARD A PORT! TORPEDOES...

FIRE!

FOUR OMINOUS WHITE TRACKS OF AIR BUBBLES GREW IN THE WATER ~ STREAKING FOR THE CRUISER ~ DESPERATELY THE CAPTAIN ALTERED COURSE — BUT TOO LATE . . .
EVERY ONE A HIT! SHE'S RIPPED OPEN FROM STEM TO STERN! WE'LL GO IN TO PICK UP SURVIVORS!

ENGINES STOPPED, THE TANKER WAS PICKING UP THE SURVIVORS OF THE U-220 WHEN THE EXPLOSIONS CAME. ANXIOUS EYES STRAINED THROUGH THE UGLY BLACK CLOUD— FOR A SECOND IT DRIFTED ASIDE . . .
THEY DID IT ~ BY GLORY, THEY'VE SUNK THE PRINZ WILHELM!

CAPTAIN, UNLESS WE GET THAT FIRE UNDER CONTROL, YOU'LL BE BACK IN THE DRINK AGAIN OR BLOWN SKY HIGH! WITH YOUR MEN TO HELP, WE'LL STAND A BETTER CHANCE OF LIVING!
STRANGE ARE THE TRICKS OF FATE, ENGLISHMAN. WE STARTED THE FIRE ~ NOW TO SAVE OURSELVES WE MUST HELP YOU!

AND AS THE GERMANS BEGAN FIGHTING THE FIRE, THE THREE WEARY BRITISH SAILORS STARTED BACK TO THE FOC'SLE . . .
WE'LL HAVE A GO AT THAT FIRE AGAIN!
COR, CHASE O'REILLY! DUNNO WHAT MADE ME FOLLOW YOU BLOKES IN THE FIRST PLACE - I'VE BEEN IN TROUBLE EVER SINCE!
THE SORT OF TROUBLE YOU CAN'T DODGE, EH, TICKER?
FOR TWENTY FOUR HOURS RELAYS OF MEN FOUGHT THAT EYE SEARING, FLESH BLISTERING BLAZE. THEY WORKED UNTIL THEY WERE READY TO DROP ~ ENGLISHMAN AND GERMAN SIDE BY SIDE ~ STRANGE ALLIES WROUGHT BY COMMON PERIL. AND AT LAST THEY WON ~ THE INFERNO WITHERED AND DIED ~ THE SHIP AND ITS PRECIOUS CARGO WAS SAVED!

AND SO IT WAS THAT FOUR HOURS LATER, EXCALIBUR BROUGHT HER CONVOY, SCARRED BUT SAFE, HOME TO PORT ON THE WEST COAST OF ENGLAND ~ AND A HERO'S WELCOME !

OFFICIALLY RELEASED FROM HER DUTIES, EXCALIBUR GLIDED GENTLY INTO POSITION ALONGSIDE A ROYAL NAVY SUPPLY SHIP . . .
TWENTY FOUR HOURS SHORE LEAVE TO ALL WATCHES, NUMBER ONE. JUST A SMALL VOLUNTEER PARTY TO REMAIN ON BOARD ~ THEY CAN GO LATER. THEN WE GO INTO DOCKYARD FOR REPAIRS !

AND THEN SUDDENLY BOB MEADOWS FOUND AT LAST HE WAS ACCEPTED BY THE CAPTAIN ~ AS A SAILOR ~ AND A FRIEND . . . !
OH BY THE WAY, NUMBER ONE ~ I'M OFF TO LONDON TO REPORT ON THE PRINZ WILHELM ~ SO YOU'LL HAVE TO PUT EXCALIBUR INTO DRY DOCK! SHE'S YOUR SHIP UNTIL I GET BACK !
AYE, AYE, SIR !

SWEDE AND KEN WENT ASHORE WITH THE FIRST LIBERTY PARTY. OUTSIDE THE GATES THEY HEADED FOR THE NEAREST RESTAURANT . . .
BIG BLOKE LOOKS A REAL MATELOT– BUT SEE HIS PAL? I DIDN'T KNOW THEY WERE LETTING SCHOOLBOYS IN THE NAVY!
BUS STOP
THANK YOUR STARS WE'VE GOT AN ARMY, CHUM!

THE NEXT SECOND A FIST WAVED IN THE SOLDIER'S FACE . . .
LISTEN, PONGO– THAT YOUNGSTER IS MORE OF A MAN THAN YOU! HE'S A ROUGH SEA-SAILOR– AND BESIDES, HE'S A PAL OF MINE!
DOUBLE UP, TICKER– SWEDE'S PAYING!
AND WITH A FINAL SNIFF, TICKER GRIMES WALKED PROUDLY OFF TO JOIN HIS TWO FRIENDS . . .

OUR STORY COULD END THERE – WITH THOSE NEW FRIENDSHIP AND TRUSTS, FORGED IN THE COMMON ENDURANCE OF PLAN AND PERIL. BUT EVEN MORE IMPORTANT WAS THE VICTORY THAT HAD BEEN WRESTED FROM THE SEA-WOLVES– THEIR GRIP ON THE SEA LANES WOULD NEVER BECOME A STRANGLE HOLD!
LIKE TIGERS THOSE BRITISH WARSHIPS HUNTED US DOWN ONE BY ONE– I WAS LUCKY TO GET MY DAMAGED SHIP HOME. BUT WHAT OF KAPITAN VON GROST?
NO REPORTS FROM U-220– SHE'S GONE AS WELL! OUR LOSSES ARE APPALLING– IN SHIPS AND TRAINED CREWS– THE WAR MAY BE LOST BY THIS VITAL FAILURE!

Umbrella in the Sky

"I consider it to be in the interests of the Reich no longer to permit our eastern provinces to remain unprotected in the face of the tremendous concentration of Bolshevist divisions. Thus came about the result intended by the British and Russian co-operation -- namely, the tying up of such powerful German forces in the east that the radical conclusion of the war in the west could no longer be vouched for by German High Command."

.... Adolf Hitler. June. 1941.

Chapter 1. STRUGGLE TO THE DEATH

ON JUNE 22ND., 1941, ADOLF HITLER UNFOLDED THE FINAL PHASE OF HIS PLAN FOR THE DOMINATION OF EUROPE. THE GERMAN ARMY PLUNGED INTO RUSSIA ON AN 1,800 MILE FRONT FROM THE BALTIC TO THE BLACK SEA, AND RUSSIAN FORCES FOUGHT VAINLY AGAINST THE SMASHING ADVANCE OF HITLER'S LEGIONS...

THE MASTER PLAN FOR VICTORY ORDAINED THAT MOSCOW AND LENINGRAD WERE TO BE CAPTURED ALMOST AT ONCE, THUS TAKING THE NERVE CENTRE OF THE RUSSIAN WAR MACHINE, AND CLOSING THE BALTIC PORTS TO ALLIED SUPPLY SHIPS. THE RAPID BREAK-UP OF RUSSIA WOULD FOLLOW!

SPEED WAS THE ESSENCE OF THE ATTACK! A LINE FROM ARCHANGEL TO ASTRAKHAN WAS TO BE REACHED WITHIN TWELVE WEEKS, BEFORE THE TERRIBLE RUSSIAN WINTER SET IN. SUCH WAS THE CONFIDENCE OF THE GERMAN HIGH COMMAND, THAT EIGHTY FOUR DAYS WAS CONSIDERED SUFFICIENT TO ENSURE VICTORY IN RUSSIA . . .

BUT IN ALL SECTORS, THE RED ARMY AND AIR FORCE FOUGHT WITH UNPRECEDENTED FEROCITY AND DETERMINATION, SLOWING THE MASSIVE ADVANCE OF THE ENEMY, AND ON JULY 19TH, BRINGING THE FRONT TO A STANDSTILL . . .
THE FIRST PHASE OF THE BATTLE IS NOW AT AN END. THE ENEMY HAS ADVANCED SOME TWO HUNDRED MILES INTO SOVIET TERRITORY, BUT WE HAVE HALTED THEM. NOW IT IS OUR TURN TO STRIKE BACK, BEFORE THEY ATTACK.

GERMAN FORWARD ASSAULT TROOPS HAD ADVANCED TOO FAR AHEAD OF SUPPORTING UNITS, AND THE RUSSIANS SAW IN THIS A GREAT CHANCE TO THREATEN THEIR LINES OF COMMUNICATION. . .
WE ARE GOING IN BEHIND ENEMY POSITIONS TO OPERATE IN SMALL BANDS OF GUERILLAS, THE FIRST OF WHOM WILL BE FROM THIS UNIT, LED BY MAJOR SAROV HERE. FIGHT WELL, AND GOOD LUCK!

WITHIN TWELVE HOURS, THE SOVIET GUERILLAS HAD MOVED THROUGH GAPS IN THE GERMAN LINE ON THE LENINGRAD FRONT AND MAJOR SAROV'S TROOPS FANNED OUT RIGHT AND LEFT. . .
INTELLIGENCE REPORTS COLUMNS OF VEHICLES AND SUPPORT TROOPS MOVING EAST TO REINFORCE MOTORISED UNITS ON THE LENINGRAD FRONT. THEY WILL BE USING THIS ROAD SOUTH OF HERE. SECTIONS A, B AND C, HERE ARE YOUR ORDERS—

TWO SECTIONS WOULD HOLD POSITIONS ON EITHER SIDE OF THE ROAD AHEAD OF ENEMY COLUMNS, WHILE THE THIRD WOULD FIND AND ENGAGE THE ENEMY FORCE, SO THAT IT WOULD COME UNDER FIRE FROM EVERY CORNER OF THE RUSSIAN TRIANGLE . . .
MINE THE ROAD AT THIS POINT, THEN WITHDRAW AND TAKE UP ATTACK POSITIONS. AS SOON AS THE COLUMN REACHES THE MINED AREA, OPEN FIRE. UNDERSTOOD?
RIGHT, SERGEANT!
GOOD. LET'S GO!

IN THE COLD SILENCE OF THE RUSSIAN COUNTRYSIDE, THE DISTANT WHINING OF HEAVY LORRIES CARRIED FAR AND EVENTUALLY THE FEEBLE RAYS OF DIMMED HEADLAMPS APPEARED HALF A MILE AWAY . . .
HERE THEY COME! ABOUT TEN TRUCKS. MOVE IN WITH HEAVY FIRE WHEN I GIVE THE ORDER, AND WITHDRAW RAPIDLY TO THE BASE WHEN ORDERED. . . GOOD LUCK, COMRADES!

UNAWARE OF THE CHAOS THAT WAS ABOUT TO ENGULF THEM, THE GERMAN TROOPS DOZED IN THE LURCHING TRUCKS. THE ROADS HAD BEEN CHURNED INTO LITTLE BETTER THAN MUD TRACKS BY THE ADVANCING TANKS, BUT DESPITE THE HARDSHIPS OF TRAVEL, GERMAN MORALE WAS HIGH.
WHAT A COUNTRY! NOTHING BUT MUD AND SLUSH! I DON'T BLAME THE IVANS FOR PULLING OUT OF THIS MESS, WHO WANTS TO FIGHT FOR A PIG STY LIKE THIS?
BE CONSOLED, MY FRIEND, IN THE KNOWLEDGE THAT WE WON'T BE HERE MUCH LONGER! A FEW MORE WEEKS AND WE WILL STAND AMONG THE RUINS OF MOSCOW ITSELF.

TEN MINUTES LATER, THE HUGE TYRES OF THE GERMAN VEHICLES WERE GRINDING PONDEROUSLY TOWARD THE LAND MINES IN THE MUD. THEN...
HOLD IT, MEN, HOLD IT!

EXPLOSION AFTER EXPLOSION ROCKED THE ENEMY COLUMN AND THE GERMANS TUMBLED IN CONFUSION OUT OF THEIR TRUCKS. A SHRILL CRY WENT UP FROM THE DARK FIELDS AROUND . . .
FIRE, FIRE, FIRE!

WITH MORTARS, GRENADES AND SMALL ARMS, THE SOVIET TROOPS BLASTED THE ENEMY. A LURID GLOW ILLUMINATED THE TARGET, SHOWING GERMAN TROOPS STRUGGLING TO GET UNDAMAGED TRUCKS PAST THE WRECKAGE, AND ALONG THE ROAD TO SAFETY . . .
CONCENTRATE ON THE TRUCKS IN THE REAR! THE OTHERS WON'T GET FAR!

FOR FOUR MINUTES THE FEROCIOUS ASSAULT CONTINUED AND ONLY A HANDFUL OF GERMAN TRUCKS BLUNDERED PAST THE PILE OF MINE DEBRIS, AND SPED OFF INTO THE DARKNESS.
MOVE IN SLOWLY AND MOP UP! BURN ALL REMAINING EQUIPMENT.
THAT'S ONE HUN TANK DIVISION THAT WON'T SEE ITS SUPPORT COLUMN!

AS THE SMALL RUSSIAN FORCE WITHDREW FROM THE SCENE OF DESTRUCTION, A BRILLIANT YELLOW GLOW APPEARED IN THE SKY ABOUT A MILE TO THE EAST. IT TOLD THEM THAT A AND B SECTIONS HAD STRUCK AT THE ENEMY TRUCKS THAT HAD ESCAPED. SERGEANT ROSLOV SMILED GRIMLY AS HE PAUSED TO LOOK BACK.
WE WILL STRIKE WHERE THEY DO NOT EXPECT US TO BE. TO THE GERMANS EVERY RUSSIAN ROCK AND TREE WILL SEEM TO HARBOUR A MACHINE-GUN OR A GRENADE!

LATER THAT EVENING, SERGEANT ROSLOV REPORTED TO THE FARMHOUSE HEADQUARTERS BEHIND THE GERMAN LINES. MAJOR SAROV LISTENED INTENTLY TO THE REPORT...
WE ENGAGED A COLUMN OF FOURTEEN HEAVY TRANSPORT VEHICLES PROCEEDING TO TANK UNITS ON THE LENINGRAD FRONT. THE ENEMY FORCE WAS DESTROYED, SIR!
WE HAVE HAD FAVOURABLE REPORTS FROM OTHER AREAS, SERGEANT. AND THIS RAID POLICY WILL CONTINUE UNTIL THE ENEMY OFFENSIVE RE-OPENS ON THE FRONT!

BUT THE BREATHING SPACE ON THE RUSSIAN FRONT ONLY LASTED FOR TWO WEEKS. IN EARLY AUGUST, THE GERMAN ADVANCE WAS RESUMED, AND IN THREE MONTHS THE LEGIONS OF THE REICH HAD STORMED FORWARD UNTIL THE GREAT CITY OF KIEV WAS WITHIN THEIR SIGHTS. IN THE NORTH, THE WAY TO LENINGRAD LAY OPEN AND MAJOR SAROV'S TROOPS HAD BEEN WITHDRAWN TO NEW DEFENCES.
A MOST TERRIBLE AND SAVAGE BATTLE FOR THE CONTROL OF LENINGRAD HAD BEGUN.

THE RUSSIAN FORCES COUNTER-ATTACKED AGAIN AND AGAIN FOR IF LENINGRAD FELL, THEY WOULD LOSE CONTROL OF THE RAILROAD TO MURMANSK, AND DESPERATELY NEEDED SUPPLIES FROM BRITAIN AND AMERICA WOULD BE CUT OFF. THE RED AIR FORCE FACED A HUGE TASK IN SUPPORT OF THEIR GROUND FORCES.
HEAVY FIGHTING IS RAGING ON ALL SIDES OF THIS CITY. WE ARE TO BEAT UP THE FIGHTER AIRFIELD WHICH IS PROVIDING SUPPORT FOR THE ENEMY FORCES IN OUR OWN AREA.

ON THE GRASS AIRFIELD, NINE LAVOCHKIN 5 FIGHTERS HAD BEEN WARMING UP FOR TAKE-OFF. ONE BY ONE THE FIGHTERS DRONED NOISILY INTO THE SKY AND TOOK UP FORMATION.
WE WILL APPROACH FROM THE NORTH. FUEL AND AMMUNITION DUMPS WILL BE DEAD AHEAD AS WE ATTACK. I WILL LEAD IN — THE REST FOLLOW!

AFTER ONLY TWENTY MINUTES OF FLYING, THE ADVANCE GERMAN AIRFIELD WAS IN SIGHT. BELOW, SEVERAL Me.109'S WERE BEING ARMED UP, AND IT BECAME OBVIOUS TO YEGOROV, THE FLIGHT LEADER, THAT THE ATTACK SHOULD BE A REWARDING ONE.
A FIELD DAY, BOYS, THEY'RE ALL AT HOME. LET THEM HAVE IT HARD, AND GET OUT AS SOON AS YOU CAN. HERE WE GO!

FOLLOWING THE FLIGHT LEADER IN, THE RUSSIAN PILOTS ATTACKED THE ENEMY AIRFIELD WITH ZEAL AND DETERMINATION. BUT THE GERMAN ANTI-AIRCRAFT CREWS ON THE GROUND WERE READY AND WAITING FOR THEM...

IN SPITE OF THE CONCENTRATED AND ACCURATE ACK-ACK FIRE OF THE ENEMY, THE RUSSIAN FIGHTERS MADE PASS AFTER PASS AT THE ENEMY INSTALLATIONS BELOW.
I'VE FOUND IT! THAT EXPLOSION, IT'S THE BOMB DUMP! PILE IN AND FINISH IT OFF, BOYS!

AFTER FIFTEEN MINUTES OF DETERMINED STRAFING, ONLY FIVE OF THE NINE SOVIET FIGHTERS REMAINED, AND WITH AMMUNITION NOW VERY LOW, THE FLIGHT LEADER, MAJOR YEGOROV, CALLED OFF THE ATTACK. BELOW, SEVERAL ENEMY AIRCRAFT LAY BURNING, AND CLOUDS OF SMOKE TOLD OF HITS ON AMMUNITION AND FUEL DUMPS...
THAT'S ENOUGH, BOYS! FAN OUT AND KEEP DOWN LOW. GOOD WORK!

AS THE RUSSIAN FIGHTERS, MANY OF THEM BADLY HOLED, RETURNED TO BASE, THE PILOTS LOOKED SADLY DOWN AT THE MAMMOTH STRUGGLE OF THE RED ARMY WITH THE MIGHT OF THE INVADERS. TO THEM IT SEEMED THAT THERE WERE TOO MANY JOBS TO BE DONE, AND TOO FEW HOURS TO FIGHT IN. SOVIET SOLDIERS LOOKED UP, BUT WITH DIFFERENT THOUGHTS...
WHAT THE DEVIL ARE OUR FLYERS DOING? WHY DON'T THEY HELP US? CAN'T THEY SEE THE SITUATION DOWN HERE?
THOSE FIGHTERS ARE PROBABLY RETURNING FROM A RAID. EVERY DIVISION NEEDS AIR SUPPORT, BUT WE ALL CAN'T HAVE IT AT ONCE. IT'S THE SAME ALL OVER RUSSIA, IF WE HAVE COVER, OTHER TROOPS WILL GO WITHOUT!

AS SOON AS THE PLANES HAD LANDED, GROUND CREWS WENT TO WORK WHILE THE PILOTS MADE REPORTS, AND WERE GIVEN THEIR NEXT MISSION. THIS WAS THE CEASELESS WAR AGAINST TIME, A STRUGGLE TO THE DEATH...
HAVE YOU GOT THREE SERVICEABLE AIRCRAFT, YEGOROV, FOR A SUPPORT OPERATION ON THE NORTHERN FLANK? I'M SORRY TO CHASE YOU AS SOON AS YOU GET IN, BUT IT'S A HIGH COMMAND ORDER.
YES, MYSELF, ALOV AND BUNEYEV HERE. WHAT'S THE OP?
COME OVER TO THE MAP. BY THE WAY, SOME GOOD NEWS! WE'RE TO BE JOINED BY A WING OF HURRICANES FROM BRITAIN. DUE TO ARRIVE ANY TIME NOW. GOOD PILOTS, ALL OF THEM!

SEEING HER ALLY IN DIRE DISTRESS, BRITAIN HAD SENT A TOKEN FORCE OF HER MUCH NEEDED HURRICANES TO THE AID OF THE RED AIR FORCE. AS THE THREE SOVIET PILOTS RUSHED TO THEIR AIRCRAFT, GLADDENED BY THE GOOD NEWS, RE-FUELLING WAS STILL IN PROGRESS.
COME ON! SPEED IT UP. STARTER WAGONS AND FIRE CREWS, OVER HERE! MOVE, MOVE.
SHE'S ALL ARMED UP, SIR; WE'LL ONLY BE A MINUTE!

THE THREE FIGHTERS TOOK OFF, AND ONCE AGAIN FLEW OVER THE SCENE OF BITTER GROUND FIGHTING. BELOW, THE SMALL RUSSIAN FORCE THAT HAD ATTACKED THE ENEMY SUPPLY COLUMN A FORTNIGHT BEFORE WAS NOW PART OF THE MAIN RUSSIAN FORCE ON THE LENINGRAD FRONT!
LOOK! THE TANKS ARE COMING UP NOW. WE CAN'T HOLD THEM. THEY'LL BREAK THROUGH. SERGEANT, ASK FOR REINFORCEMENT IN THE REAR.
YES, SIR!

In a few minutes, the reply came through...
TANK REINFORCEMENTS WILL BE MOVED UP IMMEDIATELY, SIR. FORWARD INFANTRY UNITS ARE TO WITHDRAW AT ONCE TO A MINEFIELD ONE MILE IN OUR REAR. WE MUST DIG IN THERE.
RIGHT, ROSLOV, TELL THE MEN TO MOVE BACK.

AS HIS TROOPS WITHDREW, MAJOR SAROV RADIOED H.Q. AGAIN.
HEADQUARTERS, THIS IS SAROV, 'E' BATTALION. I REPEAT, STRONG FORCE OF ENEMY TANKS MOVING UP, POSITION B-SEVEN, F-THREE. THIS IS A MAJOR ENEMY THRUST AND I STRONGLY REQUEST AIR SUPPORT WITHIN THE NEXT FORTY EIGHT HOURS! WITHDRAWING AS ORDERED... OUT!

AS THE INFANTRY WITHDREW, MAJOR SAROV FEARED THAT THE ENEMY WERE ABOUT TO BREACH THE RUSSIAN DEFENCE LINE ON HIS SECTOR. A COUNTER-ATTACK COULD ONLY BE MADE WITH AIR SUPPORT. BUT WERE THE AIRCRAFT AVAILABLE, WOULD THEY COME IN TIME?

Chapter 2. ANOTHER COUNTRY'S WAR
A FORCE THAT COULD SUPPLY THE ANSWER TO EVERY RUSSIAN INFANTRYMAN'S DREAM WAS EVEN AT THAT MOMENT, FLYING OVER THE ENDLESS WASTE OF THE TUNDRA. A WING OF ROYAL AIR FORCE HURRICANES WERE ON THE LAST LAP OF A LONG JOURNEY. THE AIRCRAFT HAD BEEN SHIPPED TO MURMANSK, AND THERE ASSEMBLED FOR ACTION IN THE LENINGRAD AREA. . .
LET DOWN TO TEN THOUSAND AT FIVE HUNDRED FEET PER MINUTE. ETA AT BALKOV BASE, ANOTHER TWELVE MINUTES' FLYING TIME. KEEP A CLOSE EYE ON YOUR FUEL!

COMMANDING THE WING OF HURRICANES WAS SQUADRON LEADER RAYMOND MILLS, A TOUGH VETERAN OF THE BATTLE OF BRITAIN, AND WITH HIM WERE SEVERAL DISTINGUISHED FIGHTER PILOTS OF THE RAF. AS THE AIRCRAFT NEARED THE END OF THEIR FLIGHT, MANY A PILOT WAS WONDERING WHAT LIFE WOULD BE LIKE WITH THE RED AIR FORCE.
HOW ARE THE BOYS GOING TO SHAPE UP WITH THIS ASSIGNMENT? IT'S GOING TO BE A TRICKY JOB GETTING EVERYBODY TO WORK TOGETHER AS A TEAM.

THE SQUADRON LEADER'S THOUGHTS WERE INTERRUPTED WHEN, IN THE DISTANCE, THE FAMILIAR SIGHT OF A FIGHTER AIRFIELD APPEARED THROUGH THE BROKEN CLOUD. HE SWUNG HIS FIGHTER INTO A GENTLE TURN, AND GAVE ORDERS FOR LANDING...
HERE WE ARE, CHAPS! NORMAL CIRCUIT, AND LET'S MAKE THE LANDINGS GOOD.
LOOKS LIKE WE'VE GOT QUITE AN AUDIENCE, SIR!

AS WORD GOT ROUND THAT THE HURRICANES WERE ARRIVING, ALL THE PILOTS AND CREWS OF BALKOV AIRFIELD GATHERED TO WATCH THE R.A.F. PLANES LAND. THE FIRST AIRCRAFT TOUCHED DOWN AND A LOUD CHEER WENT UP FROM THE RUSSIANS...
WELL, THEY SEEM HAPPY ENOUGH TO SEE US!

WHEN ALL THE AIRCRAFT HAD LANDED SAFELY, THE PILOTS QUICKLY CHANGED IN THEIR NEW QUARTERS, AND HAD A MUCH NEEDED MEAL. AFTER THAT, THE WING WAS ASKED TO ASSEMBLE IN THE MESS.
SO THIS IS HOME!
THEY DON'T WASTE MUCH TIME, DO THEY?
DON'T EXPECT REASONABLE TREATMENT AROUND HERE! THIS WHOLE CO-OPERATION LARK WILL COME TO NOTHING, IF YOU WANT MY OPINION!

THE CYNICAL COMMENT CAME FROM FLYING OFFICER BOB HUNTER, AN UNPOPULAR, BUT VERY CAPABLE MEMBER OF THE WING.
HUNTER, I REALLY DON'T KNOW WHY YOU JOINED THE R.A.F. IN THE FIRST PLACE!
I WAS CALLED UP, AND I LIKED FLYING. IT'S AS SIMPLE AS THAT! BUT I DIDN'T JOIN UP TO FIGHT ANOTHER COUNTRY'S WAR! THERE'S QUITE ENOUGH TO DO BACK HOME.
IT'S THE SAME WAR, HUNTER, FOR THE SAME REASONS. WHAT HAPPENS OVER HERE WILL EFFECT THE WHOLE ALLIED WAR EFFORT.

TO HIS FELLOW PILOTS, HUNTER'S ATTITUDE WAS STRANGE AND HOSTILE, BUT ONE MAN IN THE SQUADRON HAD AN INKLING OF WHAT LAY BEHIND IT. THAT WAS THE FLIGHT COMMANDER, BRUCE NELSON...
POOR OLD HUNTER ISN'T GOING TO BE POPULAR WITH OUR ALLIES AT THIS RATE. PITY, BECAUSE HE'S A GOOD PILOT, AND A GOOD SCRAPPER...

NELSON KNEW THAT HUNTER HAD VOLUNTEERED FOR FLYING TO PROVE TO HIMSELF THAT HE WAS AS COURAGEOUS AS THE NEXT MAN. BUT OPERATIONAL FLYING HAD ONLY INCREASED HIS DOUBTS ABOUT HIMSELF, AND HE FOUGHT WITH RECKLESS FURY IN THE AIR, DRIVING HIMSELF TO PERILOUS ACTS OF DARING.
HE'S FIGHTING HIS OWN PRIVATE WAR AGAINST HIMSELF, AND HE FIGHTS THE BOUNCING CONFIDENCE OF THE OTHER LADS WITH A SEEMING INDIFFERENCE TO THE AIR FORCE. STRANGE THING IS, HE LIVES FOR FLYING!

NELSON'S THOUGHTS WERE INTERRUPTED WHEN THE RUSSIAN STATION COMMANDER, COLONEL SERGEI LUDERKIN, ENTERED TO WELCOME THE NEW ARRIVALS...
WELCOME, BRITISH FRIENDS. YOU COME TO US WHEN THE RED AIR FORCE IS FACED WITH A POWERFUL ENEMY OPERATING FROM WELL WITHIN THE BOUNDARIES OF OUR COUNTRY. OUR LOSSES HAVE BEEN HEAVY, BUT WE ARE DETERMINED TO STEM THE GERMAN ADVANCE! THE SOVIET AIR FORCE WELCOMES YOU MOST WARMLY TO ASSIST US IN THIS EFFORT!

BUT FLYING OFFICER HUNTER WAS STILL NOT IMPRESSED . . .
ALL VERY TOUCHING! HE NEARLY HAD ME BELIEVING THAT I SHOULD BE HAPPY FIGHTING ANOTHER COUNTRY'S WAR, BUT I'M AFRAID I'M STILL UNCONVINCED!
EXCUSE ME, FLYING OFFICER...

YOU FAIL TO UNDERSTAND THE COLONEL'S POINT! BOTH OF OUR COUNTRIES ARE FIGHTING A COMMON ENEMY, AND WE CAN DO THIS BETTER TOGETHER, THAN EACH ON HIS OWN. DISREGARD THE PLIGHT OF THE SOVIET UNION IF YOU WISH, BUT DO NOT THINK YOU ARE FIGHTING FOR US ALONE!
THANK YOU, LIEUTENANT, FOR YOUR MOST CLEAR EXPOSITION!

BOB HUNTER HAD MADE HIS FIRST ENEMY IN RUSSIA: HE COULD SEE THE ANGER IN THE YOUNG RUSSIAN'S EYES, AND HE SENSED THE HOSTILITY OF THE OTHER RED AIR FORCE PILOTS. THE FOLLOWING DAY, BATTLE ORDERS ARRIVED FOR THE R.A.F...
WE WILL USE FOUR HURRICANES AND FOUR LAVOCHKINS. WE ARE TO GIVE CLOSE SUPPORT TO 'E' BATTALION, ON THE LENINGRAD FRONT. THE ENEMY HAS BROKEN THROUGH, AND THE SITUATION IS GRAVE. WE WILL BE MET BY OUR DIVE BOMBERS OVER THE TARGET.
THAT'S QUITE CLEAR, MAJOR! OUR BOYS WILL BE KEEN TO GET IN SOME FIGHTING. I'LL PASS ON THE DETAILS!

WITHIN AN HOUR, THE EIGHT ALLIED AIRCRAFT WERE WARMING UP. IN THE COCKPIT OF ONE OF THE HURRICANES, BOB HUNTER STROVE TO STIFLE THE ATTACK OF NERVES THAT OVERTOOK HIM BEFORE EACH MISSION...
BALKOV TOWER, THIS IS AIR FORCE THREE-O FOUR. RADIO CHECK AND TAXI CLEARANCE, OVER!
THREE-O-FOUR, YOU ARE CLEAR TO TAXI. THE VERY BEST OF LUCK, COMRADE!
6

HUNTER FOUND HIMSELF STRANGELY TOUCHED BY THE UNEXPECTED GOOD WISHES. A FEW MINUTES LATER, THE SQUADRON WAS AIRBORNE, HEADING FOR ITS FIRST OPERATION IN THE RUSSIAN THEATRE . . .
YOU BOYS UP TOP THERE, KEEP A LOOK-OUT FOR ENEMY FIGHTERS. JOIN US WHEN I GIVE THE ORDER.

AS THE FIGHTERS DRONED THROUGH THE SMOKE-BLACKENED SKY, FLYING OFFICER HUNTER SCANNED THE HORIZON UNCEASINGLY, HIS EYES MOVING WITH MECHANICAL THOROUGHNESS ACROSS HIS WHOLE FIELD OF VISION. SUDDENLY, HE BROKE RADIO SILENCE . . .
SEVEN ENEMY FIGHTERS, TEN O'CLOCK, OUR ANGELS!

THE FLIGHT LEADER, MAJOR YEGOROV, SNAPPED QUICK ORDERS TO HIS PILOTS. SOMEHOW THEY MUST AVOID AN ENGAGEMENT WITH THE ENEMY FIGHTERS...
ALOV, DESCEND AND JOIN US DOWN HERE. OTHER COVER FIGHTERS MAINTAIN ALTITUDE AND ENGAGE THE ENEMY IF NECESSARY. LEAD THEM AWAY FROM US. OUT!

A MILE AWAY, THE LUFTWAFFE FLIGHT LEADER WAS CALCULATING HIS COURSE OF ACTION.
THREE OF THEM, PLUS ONE BREAKING AWAY! NO SIGNS OF ANYTHING ELSE AROUND. PERHAPS THEY'RE TRYING TO FOOL ME.
LET'S GO AND GET THEM!

HUNTER HAD BEEN WATCHING CLOSELY ALL THE TIME, AND AS SOON AS HE SAW THE ENEMY BANK TO OPEN THE ENGAGEMENT, HE WENT INTO A FAST, TIGHT TURN, FOLLOWED BY HIS TWO COMPANIONS . . .
THEY'LL BE EXPECTING US TO RUN FOR IT. LET'S SURPRISE THEM WITH A BEAM ATTACK!

HUNTER AND HIS TWO WINGMEN RIPPED THROUGH THE ENEMY FORMATION, GUNS BLAZING, AND BROKE AWAY INTO THE SKY IN ALL DIRECTIONS TO DRAW THE ENEMY AFTER THEM.
THAT'LL ANNOY THEM! THEY HAVEN'T SEEN THE OTHERS.

THE FOCRE WULF 190's SWUNG ROUND ON THE THREE ALLIED FIGHTERS; AND SOON HUNTER FOUND TWO GRIMLY DETERMINED GERMANS ON HIS TAIL.
THIS LOOKS BAD; THESE TWO REALLY MEAN BUSINESS!

THE SKY WAS ALIVE WITH TWISTING AIRCRAFT. BUT EVEN SO, ON SEEING HUNTER'S DESPERATE PLIGHT, ONE OF THE RUSSIAN PILOTS MANOEUVRED VIOLENTLY THROUGH THE PACK TO COME TO HIS AID.
BREAK RIGHT, BRITISHER! I'M RIGHT BEHIND YOU. BREAK NOW!

WITH SPLIT-SECOND RESPONSE, HUNTER FLUNG HIS AIRCRAFT ROUND AND AS IT ROCKETED SKYWARDS, HE SAW A BRIGHT FLASH OUT OF THE CORNER OF HIS GOGGLES . . .
GREAT SHOOTING, IVAN — THANKS!

BOB HUNTER WAS PRESSED HEAVILY INTO HIS SEAT UNDER THE BIG 'G' FORCES AND THROUGH THE GREY MIST THAT CLOUDED HIS EYES, HE VAGUELY SAW THE SHAPE OF THE FOCKE WULF WHICH HAD SO RECENTLY BEEN ON HIS TAIL.
OKAY, JERRY, NOW YOU'RE ON THE RECEIVING END!

CONTROL COLUMN FORWARD, THUMB ON THE FIRING BUTTON, HUNTER SKILFULLY MANOEUVRED THE ENEMY INTO HIS SIGHTS . . .

BUT MEANWHILE, THE THIRD RUSSIAN PILOT WAS CONDUCTING A LONE, LOSING BATTLE AGAINST THE REMAINING ENEMY FIGHTERS.
WHERE ARE YOU, KONSTANTIN? I'M IN BAD TROUBLE! COME IN, COME IN!

AT FULL BOOST, HUNTER AND HIS WINGMAN STREAKED TO THE AID OF THE OUTNUMBERED RUSSIAN BUT THE GERMAN VULTURES HAD ALREADY CLOSED IN FOR THE KILL. IT WAS ALL OVER IN ONE TERRIBLE, BLINDING SECOND.

THE AIR BATTLE HAD LASTED FOR BARELY THREE MINUTES AND ONLY THE SMOKE FROM THE EXPLOSION HUNG IN THE SKY LIKE A DARK GHOST AS EVIDENCE OF ITS SHORT-LIVED FURY.
I'M EXTREMELY SORRY ABOUT YOUR MAN. I'M AFRAID HE DIDN'T HAVE A CHANCE WHILE WE WERE BUSY.
WAR IS NO RESPECTER OF PERSONS, COMRADE. HE WAS A GOOD FIGHTER. HE DIED AS A MAN SHOULD!

THE PILOTS FLEW ON IN SILENCE, AND SOON THEY WERE LEVELLING OUT FOR LANDING ON THE HOME AIRFIELD.
THREE-O-FOUR AND THREE-ONE-SEVEN LANDING. THREE-ONE-NINE REPORTED DESTROYED.

THE RUSSIAN, LIEUTENANT SAVCHENKO, TAXIED OFF THE RUNWAY, SHUT DOWN HIS ENGINE, AND WENT TO ESCORT HIS R.A.F. WINGMAN BACK TO THE BRIEFING HUT...

SAVCHENKO WALKED OVER TO THE HURRICANE AND SUDDENLY STOPPED DEAD IN HIS TRACKS, STARING BLANKLY AT THE EQUALLY ASTONISHED FACE OF FLYING OFFICER HUNTER. UNTIL THAT MOMENT, NEITHER HAD REALISED THE IDENTITY OF THE OTHER...
HUNTER! I LEFT MY COMRADE TO ASSIST THIS CLOWN!

LIEUTENANT SAVCHENKO COULD NOT CONTAIN HIS ANGER . . .
SO MY COMRADE DIED WHILE I WAS HELPING YOU! HAD I KNOWN IT WAS YOU, . . I WOULD HAVE LEFT YOU TO FIGHT YOUR OWN BATTLE!

THE BITTERNESS IN THE RUSSIAN'S VOICE BURNED LIKE ACID INTO HUNTER'S BRAIN. FOR THE FIRST TIME, HE CLEARLY SAW THE HARM HIS CYNICAL ATTITUDE COULD CAUSE AND HE DEEPLY REGRETTED THE EPISODE OF THE DAY BEFORE. HE WALKED SLOWLY BACK TO THE FLIGHT ROOM ALONE . . .
SAVCHENKO MEANT EVERY WORD HE SAID — AND I DESERVED IT!

Chapter 3. HURRICANES!
MEANWHILE THE SUPPORT FORCE OF FIVE FIGHTERS FROM WHICH HUNTER AND HIS COMPANIONS HAD BEEN DETACHED, WAS FAST NEARING THE BATTLE AREA, AND SOVIET TANK CREWS LOOKED IMPATIENTLY SKYWARD FOR THEIR PROMISED ILIUCHIN STORMOVIK DIVE-BOMBER COVER...
WHERE ARE THOSE AIRCRAFT? WE ARE ONLY THREE MILES FROM THE ENEMY NOW, AND WE'RE GOING TO NEED THOSE BOMBERS BADLY!
270

FIGHTERS AND DIVE-BOMBERS MADE THEIR RENDEZVOUS DEAD ON TIME AND THE FORCE IMMEDIATELY TOOK UP POSITIONS FOR THE ATTACK ON THE ENEMY ARMOURED COLUMNS . . .
TARGET DEAD AHEAD! FOLLOW ME IN, AND KEEP LOW. TAKE YOUR TIME, AND MAKE EVERY ROCKET COUNT!

THE NOSE OF THE LEADING STORMOVIK DIPPED, ITS ENGINE NOTE RISING TO A HIGH PITCHED WAIL AS THE THROTTLE WAS OPENED. AND THEN THE ROCKETS STREAKED DOWNWARDS — TO RIP THE GERMAN ARMOURED GIANTS APART AS IF THEY WERE MADE OF TIN-FOIL.

A LOUD CHEER WENT UP FROM THE DEFENDING RUSSIAN TANK CREWS AS THE AIR REVERBERATED TO THE ROAR OF FRIENDLY AIRCRAFT. THEY SOON BECAME AWARE OF THE UNUSUAL SHAPE OF SOME OF THE FIGHTERS, AND SLOWLY THE WORD SPREAD AMONG THE ADVANCING INFANTRYMEN . . .
HURRICANES!
HURRICANES!
HURRICANES!

THE AIRCRAFT HAD STRUCK THE OPENING BLOW AND THE SOVIET TANKS BEGAN TO ROLL FORWARD MENACINGLY. SOON A MASSIVE TANK BATTLE HAD DEVELOPED. THE RUSSIAN COUNTER-ATTACK WAS GOING WELL . . .
THE ENEMY HAS BROKEN FORMATION. CONCENTRATE ON THE MAIN FORCE, AND LEAVE ISOLATED TANKS FOR THE AIRCRAFT TO KNOCK OUT

ACHTUNG! ACHTUNG! THIS IS 'Z' FORCE COMMANDER. THE ENEMY HAS SPLIT THE ADVANCE. ALL TANKS WITHDRAW TO REARGUARD POSITIONS. FIGHTER COVER HAS BEEN REQUESTED.

WITH THE MAIN ENEMY BATTLE FORCE GIVING GROUND, AND ISOLATED POCKETS OF GERMAN TANKS BATTLING DESPERATELY TO CONTAIN THE MASSIVE RUSSIAN COUNTER-ATTACK, THE SCENE WAS SET FOR THE DRIVE TO THE MAIN OBJECTIVE, THE VILLAGE OF KRUSLOV...
RIGHT! THE AIRCRAFT HAVE STARTED THE ROT. WE MUST MAKE THE OUTSKIRTS OF KRUSLOV BY DUSK WHEN OUR TANKS WILL WITHDRAW. THEN IT WILL BE UP TO US!
JERRY WILL BE WAITING FOR US, MAJOR, THAT'S FOR SURE. I'LL BET KRUSLOV IS CRAWLING WITH SNIPERS AND MORTARS!

THE VETERAN MAJOR SAROV KNEW ONLY TOO WELL THAT THE BATTLE WAS JUST BEGINNING. THE SPECTACULAR REPULSION OF THE ENEMY TANK ATTACK HAD MERELY OPENED THE WAY FOR THE MAIN CLASH OF THE DAY.
WE THOUGHT THE RETREAT WAS ROUGH, BUT THIS IS GOING TO BE MURDER. THANK HEAVEN FOR THE TANKS!
DON'T KID YOURSELF, COMRADE! THIS LITTLE SHOW IS RESERVED STRICTLY FOR THE DEAR OLD FOOTSLOGGER. THAT MEANS YOU! THESE TANKS ARE AS BLIND AS BATS AT NIGHT. THEY WON'T BE WITH US MUCH LONGER!

AN HOUR PASSED — THE AIRCRAFT HAD LONG SINCE FINISHED THEIR JOB, AND HAD RETURNED TO BASE — THE EVENING COUNTRYSIDE WAS THROBBING WITH THE RUMBLE OF DISTANT GUNS AND THE RATTLE OF MACHINE-GUNS. THE BATTLE AREA WAS NEAR...
ALL RIGHT, EVERYBODY OFF. KRUSLOV IS TWO MILES AWAY. SPREAD OUT, AND WATCH FOR ENEMY FOXHOLES ALL THE WAY...

THE TANKS WERE LUMBERING FORWARD SLOWLY NOW WITH THE GAUNT SHAPES OF DAMAGED BUILDINGS LOOMING UP THROUGH THE DUSK. AS THE INFANTRYMEN MOVED UP WITH THE TANKS, HEAVY ENEMY SHELLFIRE GREETED THEM . . .
HERE IT COMES! GET DOWN, AND HOLD TILL IT EASES OFF. THEY WON'T BE ABLE TO SEE US FOR MUCH LONGER, COMRADES, THE LIGHT'S GOING FAST.

DESPITE THE APPALLING BARRAGE, THE SOVIET INFANTRYMEN REACHED THE OUTSKIRTS OF THE SHATTERED RUIN THAT WAS ONCE KRUSLOV. SUDDENLY, A SHRILL CRY WENT UP . . .
SNIPERS! UP THERE, DEAD AHEAD, IN THAT WINDOW!

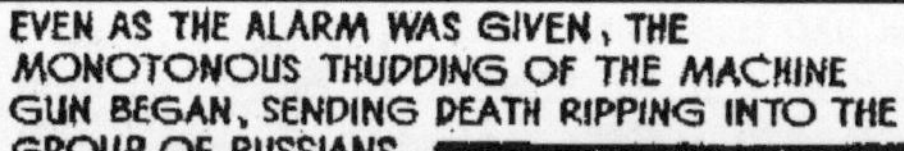
EVEN AS THE ALARM WAS GIVEN, THE MONOTONOUS THUDDING OF THE MACHINE GUN BEGAN, SENDING DEATH RIPPING INTO THE GROUP OF RUSSIANS.

BUT ANOTHER RUSSIAN TANK EDGED FORWARD AND A STREAM OF BULLETS FROM ITS GUN CARVED A LINE UP THE WALL UNTIL THE SNIPERS WERE SILENCED.
THAT'S FIXED THEM!

THE TANKS WERE GROPING THEIR WAY AWKWARDLY OVER THE RUBBLE-STREWN STREETS. THEY WERE EASY, BULKY TARGETS FOR HIDDEN GERMAN "PANZERFAUST" ANTI-TANK WEAPONS IN THE DUSK...
THE ORDER'S COME THROUGH FOR THE TANKS TO PULL OUT! WE'RE ON OUR OWN NOW...

BY THE TIME DARKNESS HAD FALLEN, EVERY SOVIET TANK HAD LEFT EMBATTLED KRUSLOV. IT WAS LEFT TO THE SOVIET INFANTRYMEN TO MOP UP THE VILLAGE.
GRENADES, OVER THERE! WATCH EVERY WINDOW AS YOU MOVE ON.

FOR HALF THE NIGHT, THE GRUELLING BATTLE AGAINST THE UNSEEN ENEMY WENT ON, AND FINALLY A LARGE PART OF THE VILLAGE HAD BEEN OCCUPIED BY RUSSIAN TROOPS, AND THE LAST SNIPERS WERE BEING FERRETED OUT...
REPORT BACK TO H.Q. THAT KRUSLOV HAS BEEN TAKEN. LIMITED ENEMY RESISTANCE REMAINS, BUT THE SITUATION IS IN HAND.
IMMEDIATELY, MAJOR.

WE HAVE RECOVERED OUR FORMER POSITION, AND HERE WE WILL STAY! ALL OUR TROOPS ARE ON THIS SIDE OF THE STREET, SO FIRE AT ANYTHING THAT MOVES OVER THERE...

MEANWHILE, AT BALKOV FIGHTER AIRFIELD, THE PILOTS OF THE SUCCESSFUL SUPPORT SORTIE CELEBRATED IN THE MESS. FLIGHT LIEUTENANT NELSON WAS PROUD OF THE GOOD PERFORMANCE OF HIS PILOTS...
WE HAVE JUST HAD NEWS. THAT SOVIET TROOPS HAVE RETAKEN KRUSLOV. SPECIAL THANKS TO OUR BRITISH FRIENDS FOR THEIR PART IN THE OPERATION. TWO PILOTS OF THIS WING, LIEUTENANT SAVCHENKO, AND FLYING OFFICER HUNTER SHOT DOWN ENEMY AIRCRAFT, BRINGING OUR TOTAL TO THIRTY-SIX ENEMY AIRCRAFT DESTROYED!

...ONE OF OUR PILOTS WAS LOST. COMRADE LIEUTENANT BUNEYEV WAS KILLED IN ACTION TODAY. THE SPIRIT OF THIS YOUNG MAN OF NINETEEN, WHO HAD SEVEN ENEMY AIRCRAFT TO HIS CREDIT, IS AN EXAMPLE AND AN INSPIRATION TO US ALL.

COMRADE LIEUTENANT BUNEYEV WAS A GOOD FRIEND TO ALL OF US, AND A GREAT ASSET TO THIS WING. HE WILL BE SADLY MISSED.

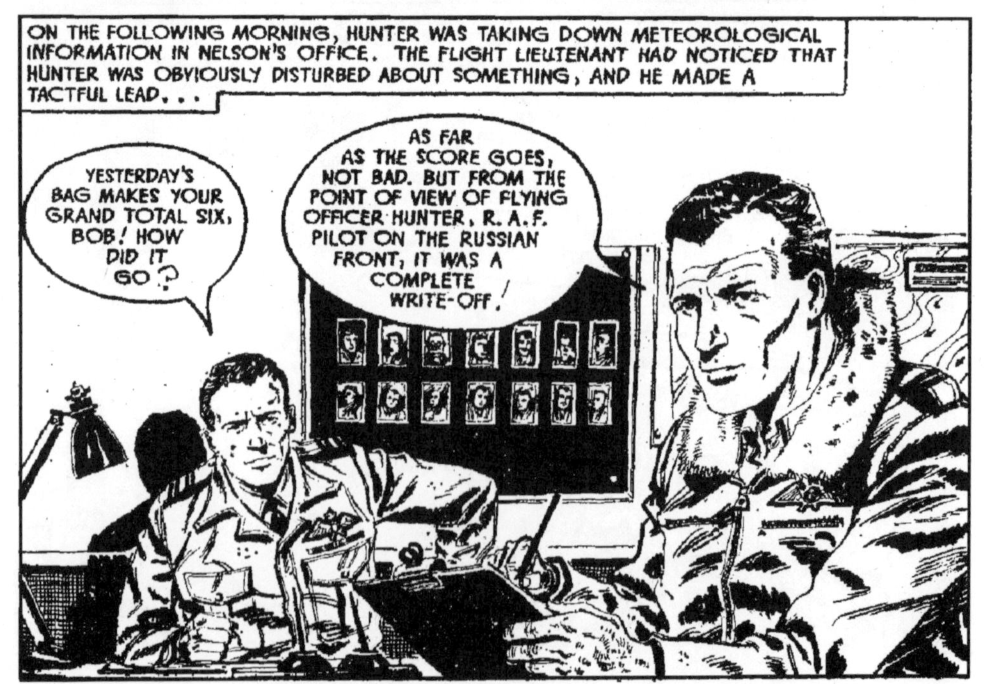
ON THE FOLLOWING MORNING, HUNTER WAS TAKING DOWN METEOROLOGICAL INFORMATION IN NELSON'S OFFICE. THE FLIGHT LIEUTENANT HAD NOTICED THAT HUNTER WAS OBVIOUSLY DISTURBED ABOUT SOMETHING, AND HE MADE A TACTFUL LEAD...
YESTERDAY'S BAG MAKES YOUR GRAND TOTAL SIX, BOB! HOW DID IT GO?
AS FAR AS THE SCORE GOES, NOT BAD. BUT FROM THE POINT OF VIEW OF FLYING OFFICER HUNTER, R.A.F. PILOT ON THE RUSSIAN FRONT, IT WAS A COMPLETE WRITE-OFF!

SLOWLY, HUNTER TOLD OF THE CIRCUMSTANCES THAT LED TO THE SHOOTING DOWN OF THE RUSSIAN PILOT. NELSON COULD SEE THAT HUNTER WAS VERY MUCH ALONE IN HIS PROBLEM BUT HE TRIED TO EASE THE OTHER'S MIND...
BOB, REMEMBER THIS. MEN MUST ALWAYS DIE IN A WAR. YOU CAN'T START BLAMING YOURSELF FOR THAT. SAVCHENKO HAD HIS CHOICE, AND HE DECIDED YOU WERE MOST IN NEED OF ASSISTANCE. IT'S NOT A QUESTION OF PERSONALITIES.
I DON'T THINK SAVCHENKO WOULD AGREE WITH THAT, BRUCE!

SO ENDED THE FIRST OF HUNDREDS OF OPERATIONS MADE BY THE R.A.F. VISITORS IN RUSSIA. IN THE MONTHS TO COME, THEY WERE TO PROVE THEMSELVES EXCELLENT PILOTS AND POPULAR ALLIES, WITH THE POSSIBLE EXCEPTION OF FLYING OFFICER HUNTER... THE MAN WITH A LOT OF ICE TO CRACK!

Chapter 4. THE SUPREME TEST
WITH SIX KILLS TO HIS CREDIT, HUNTER HAD PROVED HIMSELF TO BE ONE OF THE FINEST PILOTS IN THE SQUADRON. BUT AS THE MONTHS PASSED, HIS RECKLESSNESS IN COMBAT INCREASED FOR, TRY AS HE MIGHT, HUNTER COULD NOT SHAKE OFF HIS DOUBTS ABOUT HIS OWN PERSONAL COURAGE. SO HE STROVE TO CONCEAL HIS FEARS FROM HIS FELLOW PILOTS WITH RECKLESS FEATS OF DARING.
DON'T BE A FOOL, HUNTER. YOU DON'T STAND A CHANCE AGAINST HALF A DOZEN OF THEM!

BUT HUNTER'S TACTICS HAD NOT DECEIVED THE VETERAN, MAJOR YEGOROV. THE RUSSIAN UNDERSTOOD WHY HUNTER HAD ABANDONED HIMSELF TO THE FORTUNES OF CHANCE, AND HE REALISED THAT HUNTER WOULD HAVE TO FIND HIS OWN SOLUTION TO HIS PROBLEM. YEGOROV BELIEVED IN HIM, HOWEVER . . .
HUNTER, THIS IS OUR NEW MAN, LIEUTENANT ZHILIN. HE WILL BE JOINING THE WING ON THE SUPPORT MISSION PLANNED FOR LATER TODAY. KEEP AN EYE ON HIM, WILL YOU?
I'LL BE GLAD TO LOOK OUT FOR YOU, ZHILIN. DON'T TRY ANYTHING AMBITIOUS, LEAVE ALL THAT FOR LATER!

THE ADVICE SOUNDED STRANGE COMING FROM HUNTER. HE ADVOCATED CAUTION, BUT NEVER PRACTISED IT. THAT AFTERNOON, AS THE SQUADRON HEADED FOR THE BATTLE AREA, ZHILIN, WAS WEAVING UNEASILY IN FRONT OF HUNTER'S NOSE, TRYING HIS BEST TO MAINTAIN FORMATION . . .
NOW TAKE IT EASY, ZHILIN, DON'T KEEP JUGGLING THE THROTTLE. JUST SETTLE DOWN AND LET HER FLY HERSELF.

MEANWHILE, MAJOR YEGOROV AND THE REST OF THE SQUADRON HAD BEEN OBSERVING A GROUP OF ENEMY FIGHTERS, FLYING IN THE SAME DIRECTION BUT AT A SAFE DISTANCE FROM THE FORMATION.
WE'RE TOO MANY FOR THEM SO THEY WON'T ATTACK, JUST WAIT FOR SOME ROOKIE TO STRAY OUT OF LINE AND THEN PICK HIM OFF!

AS THE TRAILING PROCEDURE WAS SO COMMON, NONE OF THE PILOTS HAD REPORTED THE PRESENCE OF THE ENEMY — UNTIL ZHILIN SUDDENLY NOTICED THEM...
BANDITS! FOUR OF THEM ON THE STARBOARD SIDE!

ZHILIN EXCITEDLY PULLED HIS AIRCRAFT UPWARDS IN A STEEP CLIMB TO GET TACTICAL HEIGHT ADVANTAGE. ALL HIS DISCIPLINE TRAINING WAS FORGOTTEN, AND WITHIN AN INSTANT, HE WAS ALONE, TWO HUNDRED FEET ABOVE AND BEHIND THE ALLIED FORMATION . . .
WHAT THE... COME BACK HERE, YOU FOOL!
GO GET HIM, HUNTER!

TWO OF THE ENEMY AIRCRAFT WERE ALREADY PEELING OFF IN A SINISTER FASHION AFTER THE LONE LAVOCHKIN AS HUNTER LOOPED HIS HURRICANE, ROLLED OFF THE TOP AND RACED TO JOIN THE YOUNG RUSSIAN PILOT. . .
ZHILIN! THIS IS HUNTER. TURN HARD TO STARBOARD AND OPEN THE THROTTLE. YOU'RE IN REAL TROUBLE, SON! I'M WITH YOU!

THE BATTLE-HARDENED LUFTWAFFE PILOTS SOON SAW IN THE RUSSIAN'S FUTILE MANOEUVRES THE HALLMARK OF THE 'ROOKIE PILOT'; AND THEY CONVERGED LIKE A PACK OF WOLVES, GREEDY FOR THE KILL.

HUNTER'S AIRSPEED INDICATOR WAS ROTATING FURIOUSLY AS HE CLOSED THE GAP BETWEEN HIMSELF AND THE ENEMY. THEN, AN ME. 109 MOMENTARILY HOVERED IN HIS GUNSIGHT. . .
GOT HIM! KEEP WEAVING, ZHILIN! THERE'S ONE RIGHT ON YOUR TAIL!

THE HURRICANE PLOUGHED THROUGH THE WRECKAGE OF THE SHATTERED ENEMY FIGHTER, AND AS THE SMOKE CLEARED, HUNTER BECAME AWARE OF A DIM SHAPE DANCING IN HIS REAR VIEW MIRROR . . .
VERY NEAT, JERRY! I CAN SEE YOU'VE BEEN IN A SCRAP OR TWO! WELL, SO HAVE I!

THROWING HIS AIRCRAFT INTO A VIOLENT PORT TURN, HUNTER FELT HIS HURRICANE SHUDDER AS THE STARBOARD AILERON WAS TORN BY A STREAM OF BULLETS FROM BEHIND . . .

THE LIGHTNING MANOEUVRE HAD SAVED HIM FROM DESTRUCTION, BUT AS HUNTER TURNED IN TO ASSIST THE RUSSIAN, HE COULD SENSE THE LOSS OF CONTROL. . .
OKAY, ZHILIN, I'M RIGHT BEHIND THE JERRY THAT'S CHASING YOU! BREAK AWAY AND RUN FOR IT!

THE UNEXPECTED FIRE FROM HUNTER'S AIRCRAFT CAUSED THE GERMAN PILOT TO BREAK AWAY. BY SKILFUL TACTICS, HUNTER HAD SEPARATED THE TWO ENEMY AIRCRAFT, GIVING THE RUSSIAN A CHANCE TO ESCAPE.
FLY O-NINE-FIVE DEGREES AT FULL THROTTLE, ZHILIN. YOU'LL SOON FIND THE OTHERS. I'LL FOLLOW ON!
THANK YOU, FLYING OFFICER! SEE YOU LATER...

ALTHOUGH HE SOUNDED CONFIDENT, HUNTER KNEW HIS POSITION WAS FRAUGHT WITH DANGER
THE GERMANS WERE NOT LIKELY TO LEAVE A DAMAGED ENEMY PLANE ALONE...
THIS COULD BE IT! THERE'S NO DUCKING OUT OF THIS ONE!

WITH CHARACTERISTIC DESPERATION, HUNTER HURLED HIS AIRCRAFT STRAIGHT AT THE ADVANCING ENEMY, ALL GUNS BLAZING.
LOOK OUT, KARL, THIS CRAZY ENGLANDER IS TRYING TO RAM US!

ONE GERMAN HAD GIVEN GROUND BUT THE OTHER BORE ON — THEY WERE ON A COLLISION COURSE. DESTRUCTION WOULD BE SWIFT FOR THE FIRST TO PULL OUT . . .

WHOSE NERVES WOULD FAIL FIRST ?

A SPLIT-SECOND LATER, HUNTER SAW A DARK BULLET-RIDDLED SHAPE FLASH ABOVE HIS COCKPIT— AND HE KNEW THAT HE HAD WON THE BATTLE OF NERVES. HE PUT HIS HURRICANE INTO A GENTLE TURN, AND BEHIND HIM, THE MESSERSCHMITT SPIRALLED SLOWLY TO EARTH, TRAILING SMOKE...

THAT SEEMS TO WIND UP THIS LITTLE PARTY. YOUR PAL MUST HAVE TAKEN OFF.

WITH THE COOLING FLUID LEAKING OUT, THE POWERFUL AERO-ENGINE WAS OVERHEATING RAPIDLY. HUNTER'S CHANCES OF MAKING BASE WERE PRETTY SLIM, YET HE DOGGEDLY HEADED THE HURRICANE TOWARDS HIS OWN LINES.
I'M LOSING ALTITUDE FAST AND THE WHOLE CRATE COULD GO UP IN FLAMES ANY MOMENT, BUT I'M HANGED IF I'M GOING TO LET THE JERRIES GET ME.

HUNTER HAD BEEN NURSING THE FAILING HURRICANE FOR SEVEN MINUTES WHEN HE SUDDENLY BECAME AWARE OF THE FACT THAT HE WAS ACTING WITH SUPREME COOLNESS IN A DESPERATE SITUATION. FOR THE FIRST TIME HE SAW THAT COWARDICE AND FEAR WERE NOT THE SAME THING . . .
PERHAPS I'VE BEEN WRONG! I COULD HAVE BALED OUT AND BEEN TAKEN AS A P.O.W., AND THE WAR WOULD BE OVER FOR ME! BUT HERE I AM, STRAPPED TO A FLYING COFFIN, TRYING TO MAKE BASE AND GET BACK INTO THE WAR . . .

A LOUD CLATTER FROM THE ENGINE TOLD HUNTER THAT THE TORTURED PISTONS HAD SEIZED UP. INSTANTLY HE CLOSED THE THROTTLE TO PREVENT FIRE AND PULLED THE COCKPIT EXTINGUISHER...
LOOKS AS IF I'M OVER SOVIET-HELD TERRITORY ACCORDING TO MY MAP. THAT MEANS I'LL CRASH LAND ABOUT THIRTY MILES FROM BASE.

AS THE CRIPPLED PLANE GLIDED TOWARDS THE GROUND, TWO RUSSIAN INFANTRYMEN WATCHED IT WARILY.
WHAT IS IT? DOESN'T LOOK LIKE A HUN!
NOT A SOVIET FIGHTER EITHER. I CAN'T SEE THE MARKINGS FROM HERE. GET READY FOR TROUBLE, COMRADE!

THE HURRICANE CAME IN JUST ABOVE STALLING SPEED, GOUGING A DEEP TRAIL IN THE SOIL. SUDDENLY THE OIL COOLER RADIATOR UNDER THE FUSELAGE CAUGHT ON A PROJECTING ROCK, AND THE NOSE WENT IN . . .

QUICKLY! IT'S A BRITISH FIGHTER. THE PILOT WILL BE BURNED ALIVE!
WILL WE BE ABLE TO GET NEAR THE THING FOR THE FLAMES?

THEY FOUND THE PILOT SLUMPED FORWARD, UNCONSCIOUS. HE HAD STRUCK HIS HEAD ON THE GUNSIGHT WITH THE IMPACT OF LANDING...
LET'S GET HIM OUT OF HERE; THIS WRECK IS GOING TO EXPLODE ANY SECOND NOW...

DOWN! FALL FLAT ON THE GROUND!

A SERIES OF VIOLENT EXPLOSIONS ROCKED THE EARTH AROUND THE RESCUERS, AND WHEN THE NOISE HAD DIED DOWN, THEY STAGGERED TO THE COVER OF SOME TREES, TAKING HUNTER WITH THEM.
THIS PILOT MUST HAVE A CHARMED LIFE, COMRADE!
W- WHAT HAPPENED?

HUNTER SLOWLY BECAME AWARE OF THE MEN WITH HIM, AND HIS MUSCLES TENSED. HIS RIGHT HAND DROPPED INSTINCTIVELY TO HIS REVOLVER — IF THEY WERE GERMANS... THEN HE SAW THEY WERE RUSSIAN SOLDIERS.
IVANS! YOU SAVED MY LIFE!
WHAT ELSE COULD WE DO, COMRADE? YOU FIGHT FOR US AND WOULD DIE FOR US IF NECESSARY — SHOULD WE NOT DO THE SAME FOR YOU?

MEANWHILE, BACK AT BALKOV FIGHTER FIELD, THE SQUADRON HAD RETURNED, AND THE YOUNG RUSSIAN PILOT, LIEUTENANT ZHILIN, WAS MAKING HIS REPORT TO THE INTELLIGENCE OFFICER...
I SAW HUNTER GET ONE, BUT HE WAS HIT HIMSELF. I CAN'T SAY HOW BADLY. HE ORDERED ME BACK TO THE FORMATION, SAID HE WOULD FOLLOW ON. THERE WERE TWO HUNS LEFT AT THAT TIME.
POOR OLD HUNTER, IT LOOKS BAD FOR HIM.

LATER THAT EVENING, ALL THE PILOTS WERE GATHERED IN THE MESS TO LISTEN TO THE DAY'S NEWS ON THE RADIO. SEVERAL HOURS HAD PASSED SINCE HUNTER HAD LAST BEEN SEEN AND THEY HAD GIVEN UP HOPE FOR HIM. SUDDENLY THE DOOR OPENED...
GOOD EVENING, MAJOR, I AM SAROV, RED ARMY. MY MEN PICKED UP THIS AIRMAN THIS AFTERNOON, HE CLAIMS TO...
FLYING OFFICER HUNTER! SO YOU MADE IT! WELCOME BACK!

FOR THE FIRST TIME IN HIS LIFE, HUNTER FOUND HIMSELF GREETED WITH WARMTH BY HIS COMRADES. ZHILIN WAS ONE OF THE FIRST TO COME FORWARD . . .
I AM TRULY DELIGHTED TO SEE YOU, FLYING OFFICER. THANK YOU AGAIN FOR YOUR HELP THIS AFTERNOON.
SAROV, I'M SURE YOU WILL WANT TO MEET THE R.A.F. YOU WILL RECALL THAT THEIR HURRICANES SERVED YOUR UNIT WELL AT KRUSLOV, ON THE LENINGRAD FRONT.
INDEED, THEY DID! WONDERFUL CO-OPERATION — WONDERFUL!

A FEW MINUTES LATER, HUNTER'S OLD ENEMY, LIEUTENANT SAVCHENKO APPROACHED HIM, AND FOR THE FIRST TIME, THE BRITISH PILOT DID NOT SEE HOSTILITY IN HIS FACE . . .
FLYING OFFICER HUNTER, MAY I SPEAK TO YOU?

THE RUSSIAN'S MANNER WAS AWKWARD AND EMBARRASSED— BUT HE WAS OBVIOUSLY SINCERE . . .
ZHILIN TOLD ME OF YOUR BRAVE ACTION IN SAVING HIM THIS AFTERNOON. I FEEL THAT I OWE YOU AN APOLOGY FOR THE INCIDENT THAT OCCURRED WHEN COMRADE BUNEYEV WAS SHOT DOWN. I CRUELLY MISJUDGED YOU, COMRADE.
YOU HAD CAUSE TO, LIEUTENANT SAVCHENKO. IT WOULD SEEM THAT I PROVOKED THE COMMENTS THAT YOU MADE. I AM ALSO TO BLAME.

MAJOR YEGOROV AND FLIGHT LIEUTENANT NELSON WATCHED THE REUNION WITH MUTUAL SATISFACTION.
IT SEEMS THAT YOUR FLYING OFFICER HUNTER HAS AT LAST LEARNED THE DIFFERENCE BETWEEN FEAR AND COWARDICE, COMRADE.
I WAS THINKING THE SAME THING, MAJOR. IT TAKES TIME FOR A YOUNG PILOT TO LEARN THAT WE ALL HAVE MOMENTS OF FEAR IN THIS WAR. ONE CANNOT TELL THEM, THEY ONLY BECOME ANNOYED THAT THEY SHOW THEIR FEELINGS SO CLEARLY. THEY HAVE TO FIND IT OUT FOR THEMSELVES.

SO, IT WAS THAT FLYING OFFICER HUNTER FOUND HIS TRUE SELF IN THE AIR WAR ON THE RUSSIAN FRONT. HIS SCORE MOUNTED STEADILY EACH WEEK AND NOT FAR BEHIND WAS LIEUTENANT SAVCHENKO OF THE RED AIR FORCE. A FRIENDLY RIVALRY HAD GROWN BETWEEN THEM . . .
RUNWAY CLEAR FOR TAKE OFF! OUT!

AND MINUTES LATER . . .
I'LL WAGER YOU DON'T ADD TO YOUR SCORE, COMRADE!
TAKEN, SAVCHENKO. I THINK YOU'LL BE DISAPPOINTED — I FEEL LUCKY TODAY.
HUNTER'S PERSONAL WAR WAS FINALLY AT AN END. HE KNEW HE WOULD BE FLYING WING TO WING WITH THE REST, WHATEVER THE SCORE.

CRASH CALL

TO THE OFFICERS AND MEN WHO MANNED THE HIGH SPEED AIR SEA RESCUE LAUNCHES OF THE ROYAL AIR FORCE DURING WORLD WAR TWO, THE SIGNAL "CRASH CALL" MEANT INSTANT ACTION. REGARDLESS OF THE PERIL FROM THE ELEMENTS OR FROM ENEMY ACTION, THEIR SMALL CRAFT WOULD ROAR OUT TO SEA TO THE AID OF ALLY AND FOE ALIKE. THEIR MOTTO WAS "THE SEA SHALL NOT HAVE THEM".
THIS IS THE STORY OF HIGH SPEED LAUNCH 2575, ONE OF MANY THAT ALSO SERVED...
2575
25

Chapter 1. FORTUNES OF WAR

ALONGSIDE AN ANCIENT WOODEN JETTY ON THE NORTHERNMOST TIP OF THE LONELY, WINDSWEPT SHETLAND ISLANDS, THE CREW OF NEWCOMER HIGH SPEED LAUNCH 2575 WATCHED HER SISTER BOATS RETURN FROM A SUCCESSFUL OPERATION . . .

LISTEN TO THOSE CROWING BLIGHTERS **SHOUTING AT US**! WE SAW MORE ACTION IN THE CHANNEL THAN THEY'LL EVER SEE!

2573

2575

WE'LL HAVE TO PROVE THAT TO 'EM! **AND THERE'LL BE NO LIVING WITH 'EM UNTIL WE DO**!

H.S.L. 2575 HAD EARNED A NAME FOR HER RESCUE OPERATIONS ON THE SOUTH COAST. BUT THAT MEANT NOTHING TO THE VETERAN SHETLAND LONG-RANGE CREWS!

THE MEN OF 2575 HAD TO GRIN AND BEAR THE FUN. BUT THE RIVALRY WAS FORGOTTEN AS THEY WASHED OFF THE GRIME OF THE DAY AND MADE THEMSELVES READY FOR THE STATION DANCE ... FOR ENTERTAINMENT WAS ALMOST AS RARE AS TRAINS ON BRITAIN'S NORTHERN ISLANDS!
BRUSH ALL NIGHT, GINGER ... YOU WON'T IMPROVE THAT MUG!
HEY, FELLOWS— WAIT! I'VE GOT ME A DATE WITH THAT LITTLE REDHEAD FROM THE COOKHOUSE!
CALL

FLYING OFFICER JOHN HAIG, YOUTHFUL SKIPPER OF H.S.L. 2575, CAME IN FOR HIS SHARE OF THE BANTER WHEN THE RETURNING LAUNCH COMMANDERS BROUGHT THE SURVIVORS TO THE BASE OFFICERS' MESS. HAIG LET THEM HAVE THEIR MOMENT OF TRIUMPH. HE KNEW HIS BOAT, KNEW HIS CREW, AND KNEW HIS CHANCE WOULD COME BEFORE LONG ...
COME AND MEET SOME SURVIVORS, HAIG. YOU'RE UNFAMILIAR WITH THE SPECIES, I BELIEVE?
FLYING OFFICER HAIG SKIPPERS THE JETTY MASCOT!
HEY! STEADY ON THE KIDDING, FELLERS!

BACK AT THE JETTY, WATCHING HIS DEPARTING CREWMEN WITH A DISAPPROVING EYE, VETERAN FLIGHT SERGEANT CHIEFY WELSH, COXSWAIN OF 2575, ISSUED A LAST STERN WARNING TO THE WOULD-BE MERRYMAKERS...
TRANSPORT'S ALL BEEN SNAFFLED UP BY THE OTHER CREWS — HAVE TO HOOF IT... WE'VE HAD IT AGAIN.
REMEMBER WHAT LAUNCH YOU SERVE ON AND KEEP YOUR NOSES CLEAN TONIGHT, YOU ERKS — OR YOU'LL ANSWER TO ME!

THE STATION DANCE WAS IN FULL SWING WHEN THEY ARRIVED...
WELL, HERE WE GO! LET'S GIVE THE GIRLS A TREAT!
THE BEST LOOKING ONE IS MY DATE! LAY OFF!
TELL THAT TO YON FLASH HARRY, THAT CORPORAL FITTER, GRUBBY! HE'S WITH YOUR REDHEAD... **YOU'VE HAD IT!**

THE LITTLE MECHANIC PUSHED HIS WAY INTO THE THRONG...
MAY I CUT IN — AAAGH!
BEAT IT, GREASEBALL! GO FIX YOUR DUD ENGINE! DON'T YOU KNOW THAT CORPORALS AND COMMON AIRMEN HAVE NOTHING IN COMMON?

THE INSULT MADE GRUBBY FORGET HIS MANNERS IN FRONT OF A LADY... AND CHIEFY WELSH'S WARNING!
TAKE THAT, YOU TAILOR'S DUMMY! YOU WAIT... I'LL HAVE MY STRIPES ONE DAY!
ARREST THAT MAN!

SO A SORRIER AND MUCH-WISER GRUBBY GRAY, UNDER CLOSE ARREST, WATCHED HIS LAUNCH HEAD TO SEA FOR THE NEXT OPERATION. AND INSTEAD OF BEING AT THE CONTROLS IN HIS BELOVED ENGINE-ROOM, HE WORKED AT MENIAL TASKS UNDER THE EYE OF A GUARD...
CRASH CALL, GRUBBY! THINK THAT LAUNCH OF YOURS WILL MAKE IT... AS FAR AS THE HARBOUR ENTRANCE!
VERY FUNNY, FATSO! I FIXED THOSE ENGINES MYSELF... A WEEK'S PAY SAYS SEVENTY-FIVE'LL BE FIRST BACK WITH SURVIVORS!

IN THE TINY WHEELHOUSE OF H.S.L. 2575, FLYING OFFICER HAIG BROKE DETAILS OF THE OPERATION TO HIS VETERAN COXSWAIN . . .
TAIL-END CHARLIE AT PRESENT, FLIGHT. BUT WE'LL SOON LEAVE THE OTHERS FAR BEHIND IN THIS BOAT . . .
AYE AYE, SKIPPER . . . GOOD TO BE ON THE JOB AGAIN!
2573

HERE'S OUR CHANCE TO PROVE OUR WORTH TO THESE SHETLAND BARNACLES. SOME OF OUR TRAWLERS OFF THE FAROES ARE TAKING A SAVAGING FROM RELAYS OF HUN MINELAYING AIRCRAFT OUT FOR A LITTLE BLOOD SPORT . . . THOSE FISHERMEN WILL NEED OUR HELP!
BIT OF A DIFFERENT JOB TO THE ONES WE HAD OFF DOVER, SIR.

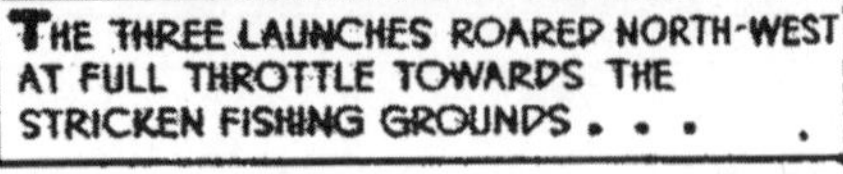
THE THREE LAUNCHES ROARED NORTH-WEST AT FULL THROTTLE TOWARDS THE STRICKEN FISHING GROUNDS . . .

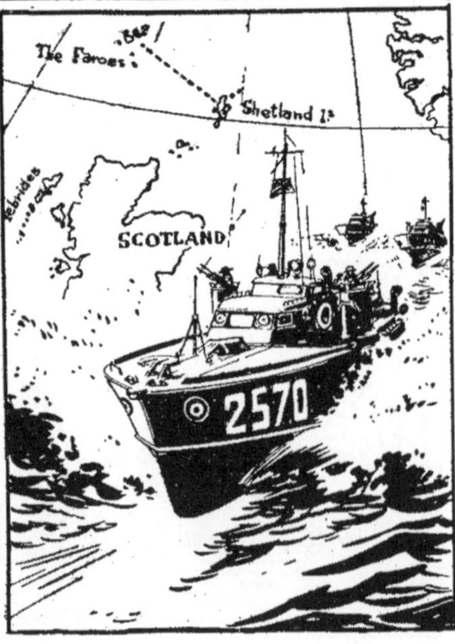
The Faroes
Shetland Is
Hebrides
SCOTLAND
2570

FINDING THE SPORT GOOD, A GERMAN MINELAYING SQUADRON RETURNING FROM AN OPERATION IN ICELANDIC WATERS, DALLIED TO WREAK HAVOC ON THE NEAR-DEFENCELESS FISHING VESSELS.
DIRTY HUN MURDERERS! WHY DON'T YOU PICK ON A DESTROYER..?

ACH, KURT... MINELAYING IS A DULL TASK. THIS IS HOW WAR SHOULD BE!
JA! AND SEE WHAT THE BRITISH FOOLS HAVE SENT TO DRIVE US OFF!
1045

THE SIGHT OF THE THREE RESCUE LAUNCHES WAS THE CAUSE OF THE CO-PILOT'S MIRTH. UNDAUNTED BY THE OPPOSITION, THE THREE LITTLE H.S.L'S CLOSED IN TO EXECUTE THEIR ERRAND OF MERCY...

SEE YOU KEEP THOSE JERRIES BUSY, GINGER! AT LEAST UNTIL I GET MY SURVIVORS TO THE SICK-BAY!

THAT'S WHAT I'M HERE FOR, DOC!

HAIG TOOK HIS LAUNCH SKILFULLY ALONGSIDE — SEEMINGLY IMPERTURBED BY THE HAIL OF BULLETS NOW DIRECTED AT HIS CRAFT.
GOOD TO SEE YOU, LADS!
LESS TALK THERE AND GET A MOVE ON! OUR FUEL TANKS COULD BLOW ANY SECOND IN THIS HEAT!
2575

SCORCHED AND CHOKING, THE LAUNCH'S GUNNERS FIRED CALMLY AND ACCURATELY AT THE ENEMY . . .
BLOOD TO SEVENTY-FIVE, SIR! IT MUST BE HOT WORK FOR 'EM!
GOOD SHOW, YOUNG HAIG!
2575

RESCUE WORK COMPLETE, H.S.L. 2575 BEGAN TO CLEAR THE BURNING WRECK . . .
FULL ASTERN BOTH, HELMSMAN! WE'RE GETTING OUT OF HERE!

... BUT THE FORTUNES OF WAR... ARE UNPREDICTABLE!
2575
WE MUST HAVE CAUGHT SOMETHING MIGHTY BIG WITH OUR PROPS! CUT ENGINES...!

A HALF-SUBMERGED FISHING NET HAD SUCCEEDED IN STOPPING THE LAUNCH AFTER FIRE AT SEA AND ENEMY ATTACK HAD FAILED.
OUR LUCK IS RUNNING TRUE TO FORM AGAIN FLIGHT... ALL BAD!
NO ONE COULD HAVE FORESEEN THIS LOT, SIR.

THE H.S.L. NOW DRIFTED HELPLESSLY AT THE MERCY OF THE TIDE... UNABLE TO MANOEUVRE UNDER ATTACK...
BADLY BURNED MEN ABOARD... MUST RETURN TO BASE... CAN YOU COPE?
WE'LL MAKE OUT. TAKE OUR SURVIVORS AND GET 'EM HOME. GOOD LUCK!
2575

AND BACK AT BASE, GRUBBY GRAY SERVED OUT HIS PUNISHMENT— PUNISHMENT WORSENED BY THE THOUGHT OF NOT BEING WITH HIS LAUNCH ON AN ACTIVE OPERATION . . .
WHAT ODDS TWO- FIVE- SEVEN- FIVE NOW, GRUBBY ? STILL WANT TO LOSE YOUR MONEY ?
DON'T WORRY, FATSO ! SHE'LL BE DOING HER STUFF TODAY... WISH I WERE ABOARD !

LADEN WITH SURVIVORS AND WOUNDED, THE TWO LAUNCHES SET OFF FOR BASE, LEAVING THEIR UNLUCKY SISTER SHIP BEHIND. FORTUNATELY, THE GERMAN AIRMEN WERE ALSO LEAVING AFTER LOSING TWO OF THEIR AIRCRAFT AS PAYMENT FOR THEIR SPORT.
TOUGH GOING FOR HAIG AND HIS MEN... THEY'D DONE A GREAT JOB !
YES. THERE BUT FOR THE GRACE OF FATE WOULD BE US !
2573

2575 WAS LEFT TO HER OWN DEVICES...
DO WHAT YOU CAN, LAD...
BE WITH YOU IN A MOMENT, DODDS!

WITH THE WIND AND SEA RISING, THE TWO MEN HACKED AT THE PONDEROUS WEIGHT OF NET...

BUT THE POWER OF THE LAUNCH'S ENGINES HAD SPUN A WEB THAT DEFEATED THE GALLANT EFFORTS OF THE PAIR.
NO GO, CHIEFY— BASE JOB, THIS LOT...
THIS BREAKS MY HEART. HOW THOSE BODS BACK AT BASE WILL CHORTLE...

... SIGNAL REQUEST FOR TOW!
CHEER UP, FLIGHT! IT'S ALL THAT'S LEFT FOR US...

A WELCOMING THRONG CROWDED THE LITTLE JETTY AT THE SHETLAND BASE AS THE LAUNCHES RETURNED . . .
NO EMPTY BEDS IN OUR HOSPITAL . . . NOT WITH THOSE BOATS TO KEEP GRABBING PATIENTS OUT OF THE SEA !

BUT THE CROWDS HAD DISPERSED AND THE JETTY WAS DESERTED WHEN 2575 HOVE IN SIGHT . . .
WHAT DID WE TELL YOU, GRUBBY !
SHE GOES TO RESCUE — AND IS RESCUED HERSELF ! WHAT AN ASSET !
C'MON, GUARD ! YOU CAN LOCK ME UP AND THROW AWAY THE KEY !

Chapter 2. OPERATION RESCUE

IN A SHELTERED FIORD SOUTH OF TRONDHEIM, NORWAY, A GERMAN RAIDER FORCE OF HEAVY UNITS PREPARED TO ASSAULT THE ATLANTIC CONVOYS THAT WERE THE LIFELINE OF BRITAIN. WELL CAMOUFLAGED, THEY MADE READY FOR SEA, THEIR SECRETS SAFE IN THE EYES OF THE GERMAN HIGH COMMAND UNTIL . . .

RAPID FIRE! HOW DID THAT BRITISH DOG MANAGE TO AVOID OUR DEFENCE SYSTEM AND STUMBLE UPON US AT THIS TIME..?

9

3

AN ORDER WAS GIVEN — THE INTRUDER MUST NOT GET AWAY!
THAT RECCE AIRCRAFT WOULD NO DOUBT BE USING A CAMERA TO UNCOVER OUR SECRETS. SUCH PHOTOGRAPHIC EVIDENCE WOULD SOON REVEAL OUR STRENGTH AND THE BRITISH HOME FLEET WOULD BE ALERTED.
I THINK OUR SECRET IS SAFE YET, HERR GROSS-ADMIRAL! THE WHOLE COAST HAS BEEN ALERTED. EVERY EXIT HAS BEEN SEALED TO THE BRITISHER!

BUT THE LONE CATALINA WAS STILL AIRBORNE AS SHE LIMPED ACROSS THE NORWEGIAN COASTLINE WITH HULL RIPPED, PORT ENGINE DEAD, AND GUNS MANNED BY HUDDLED CORPSES. HER WOUNDED PILOT LISTENED ANXIOUSLY TO THE RAGGED BEAT OF THE STARBOARD MOTOR . . .
RA-S

CAN'T MAKE IT, SKIPPER! ENGINE REVS DROPPING... LOSING HEIGHT FAST! IT'S THE DRINK FOR US!
SIGNAL BASE AND GET THAT CAMERA UNSHIPPED... WE PAID DEARLY FOR THOSE SHOTS!
WOLF CALLING VIXEN...

THE DARK MENACING WATERS LOOMED... THE CO-PILOT FOUGHT THE SLUGGISH AIRCRAFT DOWN TO A HALF-CRASH THAT ALLOWED A FEW PRECIOUS MOMENTS FOR ESCAPE...
EASY WITH THAT CAMERA THERE! WE'LL KEEP IT WITH US AS LONG AS WE HAVE A CHANCE OF RESCUE...
INTO THE DINGHY, SIR! SHE'S GOING DOWN!
BRRR! A COLD SHOWER AT THIS TIME OF YEAR...!

THE CRY FOR HELP FROM THE DOOMED CATALINA HAD BEEN PASSED TO THE SHETLAND AIR SEA RESCUE BASE. A VERY HURRIED BRIEFING FOLLOWED...
GLASS IS STILL FALLING... IT WILL BE A TOUGH TRIP WITH A FULL GALE THROWN IN FOR GOOD MEASURE. THE AIR MINISTRY WANT THIS PICK-UP MADE AT ALL COSTS. I'VE BEEN ORDERED TO MAKE THIS A THREE-BOAT CALL!

I KNOW YOUR BOAT IS OFF-DUTY THIS WEEK-END, HAIG, AND YOUR REGULAR CREW ARE ON ISLAND-LEAVE AND SCATTERED. BUT THIS IS A PRIORITY JOB FOR ALL HANDS... ROUND 'EM UP AND GET UNDER WAY AS SOON AS YOU CAN!
THEY'LL BE GLAD TO BE IN ON THIS, SIR!

THE DUTY AND STANDBY LAUNCHES MADE A RAPID DEPARTURE... AND 2575 REMAINED ALONGSIDE WHILE THE ISLAND WAS COMBED FOR HER CREWMEN...
... TOO BAD YOUR CREW WERE OFF-DUTY, HAIG!
WE'LL CATCH YOU UP... SEE YOU OUT THERE!
2570

THE FIRST FEW OF THE ELUSIVE CREW WERE LOCATED... AND, WITH AN UNEXPECTED ARRIVAL, HAIG'S MIND WAS MADE UP...
SIR! GRAY! HE'S BROKEN OUT OF THE GUARDHOUSE!
HE'LL DO MORE GOOD BELOW AT HIS ENGINES, FLIGHT! STAND BY TO LEAVE HARBOUR... WE'VE ENOUGH HANDS TO MANAGE!

SCARCELY HAD THE POWERFUL MOTORS THUNDERED INTO LIFE AT GRUBBY'S EXPERT TOUCH WHEN THE ENGINE-ROOM TELEGRAPHS DEMANDED ACTION...
COR! WHAT AM I — A ONE-MAN BAND! NO RELIEF FOR ME THIS TRIP... BUT IT'S BETTER THAN BEING A KITCHEN MECHANIC!

THE UNDERMANNED 2575 RACED FOR THE OPEN SEA IN THE WAKE OF HER SISTER BOATS...
STONE A CROW! NORWAY— WITH ONLY HALF A TRAINED CREW, A FEW LANDLUBBER VOLUNTEERS FROM BASE, AND A STORM! AND US A FULL HOUR BEHIND THE OTHERS...
... AND IF WE MAKE IT BACK FROM THIS JOB I'LL BE UP TO MY NECK IN DEAD TROUBLE, SURE AS MY NAME'S GRUBBY GRAY!
2575

MEANWHILE, ACROSS THE SEA, AT THE MERCY OF WIND AND TIDE, THE SMALL RUBBER DINGHY. TOSSED HELPLESSLY OFF THE ENEMY-OCCUPIED COAST...
NORWAY AND A PRISON CAMP, A WATERY GRAVE, OR A SUIT MADE OF ICICLES! WHAT A CHOICE... ANY WAY **WE LOSE**!
STOP MOANING, HARRY! AND REMEMBER TO DUMP THAT CAMERA IF WE DO GET TAKEN!

BUT THE SOUND OF ENGINES ROUSED THE SURVIVORS FROM THEIR FROZEN STUPOR. HOPEFULLY THEY PEERED INTO THE NIGHT...
IS IT ONE OF OURS?
I DON'T KNOW. CAN HARDLY BE OUR BOYS ALREADY...
SIGNAL PISTOL READY, SKIPPER!

BUT THE ENEMY WERE INTERESTED IN FINDING SURVIVORS, TOO — IF NOT FOR ENTIRELY HUMANE REASONS.
FINDING THE WING FLOAT OF THE BRITISHER WAS EASY COMPARED TO THIS, SIR. WE HAVE A COLD NIGHT AT SEA AHEAD LOOKING FOR MEN WHO MAY NOT EVEN EXIST...
PERHAPS WE ARE WASTING OUR TIME, HERR LEUTNANT. THEY COULD HAVE GONE DOWN WITH THEIR AIRCRAFT... BUT ORDERS FROM A GROSS-ADMIRAL ARE ORDERS I CARRY OUT TO THE FULL...

SEPARATED FROM THE RUBBER LIFE RAFT BY A FEW FEET OF STORM-TOSSED WATER, THE E-BOAT LOOMED OUT OF THE BLANKETED NIGHT AND WAS GONE...
WOW! AN E-BOAT... NEARLY SLICED US!
SHALL I SIGNAL? WE'LL FREEZE TO DEATH OUT HERE!
WISH YOUR TONGUE WOULD FREEZE! SHUT UP!

...BETWEEN THE SHETLAND BASE AND THE DRIFTING SURVIVORS, TWO HIGH SPEED LAUNCHES BRAVED THE GALE-LASHED WASTES...
... NEVER KNOWN SEAS LIKE THIS. LOOK, SEVEN-O HAS COPPED IT!
2573
2570
AAEEGH!

THE GALE RAGED WITH UNRELENTING FURY . . . AND THE SECOND HIGH SPEED LAUNCH BECAME A CASUALTY . . .
... CLUTCHES HAVE BURNED OUT FIGHTING THIS LOT, SIR! WE'VE HAD IT!
THEN WE'VE BOTH HAD IT!
MAN OVERBOARD STARBOARD!
2570

... AND HARD ON THE HEELS OF HER SISTER LAUNCHES CAME 2575, PLOUGHING GRIMLY INTO THE TEETH OF THE GALE ...
HANG ON, DOC! WE MAY NEED YOUR MEDICAL SKILL WHEN WE REACH THOSE SURVIVORS!
SURVIVORS! NOTHING COULD SURVIVE A NIGHT LIKE THIS ON A RUBBER RAFT... NOT UNLESS THEY'VE DRIFTED WELL INSHORE
2575

THE SEARCHING E-BOAT FARED BADLY IN THE STORM, TOO... BUT SHE REMAINED AT SEA FOR THE SAME PURPOSE AS 2575.
BASE REFUSES PERMISSION TO CANCEL SEARCH, HERR KAPITAN!
CURSED BATTLESHIP SAILORS! DO THEY REALISE WHAT IT IS LIKE ON A SCHNELLBOOT IN SUCH WEATHER?

2575 FINALLY CAUGHT UP WITH HER SISTERS... A SIGHT EVEN GRUBBY LEFT THE WARMTH OF HIS ENGINE-ROOM TO WITNESS.
UNDER TOW, BOYS? DROP YOUR HOOKS AND WE'LL TOW YOU BOTH HOME ON THE WAY BACK!
LOST A PROP, I BET! BETTER IF YOU'D LOST THE CORPORAL FITTER!

ALONE AND UNDER COVER OF THE LONG ARCTIC NIGHT, HAIG'S LAUNCH CLOSED IN TO THE NORWEGIAN COASTLINE . . .
I CAN USE SOME COCOA, LIVINGSTONE. DID YOU PUT A TOT IN IT? AND WHAT'S IT LIKE BELOW?
I PUT TWO TOTS IN IT! AND IT'S A SHAMBLES BELOW! EVERYTHING SMASHED BUT THE LADS' SPIRITS!
WE'RE ALMOST THERE, MEN! KEEP YOUR FINGERS CROSSED FOR A QUICK PICK-UP OF SURVIVORS AND A SAFE RETURN...

BUT OTHER EYES WERE ALERTED...
SCHNELLBOOT, KAPITAN! RED-FOUR-ZERO!
WE HAVE NO OTHER SCHNELLBOOTS ON THIS SEARCH IN THIS AREA ... SHE'S AN R.A.F. RESCUE LAUNCH! PREPARE FOR ACTION!
E 120

THE HEAVIER ARMAMENT OF THE E-BOAT BEGAN TO TAKE TOLL OF THE FLIMSY RESCUE CRAFT...
EMERGENCY FULL AHEAD! HARD TO STARBOARD, HELMSMAN! WE'LL MAKE A RUN FOR IT IN THE OPEN SEA...
RAPID FIRE, YOU GUNNERS!

HAIG HAD NO DESIRE TO DALLY AND SWAP SHOTS WITH HIS MAGNIFICENTLY EQUIPPED ADVERSARY...
WE'VE GOT OUT OF RANGE... BUT I JUST WISH THE SKIPPER HAD LET ME HAVE ONE REAL GO AT THAT SQUAREHEAD!
HE KNOWS WE'RE OUT HERE TO SAVE LIFE — NOT TO CHUCK IT AWAY! AN E-BOAT COULD EAT US!

... 2575'S SUPERIOR SPEED CARRIED HER OUT OF DANGER — TEMPORARILY...
WE HAVE SENT THE BRITISH DOGS SCUTTLING FOR HOME, HERR KAPITAN. IF SHE POKES HER NOSE BACK WE WILL SINK HER FOR CERTAIN!
ACH, SO! BUT SHE WOULD BE HERE FOR A PURPOSE. THERE MUST BE SURVIVORS! DOUBLE LOOKOUTS! CONTINUE SQUARE SEARCH OF THE AREA!

HAIG KNEW HE HAD A DANGEROUS ENEMY TO LOSE... AS WELL AS A TINY CRAFT TO LOCATE...
DINGHY
NORWAY

BUT ONCE RID OF THE E-BOAT, 2575 REVERTED TO COURSE AND REACHED HER SEARCH AREA... A COMPLETELY BLANK SEARCH AREA REVEALED IN A NEW DAWN FREE OF STORM CLOUDS...
JERRY HAS PROBABLY COVERED THIS AREA THOROUGHLY... WE'LL BE ORIGINAL! CUT ENGINES!
CUT ENGINES, SIR..?
YES, FLIGHT! WE'LL LET THE DRIFT OF THE TIDE LEAD US TO 'EM!

WE'VE FOUND THE DRIFT... HALF AHEAD BOTH ENGINES... HERE'S HOPING THIS WORKS OUT RIGHT!
AYE, SKIPPER. I'LL TAKE OVER THE WHEEL TO SEE THAT WE FLOW WITH THE TIDE!
2575

THE SAME TIDE DRIFT HAD CARRIED THE DINGHY. THE NUMBED, CRAMPED SURVIVORS WOKE TO FIND THEMSELVES INSIDE ENEMY TERRITORY!
LAND ON BOTH SIDES... WE'RE IN A BLOOMING FIORD!
WE'RE UP THE WELL-KNOWN CREEK! WHAT ABOUT THE AIR SEA RESCUE LARK NOW?

ON THE SHEER SIDE GUARDING THE MOUTH OF THE FIORD, A STARTLED GERMAN ARTILLERYMAN RUBBED HIS EYES AT THE SIGHT BELOW...
FELDWEBEL! THERE IS SOMETHING IN THE FIORD... HEADING FOR THE SEAPLANE BASE!
3

ACHTUNG! ACHTUNG! BOAT APPROACHING FROM SEA! ENGLANDER SCHNELLBOOT!
DUMKOPF! IT IS ONLY A RUBBER RAFT... CALL THE DUTY OFFICER AT THE SEAPLANE BASE. HE'LL GET A BOAT OUT TO INVESTIGATE...

HAIG HAD FOUND HIS SURVIVORS. CONFRONTED BY THE NARROW TRAP-LIKE MOUTH OF THE FIORD, THE AIR SEA RESCUE OFFICER DID NOT HESITATE...
WE'VE FOUND 'EM! NOT THE BEST PLACE FOR A RECOVERY... BUT THAT'S WHAT WE'RE HERE FOR! FULL AHEAD BOTH!

Chapter 3 THE FIRE TRAP
HER BOW POINTED DIRECTLY AT THE FIORD ENTRANCE, THE LAUNCH ROARED THROUGH HEAVY ENEMY CROSS-FIRE FROM THE COASTAL BATTERIES.
THANK GOODNESS THE BIG COASTAL DEFENCE GUNS CAN'T FIRE INTO THE FIORD!

THE DRIFTING DINGHY HAD BECOME A PAWN IN A DEADLY GAME...
HIMMEL! THE BRITISH DOGS DARE TO ENTER OUR BASE!

... A GAME HAIG PLAYED WELL!
CHECKMATE!
2575

THE SURVIVORS, HARDLY BELIEVING WHAT THEY CONSIDERED A MIRACLE, ALLOWED HOPE TO RETURN AS THEY WERE HELPED FROM THE TINY RUBBER COCKLESHELL ...
HURRY IT UP, LIVINGSTONE! THE NATIVES AREN'T FRIENDLY!
ENEMY FIRE DIRECTED AT US FROM SEAPLANE BASE, SIR!
2575

... AND THE RESCUED MEN'S FIRST THOUGHTS WERE FOR THE CAMERA'S SAFETY.
EASY WITH THAT CAMERA! FOUR MEN HAVE DIED FOR THAT!

FROM THE GERMAN SEAPLANE BASE UP THE FIORD, THE MOTIONLESS LAUNCH MADE A FINE TARGET...
ARE THE BRITISH MAD? THEY COME HERE AND EXPECT TO LIVE?
GET THEM, KURT!

GINGER DODDS SWUNG HIS OERLIKON TO ANSWER THE GERMAN CHALLENGE...
THAT'LL TEACH YOU TO INTERFERE, YOU HUN!

ENCOURAGED BY HIS SUCCESS, THE GUNNER TURNED HIS OERLIKON ON THE OTHER MOORED SEAPLANES...

BUT THE EXULTANT GINGER WAS SOON DEFLATED BY FLIGHT SERGEANT WELSH!
DODDS! DON'T WASTE AMMUNITION! WE'RE NOT HERE TO WIN THE WAR!
COR! I SHOOT UP FOUR AIRCRAFT — AND DROP A CLANGER! WHAT A LIFE!
THE FLIGHT SERGEANT IS RIGHT... YOU MAY REGRET THOSE SHELLS YOU USED UP... LOOK! JUNKERS CIRCLING OVERHEAD!

ENGINES RACING, WHEEL HARD TO STARBOARD, THE LAUNCH SPUN IN A SHARP CURVE TO MAKE GOOD HER ESCAPE — IF SHE COULD...
WHAT WAS ALL THE NOISE, GINGER? I COULDN'T HEAR MYSELF THINK DOWN THERE!
GET YOUR FAT HEAD BELOW BEFORE I PUT A SHELL THROUGH IT! IF IT CHEERS YOU UP TO KNOW... WE'VE GOT A JERRY PLANE ON OUR TAIL!

HIGH ABOVE THE NARROW FIORD A PATROLLING AIRCRAFT, ATTRACTED BY THE BILLOWING FLAMES FROM GINGER'S VICTIMS, SWOOPED TO INVESTIGATE . . .
ACHTUNG! GUNNERS AND BOMB-AIMER TO YOUR POSITIONS . . . WE ARE GOING IN TO ATTACK!

. . . AND AT THE CLIFF DEFENCE POST HURRIED ORDERS WERE ISSUED TO SNARE THE INTRUDERS.
JUNKERS AIRCRAFT ABOUT TO ATTACK LAUNCH . . .
JA, HERR MAJOR! OPERATION FIRETRAP! AT ONCE!

THE TERSE ORDER WAS PASSED ON!
LET HER FLOOD, HEINZ!
ALL SLUICES WIDE OPEN!

... AND IN THE FIORD'S DARK DEPTHS...
... EVEN THE FISH FLED!

MEANWHILE, THE AIRCRAFT PRESSED HOME ITS FIRST ATTACK — CONFIDENT OF THE OUTCOME!

FIRST BLOOD WENT TO THE JUNKERS!
I'LL BE WAITING FOR THAT HUN SO-AND-SO NEXT TIME!
COUNT ME IN! I'VE A COLD NIGHT ON A RAFT TO MAKE UP FOR... I WANT MY POUND OF FLESH, TOO!

A FILM OF HIGHLY INFLAMMABLE AVIATION SPIRIT FROM THE UNDERWATER PIPES DISCOLOURED THE SPAN OF SEA AT THE FIORD'S NARROW MOUTH . . .
NOW I'LL SEE IT WORKING . . . I'VE WAITED LONG FOR THIS MOMENT . . .

THE FELDWEBEL SLOWLY AND DELIBERATELY AIMED HIS SIGNAL PISTOL AT THE SEA BELOW.

A BARRIER OF LEAPING FLAME SEALED THE FIORD — AND THE SEA BOILED!
WUNDERBAR! THERE IS NO ESCAPE FOR THE BRITISH DOGS!
AND THE JUNKERS IS COMING IN FOR HER SECOND ATTACK, HERR LEUTNANT!

AND AT THAT PRECISE MOMENT, FITTER GRUBBY GRAY CHOSE TO FIND OUT HOW THINGS WERE GOING OUTSIDE HIS LONELY ENGINE-ROOM...
WOW! AND I WAS WORRIED ABOUT THE TROUBLE AWAITING ME AT BASE! ONLY HOPE I LIVE TO SEE A COURT-MARTIAL!

WHILE H.S.L. 2575 FOUGHT HER LONE BATTLE TO ESCAPE THE NAZI NET CLOSING AROUND HER IN THE LANDLOCKED WATERS OF THE FIORD, HER SISTER LAUNCHES HAD LIMPED HOME TO THE SHETLAND BASE, AN OCEAN AWAY...
HERE COMES THE OLD MAN — MAYBE HE HAS NEWS OF SEVENTY-FIVE.

NO GO, SIR! THE STORM WAS TOO MUCH FOR US — LOST HIGGINS OVERBOARD...
WE SAW SEVENTY-FIVE PLOUGHING ON. ANY NEWS OF HER?
LAST SIGNAL SAID SHE'D HAD A BRUSH WITH AN E-BOAT! HAIG MUST BE MAINTAINING RADIO SILENCE — OR ELSE HE'S IN DIRE TROUBLE!

WE CAN ONLY HOPE. HAIG AND HIS MEN HAD AN EXCELLENT WAR RECORD DOWN SOUTH... MAYBE THEY'LL WIN THROUGH. IT'S TIME THEIR BAD LUCK CHANGED. LET US HOPE THIS IS IT!

THE WEARY CREWS OF THE CRIPPLED LAUNCHES FILED INTO THE BASE COOKHOUSE FOR THEIR FIRST MEAL IN SIXTEEN HOURS...
C'MON, BEAUTIFUL — HUSTLE IT UP! WE'VE BEEN AT SEA ALL NIGHT, NOT STUCK IN A COSY CELL LIKE YOUR GLAMOUR BOY, GRUBBY GRAY!

GLAMOUR BOY, EH! GRUBBY'S STILL AT SEA... WHERE REAL MEN ARE!
YOU MEAN HE'S ON SEVENTY-FIVE? WOW! YOU CAN FORGET HIM THEN! THEY'VE HAD IT!

THE CORPORAL FITTER'S CONVICTION OF THE CERTAIN FATE OF 2575 WAS ENDORSED BY A DETERMINED GERMAN AIRCREW AND THE ARTILLERYMEN STOKING THE FLAMES BARRING THE NARROW FIORD ENTRANCE... BUT NO ONE HAD INFORMED THE FIGHTING CREW OF THE LAUNCH THAT THEY WERE FINISHED!
WE'VE HIT HIM! SEE... HE'S STARTING TO BURN!
... BUT HE'S STILL COMING! THIS'LL STOP YOU, YOU SQUAREHEADED HUN!

THE TORTURED AIRCRAFT ROARED IN TO FINISH ITS RUN OVER THE LAUNCH, STILL DEFIANTLY SPITTING SHELLS . . .
DONNERWETTER! WE MISJUDGED THE ENGLANDER . . . BUT WE WILL NOT DIE ALONE!

THIS LAST GESTURE ON THE PART OF THE DOOMED PILOT WAS NOT WITHOUT EFFECT . . .
THE DEVILS! THEY'VE GOT HARRIS — AND THE SKIPPER!
DOC!

FLIGHT SERGEANT WELSH'S REACTIONS WERE BORN OF INSTINCT AND YEARS OF HARD EXPERIENCE. THE LAUNCH WAS HEADING FOR THE SIDE OF THE FIORD AT FULL SPEED BY THE TIME HE REACHED THE BRIDGE...
STARBOARD TWENTY, EMERGENCY FULL! HEAD FOR THE CENTRE OF THOSE FLAMES... WE'RE GOING THROUGH!

THE MORTALLY STRICKEN JUNKERS, MANNED BY A DEAD CREW, WAS WEAVING AND CLIMBING AND DIPPING — AND THEN...
THE LAUNCH! SHE MAKES FOR THE BARRIER! STAND BY YOUR GUNS!
LOOK AT THE JUNKERS! SHE'S HEADING FOR THE FUEL TANKS!

THE PROGRESS OF THE LAUNCH WAS FORGOTTEN IN THE TERROR OF THE MOMENT. . .

A CASCADE OF BURNING FUEL BURST LIKE A NIGHTMARISH WATERFALL ON TO THE GUN POSITIONS. . .

THE EXPLOSION ADDED FUEL TO THE FIRE AND INTENSIFIED THE RAGING HOLOCAUST H.S.L. 2575 HAD YET TO PENETRATE...
ALL HANDS BELOW! GRAB EVERY FIRE EXTINGUISHER YOU CAN LAY YOUR HANDS ON!
2575

THE LAUNCH'S BOWS CLEAVED THE BURNING SEA AS SHE SPED INTO THE FEARSOME FALLING FLAMES... THEN SHE WAS SWALLOWED IN THEIR HOT EMBRACE...
THE FLAME BELT MUST END SOMEWHERE! HANG ON, DOC!
HOPE THE FUEL TANKS ABOARD CAN TAKE IT!

THEN, ABRUPTLY, 2575 BROKE FREE INTO THE OPEN SEA. NEVER WAS CLEAN COLD AIR AND ICY SPRAY MORE WELCOME . . .
WE'VE MADE IT! BELOW THERE! ALL HANDS DOUSE DECKS!
2575

THE DIMINUTIVE INTRUDER HAD LEFT IN HER WAKE A TERRIBLE MOMENTO OF HER VISIT . . .
CURSED BRITISH DOGS! IT WAS AN EVIL DAWN THAT BROUGHT YOU HERE!

Chapter 4. SEEK AND DESTROY
NEWS OF THE UNEXPECTED AND HUMILIATING DEBACLE AT THE FIORD REACHED THE EARS OF GROSS-ADMIRAL VON RICHTLINGER, COMMANDER OF THE SECRET ATLANTIC TASK FORCE...
THIS FIORD BUSINESS — COMPLETE DEVASTATION — AND BY ONE PLYWOOD CRAFT! ARE WE GERMANS SUCH DUMKOPFS?

THE LAUNCH'S ESCAPE HAD TURNED THE GERMAN INTO A RAGING VOLCANO ERUPTING WRATH UPON HIS SUBORDINATES...
I WANT THAT LAUNCH! NOT ONLY TO STOP THAT CAMERA FROM REACHING BRITISH NAVAL INTELLIGENCE... BUT FOR MY OWN PERSONAL SATISFACTION! DO WHAT YOU LIKE ABOUT FULFILLING MY WISH — BUT GET IT DONE. THIS I PROMISE... HEADS WILL ROLL IF YOUR COMBINED EFFORTS FAIL!

MEANWHILE, CHIEFY WELSH, ACTING-SKIPPER OF 2575, WAS RALLYING HIS MEN FOR THE LONG VOYAGE HOME...
WATCH OUT FOR BURNING AMMO!
2575

GUNNER GINGER DODDS ACTED QUICKLY, SO QUICKLY HE DID NOT FEEL THE HOT METAL SEARING HIS PALMS . . .
THOUGHT YOU'D HAD IT THERE, CHUM. BUT CHEER UP, CHIEFY RECKONS THE WORST IS TO COME! HOPE YOU'VE GOT YOUR WINGS AND HARP READY, GINGER!
YOU SHOULD COMPLAIN, GRAY! AFTER THAT FIERY FIORD YOU'LL BE QUITE AT HOME WHERE YOU'LL BE GOING!

BUT AT SUCH A TIME OF CRISIS, FLIGHT SERGEANT WELSH HAD NO TIME TO SPARE FOR COMMENDING HEROICS...
STOW THAT GAB! AND GET BELOW, GRAY, DON'T SHOW YOUR FACE AGAIN UNTIL WE MAKE BASE—AS WE WILL! I'LL WANT ALL THE REVS YOU CAN MUSTER OUT OF THOSE ENGINES! IT'S MY BET HALF THE GERMAN FORCES IN NORWAY ARE OUT TO GET US!
ONLY HALF, CHIEFY?

HALF THE GERMAN FORCES IN NORWAY OUT TO GET THEM, WELSH HAD DECLARED. HE WAS NOT FAR WRONG... THE ENEMY WERE DIRECTED TO ONE OBJECTIVE...
...THE ORDER WENT OUT—SEEK AND DESTROY!

NEAREST TO THE SCURRYING LAUNCH WAS HER OLD ENEMY— THE PATROLLING E-BOAT, THIRSTING FOR BLOOD!
E-BOAT, CHIEFY! CLOSING HARD— HEADING US OFF!
WE'LL TRY TO OUT-MANOEUVRE HER . . . BUT MAKE THOSE GUNS TALK LIKE THEY'VE NEVER DONE BEFORE!
2575

THE BRITISH LAUNCH, HERR KAPITAN! SHE TURNS TO PORT...
HIMMEL! INTO OUR THICKEST MINEFIELD!
. . . AND WE'LL FOLLOW! I'D RATHER FACE MINES THAN GROSS-ADMIRAL RICHTLINGER!

THE MEN OF 2575 BECAME AWARE THAT THEY FACED A DOUBLE DANGER...
MINES AHEAD, CHIEFY! AND THE E-BOAT'S SHELLING US!
I'M NOT BLIND, LAD! PORT FIFTEEN! REDUCE TO HALF SPEED!
SOMETIMES I WISH I WERE BACK ON THAT RAFT!

CHIEFY WELSH WAS FORCED TO CUT SPEED EVEN WITH AN E-BOAT CLOSING FOR AN EASY KILL! AT LEAST GRUBBY GRAY KNEW NOTHING OF THE MINEFIELD AS HE PONDERED THE GRIM SITUATION...
SLOW AHEAD BOTH! AND WITH AN E-BOAT ON OUR TAIL! HOPE CHIEFY KNOWS WHAT HE'S UP TO! AT LEAST THE VENTILATION IN THIS PLACE HAS BEEN IMPROVED!

BUT THE GERMAN, TOO, HAD THE MINEFIELD TO CONSIDER. THE ENERGETIC PURSUIT BECAME TEMPERED WITH CAUTION AND SLOWED TO A CRAWL...
DUMKOPF! IDIOT! KEEP ON COURSE... OR WE ALL DIE BY OUR OWN MINES!

A GRIM GAME OF TAG ENSUED, A FIGHT TO THE DEATH PLAYED AT SLOW SPEED. AND ALWAYS EACH BOBBING, GLISTENING MINE OFFERED A PASSPORT TO ETERNITY!

THE E-BOAT'S SUPERIOR ARMAMENT GAVE HER THE EDGE IN SUCH A GAME...
WE HAVE THE BRITISH CURS AT OUR MERCY! RAPID FIRE! SEND HER TO THE BOTTOM!

THE GALLANT RESCUE LAUNCH WAS NOT BUILT TO SUSTAIN PROTRACTED PUNISHMENT OF THE KIND METED OUT BY THE RELENTLESS E-BOAT...
WE'RE HITTING HER WITH ALL WE'VE GOT... BUT IT'S MAKING LITTLE IMPRESSION ... AND I'VE ONLY ONE DRUM OF AMMO LEFT!
WE CAN'T HURT HER— BUT A MISS COULD! IF THAT MISS WERE IN THE RIGHT PLACE!

THERE WAS ONE WAY OUT. CHIEFY SEIZED IT LIKE A DROWNING MAN DESPERATELY CLUTCHES A STRAW. BUT BEFORE HE COULD MAKE HIS PLAN KNOWN...
THE DEVILS! BUT I'M NOT READY TO GIVE IN TO 'EM... NOT YET!

BELOW-DECKS RECEIVED A SHARE OF THE POUNDING. THE TINY SICK-BAY WAS RIDDLED WITH RAZOR-EDGED SHRAPNEL...
THIS BOX OF TRICKS HAS REALLY ROUSED A HORNET'S NEST!
SKIPPER! YOU'RE TOO WEAK TO MOVE YET...
I'M GOING TO MY BRIDGE! HELP ME... OR GET OUT OF MY WAY!

WITH A SUPERHUMAN EFFORT, THE MORTALLY WOUNDED FLIGHT SERGEANT WELSH HAD DRAGGED HIMSELF TO HIS FEET IN THE SHAMBLES OF THE BRIDGE. HE MUSTERED HIS EBBING STRENGTH TO ISSUE ONE MORE COMMAND . . .
THE MINES! AIM FOR THE MINES! HOLD YOUR FIRE UNTIL THE JERRY IS NUDGING THEM . . .

THE RESCUE LAUNCH'S GUNNERS RIPPED A HAIL OF FIRE AT THE MINES BEFORE THE E-BOAT'S BOW . . .
HERE GO MY LAST SHELLS!
E120

AS WELSH SAGGED AMONG THE DEBRIS OF THE BRIDGE, A THUNDEROUS DETONATION WAS MUSIC TO THE EARS OF THE DYING VETERAN...
ON TARGET! CHIEFY'S IDEA PAID OFF!

BUT IN TRIUMPH... THERE WAS TRAGEDY. WELSH'S NERVELESS FINGERS LOST THEIR GRIP. HE FELL, AND THE LAUNCH WAS PILOTLESS IN THE MINEFIELD...
THE BRIDGE! THERE'S NO ONE TO TAKE US THROUGH THE MINES!
GET ME UP THERE!

FLYING OFFICER HAIG RESUMED COMMAND IN THE REMNANTS OF HIS BRIDGE. ALL HIS CONCENTRATION AND SKILL WERE NEEDED TO CLEAR THE MINEFIELD. THAT TASK OVER, HE NOTICED HIS MEN EYING HIM WITH QUIET PRIDE. AT THAT MOMENT HE KNEW HE WOULD FIND THE STRENGTH AND THE GUILE TO GET THEM THROUGH.
TAKE FLIGHT SERGEANT WELSH BELOW. THEN SEE THAT HOT TEA AND RUM, AND WHATEVER FOOD IS LEFT, IS SHARED OUT...
AYE AYE, SIR!

BUT HAIG'S NEXT ORDER CAUSED ALL EYES TO TURN ON HIM IN DISBELIEF — AND EVEN DOC WONDERED ABOUT THE HEAD WOUND SUSTAINED BY THE YOUNG SKIPPER...
FULL SPEED! WHEEL HARD TO STARBOARD! WE'RE GOING BACK TO NORWAY! WE COULDN'T LAST ANOTHER HOUR IN DAYLIGHT OUT HERE...!
WHAT AGAIN? THIS IS WHERE I CAME IN... AND NO DINGHY THIS TIME.

THE ENEMY BEGAN STEPPING UP THE DESPERATE SEARCH...
OUR CONTACT WITH THE E-BOAT CEASED SUDDENLY. RICHTLINGER HAS DESPATCHED A DESTROYER TO THE SCENE. IT WAS HIS LAST ORDER BEFORE HE COLLAPSED. WHAT IS THIS BRITISHER... A POCKET BATTLESHIP? I WANT EVERY AIRCRAFT THAT CAN FLY OVER THAT AREA — NOW!
JAWOHL, HERR GENERAL! I PERSONALLY WILL LEAD THE ATTACK...

SIMILAR URGENT COMMANDS WERE BEING ISSUED ACROSS THE NORTH SEA...
RECCE REPORTS TREMENDOUS ACTIVITY OFF NORWEGIAN COAST IN THE TRONDHEIM AREA. I WANT TO KNOW WHAT'S GOING ON!
YES, SIR. A FULL SQUADRON OF MOSQUITOS ARE LEAVING NOW FOR AN OFFENSIVE SWEEP...
HQ

HAIG TOOK HIS LAUNCH AND RELUCTANT CREW BACK TO A SHELTERED CREEK ON THE RUGGED NORWEGIAN COAST THEY HAD BEEN SO GLAD TO LEAVE . . .
LOOK AT THAT BEAUTY! SHE'D HAVE FINISHED US IN TWO TICKS. YOUR SKIPPER KNOWS HIS STUFF!
2575

SO THE MEN OF 2575 SETTLED DOWN FOR THE LONGEST WAIT OF THEIR LIVES — UNTIL DARKNESS CAME TO CLOAK A FURTIVE ESCAPE FROM ENEMY WATERS.
IMAGINE HOW WE'D FARE OUT THERE! AND ME WITH NO AMMO FOR THE OLD POPGUN!
I'M FOR GETTING MY HEAD DOWN WHILE THE GOING'S GOOD... WE'VE A LONELY NIGHT AT SEA AHEAD — I HOPE!

THE DESCENT OF NIGHT WAS REGARDED AS THE BEGINNING AND THE END. THE BEGINNING FOR 2575 AS SHE DUMPED CAMOUFLAGE AND PREPARED FOR SEA... AND THE END OF HOPE FOR FRIENDS WHO WAITED AT THE LITTLE SHETLAND BASE...
THEY SHOULD HAVE RETURNED HOURS AGO! THE WHOLE AREA HAS BEEN COMBED... SHE'S JUST VANISHED. 'FRAID SHE'S HAD IT...
BAD SHOW. HAIG AND HIS CREW WERE GOOD TYPES. THE WHOLE BASE IS TAKING IT HARD!
WE RODE THEM HARD... BUT THEY TOOK IT LIKE GOOD SPORTS!

WRITTEN OFF AS LOST! YET IN THE GREY LIGHT OF DAWN, THE DUTY LOOKOUT AT BASE STARED INCREDULOUSLY, WONDERING IF HE WERE SEEING A GHOST SHIP...
IT—IT'S SEVENTY-FIVE! SHE'S MADE IT...!
LOOK AGAIN! THEY SAID SHE MUST BE ON THE BOTTOM FOR SURE!
3
2570

THE SLEEPING CAMP, ROUSED BY THE NEWS, RUSHED TO THE JETTY DISBELIEVING . . . AND BELIEVED!
LOOK AT HER . . . A FLOATING WRECK!
MAYBE! BUT SHE'S STILL THE BEST IN THE AIR SEA RESCUE FLEET!
2570
2575

THIS CAMERA WILL BE FLOWN SOUTH MINUTES FROM NOW. GLAD YOU WERE ABLE TO MAKE IT!
THERE'S GRAY ON DECK. WHAT DO WE DO IN A CASE LIKE THIS?
THERE'S THE OLD MAN . . . BETTER ASK HIM!

. . . ER . . .
ABOUT GRAY, SIR. DO WE ARREST HIM . . ?
ARREST HIM? AFTER THAT MISSION! I'LL SEE HE GETS PROMOTION!
SP

EXPERT EYES HAD SOON STUDIED THE SECRETS OF THE ATLANTIC RAIDER FORCE AS REVEALED BY THE CAMERA'S EYE. THE DIE WAS CAST FOR VON RICHTLINGER'S FLEET!
THE WHOLE OF BOMBER COMMAND HAVE BEEN PUMMELLING A CERTAIN GERMAN FLEET ALL WEEK. OUR PICTURES, IT SEEMS, WERE A HUGE SUCCESS!
THANKS TO HAIG HERE AND HIS CREW. . .
ALL WE DID WAS TO RESCUE YOU. THAT'S OUR JOB!

AND AT THE SHETLAND AIR SEA BASE LIFE RETURNED TO NORMAL... ALMOST!

THE IRON FIST
OCTOBER 1942, AND ALL THE DESTRUCTIVE FURIES OF MODERN WAR WERE SCORCHING AND SCARRING THE DESERT SANDS OF NORTH AFRICA!
FOR THREE YEARS, THE MASSIVE MILITARY MACHINE OF NAZI GERMANY HAD MARCHED RELENTLESSLY WEST THROUGH EUROPE AND SOUTH THROUGH THE MIDDLE EAST. ONLY IN EGYPT HAD THE ALL CONQUERING NAZIS BEEN HALTED. THERE, GENERAL ERWIN ROMMEL'S VAUNTED AFRIKA KORPS, THRUSTING FOR THE VITAL SUEZ CANAL, WERE HAMMERED TO A STANDSTILL BY THE DESPERATE BRITISH EIGHTH ARMY. WEEKS OF STALEMATE PASSED — AND THE ALLIED STRENGTH GREW.
THEN, ON OCTOBER 23RD, THE EIGHTH ARMY MOVED—FORWARD IN ATTACK!
THE BATTLE OF EL ALAMEIN HAD BEGUN . . .

Chapter 1. OUT OF ACTION
ALL NIGHT, A THOUSAND BRITISH GUNS HAD ROARED AND THUNDERED IN THE GREATEST BARRAGE IN HISTORY. BEFORE DAWN, ROYAL ENGINEERS BEGAN TO CLEAR MINE-FIELD GAPS . . .

AS THE DEADLY MINES WERE DEFUSED, DEEPER GAPS WERE GOUGED INTO THE PATTERNS OF HIDDEN DEATH. THEN THE INFANTRY BEGAN TO POUR INTO THE WIDE LANES . . .
M.P

AS DAWN BROKE, THE GRIM-JAWED, SUN-TANNED INFANTRYMEN REACHED THE FAR SIDE OF THE FIRST ENEMY MINE BELTS — AND BEHIND CAME THE RUMBLING ROAR OF ARMOURED GIANTS !
THE TANKS WERE GOING THROUGH !
GO ON, YOU BEAUTIES - KNOCK OLD ROMMEL'S PANZERS FOR SIX !

IMMEDIATELY, ROMMEL FLUNG HIS FAMOUS PANZER DIVISIONS AGAINST THE BRITISH TANKS — AND A BITTER BATTLE BEGAN BETWEEN THE ARMOURED MONSTERS . . .
FOR THREE DAYS THE TANK FORCES HAMMERED AND MAULED EACH OTHER IN MERCILESS CONFLICT !

A MILE FROM THE SHATTERING VIOLENCE OF THE BATTLEFIELD, A SQUADRON OF BRITISH SHERMANS SHELTERED BEHIND A HILL . . . WAITING . . . WAITING . . .
IF H.Q. DON'T GIVE US ORDERS TO GET CRACKING SOON, MISTER PIKE, THERE WON'T BE ANY JERRIES LEFT FOR US!
NOT A THING ON THE RADIO, CORPORAL — THEY JUST KEEP TELLING US TO STAND BY!

THE TANK'S GUNNER, CORPORAL JOHNNY GRAY, DUCKED BACK INTO THE TANK AND GRINNED WRYLY AT THE OTHER TWO CREW MEMBERS — THE COCKNEY DRIVER, TUG WILSON AND KEN BYRNE, THE RADIO OPERATOR.
SAME AS LAST TIME, LADS — NOT A WHISPER ABOUT GETTING MOBILE!
COR, STONE THE FLIPPING CROWS! AFTER THREE DAYS OF WAITING TO CARVE THOSE JERRY TIN CANS UP, I'M GROWING CORNS BETWEEN ME AND THIS SEAT!
MUCH LONGER LIKE THIS AND I'LL FORGET HOW TO USE THIS BOX OF TRICKS!

THEN SUDDENLY, IT HAPPENED!
FOX EASY... FOX EASY... TOP PRIORITY — MOVE FORWARD AT MAXIMUM SPEED NOW — OUT!
EASY ONE ... TWO... THREE... FOUR — START UP! ADVANCE IN ATTACK FORMATION! OUT!

ENGINES SCREAMING TO A CRESCENDO OF UNLEASHED POWER, THE RACING TANKS SWEPT FORWARD OVER THE HILL-CREST— INTO THE HUNGRY HOLOCAUST OF DEVOURING DESTRUCTION BEYOND!
IF THE SQUADRON CAN PUNCH THROUGH THE JERRIES' RIGHT FLANK AS PLANNED— WE'LL RIP HIS SUPPLY POINTS TO SHREDS, THEN TURN AND HIT HIS TANKS FROM THE REAR!

THEN THEY WERE IN THE STORM OF WHINING ARMOUR-PIERCING SHELLS AND SLICING, STEEL-JACKETED MACHINE GUN BULLETS. LIEUTENANT PIKE DUCKED INTO THE TURRET, SLAMMING THE HATCH . . .
KEEP HER RUNNING STRAIGHT, WILSON! NOW LET'S SEE IF I CAN FIND A NICE FAT TIGER TO HAVE A GO AT!
CAN'T SEE A THING YET, SIR— ONLY BURNT OUT WRECKS AND SAND CLOUDS! BUT WAIT A MINUTE!

. . . A BLACK CROSSED TANK FILLED THE TELESCOPE SIGHT! IT WAS A GERMAN TIGER— AND ITS GUN WAS SWINGING INTO DEADLY AIM ON THE SHERMAN . . .

DESPERATELY, JOHNNY TRAVERSED THE GUN A FRACTION. THE GUN MUZZLE LASHED FLAME— AND A SHELL STABBED DEEP BETWEEN THE TIGER'S TURRET AND CHASSIS...

RACING RIVULETS OF BLAZING FUEL BURST FROM THE SHATTERED TANK'S ENGINE HATCHES, AND AS THE CREW LEAPED OUT, THE SHERMAN SPED PAST —
INTO SUDDEN NEW DANGER . . .
07121

GERMAN ANTI-TANK GUNS! IN A FLASH, PIKE SWIVELLED HIS PERISCOPE AROUND TO FIND THE THREE TANKS OF HIS TROOP . . .
. . . ONLY ONE FOLLOWED HIM — THE OTHER TWO WERE MEETING THE CHALLENGE OF TWO TIGERS!

CALMLY AND SWIFTLY, PIKE GAVE HIS ORDERS — A FRONTAL ATTACK TO DRAW THE GERMANS' FIRE SO THAT THE SECOND SHERMAN WOULD STAND A CHANCE OF BREAKING THROUGH!
SMACK, ON TARGET, SUNRAY! PERMISSION REQUESTED TO PLASTER THAT OTHER RAT'S NEST!
NO- STICK TO YOUR ORDERS TO OUTFLANK THEM WHILE WE KEEP THEM BUSY!

BUT THE BATTLE - TOUGHENED GERMANS WERE A CRACK CREW — ANOTHER SHELL SLAMMED INTO THE BREECH ...
LEFT ... LEFT. SCHNELL —! SCHNELL. HALTEN ON TARGET ... FEUER !

LIKE A THUNDERBOLT, THE SOLID, ARMOUR - PIERCING SHOT BORED THROUGH THE SHERMAN'S SHELL, SCATTERING STREAKING STEEL SPLINTERS AS IT SLAMMED INTO THE ENGINE ...
AAGH !

SUDDEN RAW, BITING SMOKE FILLED THE TANK AS THE STRICKEN SHERMAN SHUDDERED TO A STANDSTILL. FOR A SPLIT SECOND, THE CREW WERE STUNNED — THEN TRAINING AND DISCIPLINE TOOK OVER ...
WE'VE HAD IT ! SHE'LL GO UP LIKE A BOMB ANY SECOND! TUG, SCRAMBLE OUT OF YOUR EMERGENCY HATCH— KEN, HELP ME WITH MISTER PIKE — AFTER I'VE PASTED THOSE JERRIES !

THE GERMAN GUNNERS WERE LINING UP ON THE OTHER SHERMAN — JUST AS GRAY HAD HOPED! THE TURRET BROWNING SPAT FLAME AND LEAD...
CAUGHT 'EM WITH THE GUN SHIELD TURNED. THE PENALTY FOR NOT FINISHING US OFF FIRST!

SOMEHOW, THEY LIFTED THE BADLY WOUNDED OFFICER CLEAR OF THE SMOKING WRECK — ACROSS THE BLISTERING SANDS THEY STUMBLED... AND THEN...
THERE GOES THE OLD BUS! LUMME, SHE WAS A TARTAR TO DRIVE SOMETIMES, BUT THERE'LL NEVER BE ANNUVER ONE 'ARF AS GOOD!
SHE DID HER BEST — RIGHT TILL THE END! BUT FOR HER, THE REST OF THE TROOP WOULD BE PINNED DOWN HERE, INSTEAD OF BREAKING THROUGH.

ALL ABOUT THEM ROARED THE THUNDER OF BATTLE AS THEY WENT BACK ACROSS THE SHELL-RIPPED SANDS. THROUGH THE WREATHING, ACRID CLOUDS OF CORDITE SMOKE — PAST A SCORE OF BURNT-OUT TIGERS AND SHERMANS — TO FIND FRIENDLY-FACED INFANTRYMEN, AND A FORWARD MEDICAL POST...

WELL, SIR, HOW IS HE?

BAD ENOUGH TO KEEP HIM IN HOSPITAL FOR THREE MONTHS! NOW, YOU CLEAR OFF — WE'RE GOING TO BE BUSY SOON WHEN THE INFANTRY ATTACK!

Chapter 2. ENTER GOLIATH

THE TAUT GRIMNESS LEFT THE OFFICER'S PALE, UNTANNED FEATURES AS HE WALKED OVER TO THE THREE TANKMEN . . .
MY NAME IS CARSON — AND I'VE BEEN POSTED OUT HERE FROM THE ARMOURED WARFARE SCHOOL TO PUT THIS EXPERIMENTAL A.F.V. THROUGH ITS PACES ON DESERT TRIALS!
COR — FAN ME WITH A TANK TRACK! HE'S STRAIGHT OUT OF THE TANK OFFICERS' NURSERY — 'E AIN'T EVEN GOT HIS KNEES BROWN YET!

WHIPLASH SWIFT, CARSON'S HARD EYES DARTED TO TUG. A TINY PULSE THROBBED IN HIS FIRM JAW — AND JOHNNY WAS SURE HE HAD HEARD THE COCKNEY'S LOUD WHISPER . . .
STOP MUMBLING, TROOPER — AND STAND UP STRAIGHT! CORPORAL, YOU'LL DRIVE THE TRANSPORTER — I'LL BE WITH YOU IN FRONT. YOU TWO OTHERS — GET UP ON TOP OF THE TARPAULIN, AND KEEP YOUR GUNS HANDY!
VERY GOOD, SIR!

SHORTLY AFTERWARDS, THE MASSIVE LORRY SNORTED ITS WAY THROUGH ALEXANDRIA AND WESTWARD ON TO THE DESERT ROAD — TOWARDS THE GROWLING RUMBLE OF POUNDING GUNS . . .
LUVADUCK! THIS NEW GEEZER'S AS GREEN AS THEY COME! I DON'T 'ARF PITY THE CREW HE GETS FOR THIS NEW TANK TRIAL CAPER! WHAT A DIFFERENCE BETWEEN HIM AND MISTER PIKE.
NEVER MIND THAT, TUG! LISTEN TO THAT BARRAGE — SIXTY MILES AWAY AND YOU CAN FEEL THE AIR SHUDDERING FROM HERE!
4th INDIAN

AFTER THREE HOURS THEY REACHED THE FORWARD DEFENSIVE AREAS... AND THEIR SQUADRON COMMAND POST...
LUMME – THEY'VE BEEN NATTERIN' FOR NEARLY TWENTY MINUTES. I WISH HE'D HURRY IT UP, THEN WE COULD START HUNTIN' AROUND FOR A NEW BUS!

THEN TUG'S IMPATIENCE WAS ANSWERED – WITH THE BIGGEST SHOCK OF HIS LIFE!
YOU LADS WANTED A TANK – WELL, YOU'VE GOT ONE. AND LIEUTENANT CARSON HAS ASKED FOR YOU AS HIS CREW!
LUMME... NO!

WITHOUT MUCH ENTHUSIASM, THE THREE TANKMEN UNLASHED THE TIE ROPES. WITH A GREAT HEAVE, THE TARPAULIN SLID FREE, AND THE TRIO STOOD IN STUNNED WONDER!
COR – A FLIPPING GOLIATH!
YOU CAN SAY THAT AGAIN, TUG!
WHAT A BEAUTY!
THE XT EIGHT! DESIGNED TO OUTGUN AND OUTFIGHT ANY KNOWN GERMAN TANK. WEIGHT FORTY TONS, SPEED THIRTY MILES AN HOUR, ARMAMENT, ONE SEVENTEEN POUNDER, AND THREE BROWNINGS! ALL IT WANTS IS A NAME – AND WILSON HAS JUST FOUND ONE – GOLIATH!

FOR THE REST OF THAT DAY, AND HALF THE NIGHT, CARSON MADE THEM WORK UNTIL THEY WERE FIT TO DROP, PREPARING GOLIATH FOR THE TRIALS. BUT AT MIDNIGHT EVERYTHING WAS READY. THE TEST AREA CHOSEN WAS SOUTH OF THE GREAT QATTARA DEPRESSION, A HUGE STRETCH OF SUB SEA LEVEL QUICKSAND FORMING THE SOUTHERN BOUNDARY OF THE FURIOUS BATTLE STILL RAGING AT EL ALAMEIN!
MEDITERRANEAN SEA
ALEXANDRIA
EL ALAMEIN
EGYP
ENEMY AREA
BRITISH ALLIED AREA
MOGHARA
QATTARA DEPRESSION
OPEN DESERT
SIWA OASIS

AT DAWN, WITH THE RUMBLING ANGER OF THE POUNDING GUNS STILL TO THE WEST, GOLIATH AND ITS CREW STARTED OFF . . .
THIS LARK AIN'T SO BAD, CHUM — EXCEPT THAT YOU HAVEN'T GOT THAT TANK OF YOUR OWN, YET — AND WE'RE OUT OF THE SHINDIG OUR OUTFIT'S HAVING WITH JERRY'S PANZERS!
IF YOUR SLAP-HAPPY DRIVING DOESN'T WRECK GOLIATH, WE'LL FINISH THE TESTS AND BE BACK IN ACTION IN TWO DAYS — SO *KEEP YOUR EYES ON THE ROAD!*

ALL THAT DAY, CARSON DIRECTED THE MASSIVE TANK WESTWARDS, BORDERING THE DEPRESSION. TESTS WERE CARRIED OUT AND ADJUSTMENTS MADE BEFORE THEY MADE NIGHT CAMP. AT DAWN THEY WENT ON AGAIN — UNTIL . . .
WHOEVER DESIGNED GOLIATH IS A GENIUS, — IT'S PERFECT, TUG SAYS IT DRIVES LIKE A DREAM!
ONE FAULT THE BIG BRUTE HAS GOT IS THAT THE AIR FILTERS KEEP CLOGGING WITH DUST. HAH — *LISTEN, THERE THEY GO AGAIN!*

HALF A DOZEN TIMES ALREADY, THE ENGINE AIR FILTERS HAD BECOME SOLID WITH SAND — AND NOT ONCE HAD CARSON OFFERED HIS HELP TO CLEAR THEM . . .
NEVER EVEN GETS HIS HANDS DIRTY— JUST SITS THERE WRITING A LOAD OF GUFF! OLD PIKEY WOULD HAVE DONE HIS SHARE ALL RIGHT!
HE'S GOT HIS JOB TO DO, TUG — AND HE KNOWS BEST HOW TO DO IT!

THEN SUDDENLY JOHNNY'S HEAD JERKED UP — CARSON TOO HAD HEARD THE DRONING WHINE IN THE SKY TO THE NORTH . . .
JERRY ME. ONE-O-NINES! MUST BE PATROLLING DOWN HERE FOR ANY FLANKING ATTACK!

THE SINISTER BLACK-CROSSED SHAPES HELD THEIR COURSE FOR A MOMENT — THEN THEY TURNED AS ONE . . .
THEY'VE SEEN US! TAKE COVER!

ENGINES SCREAMING AT FULL BOOST, THE SLEEK FIGHTERS ROCKETED DOWN — MACHINE GUNS AND CANNONS STREAMING FLAME . . .
COME ON, YOU BLACK VULTURES — I'VE GOT A HOT LEAD WELCOME WAITING !

JETS OF TRACER LICKED VICIOUSLY ACROSS THE FORWARD HULL OF GOLIATH AS THE ME. 109'S CAME IN AT POINT BLANK RANGE . . .
. . . AND LEAD FROM CARSON'S GUN CHEWED INTO THE FIGHTER'S BODY!

THE STRICKEN FIGHTER LURCHED CRAZILY — THEN CLAWED LEVEL TRAILING FLAMES AND SMOKE. IT THUNDERED OVER, TWENTY FEET ABOVE CARSON'S HAMMERING GUNS . . .
HE'S BREAKING UP IN MID AIR! YOU'VE GOT HIM, SIR!

THE BLAZING MESSERSCHMITT FELL THROUGH THE AIR. AND A MOMENT LATER, THE SHATTERED PORT WING BROKE OFF — AND THE PLANE PLUNGED INTO THE SANDS, EXPLODING IN AN EYE-SEARING FLASH OF FIRE!
KEN — GET ROUND THE OTHER SIDE AT THE DOUBLE. NUMBER TWO IS COMING IN FOR ANOTHER ATTACK!
I'VE GOT HIS SHARE READY AND WAITING!

WITH FANATICAL FURY, THE GERMAN FLUNG HIS FIGHTER DOWN, ITS GUNS STABBING LEAD AT THE TANK. THEN, IN THE LAST SECONDS, CARSON'S BROWNINGS FIRED AGAIN . . .
GREAT SCOTT! THE LONG RANGE FUEL TANKS - IF THEY EXPLODE . . .

THE NAZI PILOT'S NERVE SPLINTERED THEN — VIOLENTLY HE WRENCHED HIS BULLET-RIDDLED PLANE AWAY. BUT BEHIND HIM HE LEFT SUDDEN DEADLY MENACE — AS WRITHING FIRE ENVELOPED THE FUEL TANKS!
CORPORAL, WHAT IN HEAVENS NAME . . . GOOD GRIEF — THE TANKS!
IF THEY GO UP, WE WON'T STAND A CHANCE — GOT TO GET RID OF 'EM FAST!

FLICKERING FINGERS OF RAW HEAT JABBED AT JOHNNY AS HE LEAPED BETWEEN THE TANKS, FUMBLING WITH THEIR STEEL LOCKING STRAPS. THEN THEY FLIPPED FREE — AND DESPERATELY JOHNNY KICKED OUT TWICE . . .
... AND FIRST ONE, THEN THE OTHER OF THE BLAZING TANKS JOLTED OFF GOLIATH'S BACK!

AS THE FLAME-WRAPPED CONTAINERS ROLLED SLOWLY AWAY, GOLIATH'S CREW WATCHED WITH BATED BREATH– UNTIL . . .
HOLY SMOKE! IF JOHNNY HADN'T DUMPED THEM, WE'D BE CINDERS BY NOW!

THE AIR-SPLITTING FLASH DIED, AND THE EYES OF MARK CARSON AND JOHNNY GRAY MET, BRIGHT WITH NEW-FOUND RESPECT FOR EACH OTHER . . .
THAT WAS GREAT WORK, CORPORAL– AND QUICK THINKING!
YOU DIDN'T DO SO BAD YOURSELF, SIR– ONE JERRY PLANE SHOT DOWN AND THAT OTHER WRECK WILL BE LUCKY TO SEE ITS BASE AGAIN!

TUG AND KEN IMMEDIATELY BEGAN REPLACING THE CLEANED AIR FILTERS IN GOLIATH'S GREAT ENGINE– *AND THEN CARSON DROPPED A BOMB SHELL . . .*
WE WERE RUNNING ON THE MAIN FUEL TANK TO GET M.P.G. FIGURES. IT'S NOW THE ONLY TANK WE HAVE AND IT'S NO MORE THAN A QUARTER FULL!
CRUMBS! THAT'S ONLY ENOUGH JUICE FOR FIFTY MILES, THE WAY GOLIATH LAPS IT UP!

THE GRIM TRUTH OF THEIR POSITION WAS PLAIN...
WE'RE OVER A HUNDRED MILES FROM H.Q. — SO THAT MEANS ABOUT A SEVENTY MILE WALK AFTER WE RUN OUT OF JUICE.
AND IF WE BROKE OUR RADIO SILENCE, JERRY'D DARNED SOON PICK UP THE SIGNALS!
WE'RE NOT WALKING-AND WE'RE NOT LEAVING GOLIATH! HERE'S ANOTHER WAY-LOOK AT THIS MAP!

WE CAN'T TRANSMIT BY RADIO — BUT WE'VE HEARD THE LATEST GEN ON THE BATTLE. THE JERRIES ARE BEING PUSHED BACK — SO BY NOW THE EIGHTH ARMY IS PROBABLY OPPOSITE US ON THE OTHER SIDE OF THE DEPRESSION. THEY'RE OUR NEAREST SOURCE OF FUEL-SO WE'RE GOING STRAIGHT ACROSS TO MEET THEM!
EL ALA
TARĀ
DEPRESSION

JOHNNY STARED AT CARSON IN AMAZEMENT...
CROSS THE DEPRESSION? BUT SIR, THERE'S ONLY A THIN CRUST OF SUN-DRIED MUD OVER IT. WE'D GO THROUGH INTO THE QUICKSANDS LIKE A KNIFE INTO BUTTER!
WE'RE GOING, CORPORAL - THAT'S AN ORDER! I'LL LEAD THE WAY ON FOOT! GET ABOARD — AT THE DOUBLE!

FOR A SPLIT SECOND, JOHNNY HESITATED— THEN, TIGHT LIPPED, HE CLIMBED UP INTO THE TURRET FOLLOWED BY TUG AND KEN. IN SILENCE THEY TOOK THEIR PLACES AND GOLIATH'S ENGINE ERUPTED INTO THROBBING LIFE...
LUMME, 'E MUST HAVE SUNSTROKE, LEADING US INTO THAT BOTTOMLESS GLUE POT!
"OURS NOT TO REASON WHY, OURS BUT TO DO AND DIE", CHUM, SO GET HER ROLLING!

GROWLING AND SHUDDERING LIKE A RESTLESS GIANT, GOLIATH CRAWLED AFTER CARSON WHO WALKED ALONG THE EDGE OF THE DEPRESSION FOR SEVERAL HUNDRED YARDS AS IF SEARCHING. THEN HE STOPPED . . .
CORPORAL, YOU AND BYRNE GET ON TO THE TURRET— JUST IN CASE! WILSON, NOW WE'LL SEE IF YOU CAN REALLY DRIVE. FOLLOW TEN YARDS BEHIND ME— AND KEEP ME DEAD CENTRE IN FRONT!

SUDDEN SWEAT BEADED TUG'S FACE— AND HIS HANDS WERE SLIPPING ON THE STEERING TILLER BARS, AS WITH INFINITE CARE HE EASED GOLIATH AFTER CARSON'S BROAD BACK . . .
EASY, TUG, EASY! IF WE BREAK THROUGH THE CRUST, YOU WON'T HAVE A CHANCE OF GETTING OUT BEFORE . . .
CAUTION
MPH
. . . BUT SOMEHOW, AS THE TANK'S WIDE TRACKS GROUND INCHES DEEP INTO THE SURFACE, IT HELD FIRM!

THEN BEGAN A LIVING NIGHTMARE FOR THE YOUNG COCKNEY DRIVER — EVERY SECOND HELD ITS OWN ETERNITY OF AGONY. YET THEY MERGED INTO MINUTES . . . AND BECAME HOURS . . .
TWO HOURS — WE'VE DRIVEN ABOUT EIGHT MILES. OLD TUG MUST BE FEELING THE STRAIN — WHAT ABOUT ME RELIEVING HIM, JOHNNY?
NOT A CHANCE, KEN — ONCE WE STOPPED, SHE'D START TO SETTLE AND GO THROUGH!
GRADUALLY, THE THREE MEN IN THE TANK BECAME AWARE OF SOMETHING ELSE BESIDES THEIR OWN DRY-MOUTHED FEAR. IN FRONT OF THEM, CARSON STRODE AHEAD, SEEMINGLY UNTIRING, WITH A RELENTLESS DETERMINATION THAT HAD NO KNOWLEDGE OF FAILURE. TO TUG IT BECAME A CHALLENGE THAT MADE HIM FORGET HIS OWN ACHING MUSCLES AND SHIVERING NERVES — NO WHITE-KNEED OFFICER STRAIGHT FROM ENGLAND WAS GOING TO BEAT HIM! SO THE TENSION-FILLED MILES DRAGGED PAST, UNTIL SUDDENLY — THEY COULD SEE THE OTHER SIDE!

YARD BY YARD THEY CREPT TOWARDS IT — ONE HUNDRED . . . THIRTY . . . TWENTY YARDS TO GO — AND THEN, DISASTER! TUG'S PAIN CRAMPED GRIP ON THE TILLER BARS SLIPPED A FRACTION — AND GOLIATH SLEWED SLIGHTLY...
SHE'S GOING THROUGH! TUG, GET OUT OF THERE FAST!
NO! STAY WHERE YOU ARE, WILSON! WE CAN STILL SAVE HER! CORPORAL, GET THAT TOW ROPE OFF THE FRONT!

AT THE END OF THE TOW ROPE, CARSON FORCED THE HOOKS BETWEEN TWO LINKS — AND BARKED A COMMAND TO TUG . . .

LOCK YOUR RIGHT TRACK — NOW OPEN UP GENTLY ON YOUR LEFT. THAT'S IT, GENTLY . . . GENTLY NOW . . . DON'T JERK IT FOR PETE'S SAKE!

GREAT GUNS! GOLIATH'S WINCHING ITSELF OUT!

ONE LAST CONVULSIVE HEAVE — AND THE GREAT TANK WAS SAFE!
RECKON WE COULD MAKE THAT INTO A REGULAR TRIP, TUG?
NEVER AGAIN, MATE! BUT I'LL SAY THIS — IF I EVER OPEN MY BIG MOUTH ABOUT MISTER CARSON AGAIN, YOU PUT YOUR FOOT IN IT, QUICK!
IF HE DOESN'T, I WILL! COME ON, KEN, LET'S GET THIS CABLE OFF!

IT WAS AS THEY FINISHED THAT JOHNNY SUDDENLY REALISED WHAT HAD BEEN NAGGING AT HIS MIND FOR THE LAST FEW SECONDS . . .
THAT ARTILLERY GUNFIRE— IT'S TO THE EAST OF US. THAT MEANS . . .
. . . IT MEANS THAT THE EIGHTH ARMY HAVEN'T BROKEN THROUGH YET - SO WE'RE BEHIND THE ENEMY LINES! BUT WE'VE STILL GOT TO FIND FUEL. SO GET GOLIATH STARTED, WE'RE HEADING NORTH, HUNTING FOR THE NEAREST GERMAN SUPPLIES!

NOW THERE SEEMED TO BE A NEW BOND BETWEEN THE FOUR MEN — THE COMRADESHIP WHICH LINKS BRAVE MEN AFTER THEY HAVE FACED THE DEADLIEST OF DANGERS — AND DEFEATED IT! ONLY TUG HAD A QUESTION . . .
ONE THING STILL BEATS ME, SIR — HOW THE BLAZES DID WE GET OVER THAT MUD POND WITHOUT SINKING?
CAMELS, WILSON - CAMELS! FOR THOUSANDS OF YEARS CAMEL CARAVANS HAVE BEEN CROSSING IT, ALWAYS ON THE SAME TRAIL — AND TREADING IT SOLID! I FOLLOWED A TRACK, HOPING IT WAS HARD ENOUGH — AND IT WAS!

Chapter 3. FIGHT FOR SURVIVAL

THEY HAD ENOUGH PETROL FOR TWENTY MILES— FIFTEEN OF THEM WENT WITHOUT A SIGN OF LIFE— AND THEN . . .

DEAD SLOW— THERE'S SOMETHING UP AHEAD BEYOND THE RIDGE! TRAVERSE TURRET AND TAKE HER UP TO THE CREST SLOWLY!

ENGINE RUNNING SOFTLY, GOLIATH CREPT SLOWLY UP TOWARDS THE CREST. SUDDENLY, CARSON'S SHARP COMMAND BROUGHT A HALT AND JOHNNY SPRANG UP INTO THE TURRET . . .

ENTHUSIASTIC GRINS FROM KEN AND TUG ANSWERED CARSON'S QUICK BRIEFING AND HIS SWIFTLY MADE PLAN OF ATTACK. A MINUTE LATER, GOLIATH SURGED FORWARD . . .
SURPRISE IS ON OUR SIDE – ALL WE WANT NOW IS LUCK AND FAST SHOOTING. LET'S GO GET 'EM!

THE GERMANS KNEW NOTHING – UNTIL CARSON'S BROWNINGS CHATTERED SAVAGELY. . . AND IT WAS TOO LATE . . .
THAT'S STOPPED 'EM COLD! OKAY, CORPORAL, LET 'EM HAVE IT!

AS THEIR TRAILING TRANSPORTERS' TYRES WERE SLICED OPEN, THE TOWING TIGERS WERE DRAGGED TO A HALT— AND JOHNNY GRAY FILLED HIS SIGHTS WITH THE LEADER . . .
UNHOOK THE TRANSPORTER... AAAAGH!

DESPERATELY, THE SECOND GERMAN TOWING TANK SWUNG ITS TURRET— BUT AGAIN, GOLIATH'S GUN ERUPTED SAVAGE ORANGE FLAME . . .
YOU SAID GOLIATH WOULD OUTGUN THE JERRIES, BUT HECK, SIR, IT'S OPENING 'EM UP LIKE BULLY BEEF TINS!
AND NOW IT'S OUR TURN TO TAKE IT, CORPORAL— THE TRANSPORTER TANKS ARE LINED UP ON US! HARD RIGHT, WILSON!

GOLIATH SWUNG ROUND VIOLENTLY — A SPLIT SECOND BEFORE THE TWO GERMAN TANKS FIRED. ONE SHELL SCREAMED PAST, A FOOT WIDE — THE OTHER HAMMERED AT THE SLOPING ARMOUR — AND BOUNCED SKYWARDS!
CRIKEY, I THOUGHT IT WAS COMING THROUGH THE FLIPPING PERISCOPE!

BEFORE THE TIGERS' GUNNERS COULD RELOAD, GOLIATH STRUCK AGAIN . . . SHATTERINGLY . . .
TURRET TRAVERSE LEFT! SLAM THE THROTTLE OPEN, WILSON — WE'RE GOING TO RAM!

IN THE NICK OF TIME, JOHNNY SWUNG THE TURRET AROUND — AND THEN GOLIATH HIT THE SURVIVING TIGER WITH DEVASTATING POWER . . .
HE'S DOWN AND OUT— FOR GOOD! NOW LET'S GET AFTER THAT PETROL!
WITH THE GRINDING GROANS OF TORTURED METAL, GOLIATH REVERSED OUT OF THE WRECKAGE— AND TUG WILSON GRINNED AS HE SPOTTED THE PETROL TANKER IN FULL FLIGHT A MILE AWAY...
WHAT ABOUT THE JERRY GUNS, SIR?
THEY CAN WAIT UNTIL WE GET THAT JUICE! SO FAR WE'VE TESTED EVERYTHING EXCEPT GOLIATH'S RACING SPEED— WELL, HERE GOES!

CERTAIN THAT NO TANK COULD MATCH HIS LOADED LORRY'S THIRTY M.P.H., THE GERMAN DRIVER THOUGHT HE WAS WELL CLEAR — *UNTIL RIPPLING STREAMS OF FLAMING TRACER LASHED PAST EACH SIDE OF HIS CAB!*

DER TEUFEL! THE BRITISHER TANK HAS CAUGHT UP WITH US! IF THEY SHOOT INTO THE PETROL . . .

STOP, HANS!

THE LORRY'S POWERFUL PUMPS WERE SOON POUNDING – AND THREE MINUTES LATER, GOLIATH'S ENGINE ROARED DEAFENINGLY AGAIN. STANDING NEARBY, THE GERMANS SAW STABBING TRACER TEAR INTO THEIR VEHICLE BEFORE IT BLEW UP BLINDINGLY!

NOW GOLIATH'S OBJECTIVE FOR DESTRUCTION BECAME THE GERMAN 88mm. GUN BATTERY – BUT THE BOILING BLACK PLUME FROM THE EXPLODING TANKER BROUGHT GRIM WARNING TO THE GUNNERS . . .
TARGET BEARING TEN DEGREES . . . FIVE HUNDRED METRES . . .

TWIN COLUMNS OF SHELL-SCORCHED SAND GEYSERED BESIDE GOLIATH — AND CARSON'S HAND SLAMMED ON A LEVER BELOW THE TURRET RIM. THE NEXT INSTANT TWO MORTAR SMOKE BOMBS ROCKETED AWAY . . .
HARD LEFT TURN, WILSON, AS IF WE WERE ON THE RUN!

AS THE SPEEDING BRITISH TANK SPUN AWAY, DENSE CLOUDS OF SWIRLING SMOKE ROLLED IN FRONT OF THE GUN LINE, MASKING IT COMPLETELY. . .
LUCKY FOR THE BRITISHER HE SCUTTLED FOR SAFETY — ANOTHER HUNDRED METRES AND WE WOULD HAVE SMASHED HIM INTO THE DUST!
HIMMEL! KEEP QUIET, DOLTS — THAT TANK ENGINE IS COMING CLOSER AGAIN!

THE GERMAN OFFICER WAS RIGHT— THE GRINDING HUM GREW TO AIR-TREMBLING THUNDER— AND THEN, SUDDENLY IT HAPPENED!
DONNERWETTER— SWING THAT GUN AROUND, BLOCKHEADS— SCHNELL . . . SCHNELL . . .

THE GUNNERS MADE A FEEBLE TRY . . . AND KNEW THEY WOULD FAIL. NOTHING COULD STOP THAT CHARGING COLOSSUS OF STEEL WHICH REARED OVER THEM. AS ONE, THEY FLED . . .

BUT THE 88s WERE TOO CUMBERSOME FOR FAST RIGHT ANGLE SWITCHES — AND ONE BY ONE, GOLIATH'S GRINDING TRACKS CRUMPLED THEM WHERE THEY STOOD . . .
STAND BY TO FIRE, CORPORAL — THAT LAST GUN COULD BE DANGEROUS!

DRIVEN BY THE LASHING TONGUE OF THEIR BRAVE YOUNG LIEUTENANT, THE SWEATING GERMAN GUN CREW MADE ONE LAST EFFORT — AND THE 88mm. GUN TURNED! IT WAS DEAD IN LINE — THEN JOHNNY FIRED . . .
. . . AND WITH SUPERB ACCURACY, THE SHELL RIPPED INTO THE 88'S YAWNING BARREL, SPLITTING IT WIDE OPEN!

DAZED AND SHOCKED BY THE BLAST, THE GUN CREW STAGGERED AWAY — AS CARSON PUSHED OPEN THE TURRET HATCHES . . .
THEY'VE HAD ENOUGH, SIR – AND AFTER THAT LAST PUNCH, I CAN'T BLAME 'EM!
THAT YOUNG LIEUTENANT OF THEIRS HAS THE COURAGE THAT HAS GOT TO BE ADMIRED. WITH TEN LIKE HIM, THEY MIGHT HAVE STOPPED US! WELL, WE CAN'T TAKE PRISONERS, SO WE'LL LET 'EM GO!

GOLIATH RUMBLED IN A HALF TURN — AND IN THAT INSTANT, JOHNNY'S KEEN, SEARCHING EYES WIDENED . . .
LOOK, SIR– DUST CLOUDS COMING TOWARDS US, AND THEY'RE REALLY MOVING!
TANKS, I'LL BET– BUT WHOSE? RETREATING PANZERS – OR BREAKTHROUGH BRITISH?

WITH EVERY TAUT NERVE KEYED FOR SPLIT SECOND ACTION, THEY WAITED AS THE DUST CLOUDS RACED TOWARDS THEM — NEARER . . . NEARER . . .
THEY'RE SHERMANS!
DON'T RECOGNISE THE SHAPE, BUT SHE'S GOT NO PANZER MARKINGS — AND GREAT SCOTT, THERE ARE TWO BLACK BERETS IN THE TURRET! SHE'S ONE OF OURS!

THE SPEEDING SHERMANS STREAMED PAST WITH A CASUAL WAVE OF THE LEADER'S HAND. THEN GOLIATH BEGUN THE RUN EAST THAT WAS TO TAKE HER, HOURS LATER, THROUGH THE GREAT BATTLEFIELD AT ALAMEIN...
GOOD GRIEF, SIR — IT'S A TANK GRAVEYARD!
ROMMEL'S DIVISIONS MUST HAVE BEEN SHATTERED HERE — AND HE'LL NEVER RECOVER. ALAMEIN IS THE BEGINNING OF THE END FOR THE AFRIKA KORPS!

MILITARY POLICE DIRECTED THEM TO THE SQUADRON COMMAND VEHICLES, NOW BROUGHT FORWARD TO AN ADVANCED H.Q. WHILE CARSON MADE HIS REPORT, GOLIATH WAS LOADED ON TO A TRANSPORTER . . .
ALMOST READY, SIR.
GOOD. WELL, GOLIATH HAS HAD ALL THE TESTS WE PLANNED — AND SOME WE DIDN'T! BUT SHE DID MAGNIFICENTLY — AND I WANT TO THANK YOU CHAPS FOR YOUR FIRST CLASS WORK!

YOU SEE, I AM AN INSTRUCTOR AT THE ARMOURED WARFARE SCHOOL — AND I DESIGNED MOST OF THE XT-EIGHT! WITH THESE NOTES WE'LL BE ABLE TO GO AHEAD AND PRODUCE A WAR-WINNING VERSION OF GOLIATH!
CRIKEY! AND I THOUGHT YOU WERE A GREEN 'UN!

CHUCKLING SOFTLY, LIEUTENANT MARK CARSON SHOOK HANDS WITH TUG, KEN AND FINALLY JOHNNY . . .
AND, CORPORAL, I'VE RECOMMENDED TO YOUR C.O. THAT YOU GET COMMAND OF THE NEXT AVAILABLE SHERMAN— PLUS THE STRIPE THAT GOES WITH IT! WILSON AND BYRNE WILL STAY AS YOUR CREW!
GOODBYE, GOLIATH, YOU BEAUTIFUL BRUTE— THE JERRIES WON'T FORGET YOU IN A HURRY, AND NEITHER WILL WE!
THANK YOU, SIR— THEY'RE THE BEST TEAM I COULD HOPE FOR!

SOON AFTERWARDS, THE TRANSPORTER ROLLED AWAY. GOLIATH HAD STARTED ITS LONG JOURNEY BACK TO ENGLAND. AND THREE MEN WATCHED IT GO, THEIR FACES SOMBRE . . .
THEY'RE QUITE A TEAM THOSE TWO— GOLIATH AND THAT CHAP, CARSON!
YOU'RE DARNED RIGHT! HECK— AS SOON AS I GET TO LIKE THE BLOKE AS MUCH AS GOLIATH, THEY BOTH SCARPER!

WITHIN TWENTY FOUR HOURS, JOHNNY GRAY WAS PROMOTED SERGEANT AND GIVEN COMMAND OF A NEW SHERMAN. ONE OF THE LATEST MODELS, IT WAS DESTINED TO BECOME THEIR CRAMPED AND EVER MOVING HOME FOR SIX MONTHS OF FIGHTING AS THE VICTORIOUS EIGHTH ARMY BATTLED WESTWARDS FOR A THOUSAND MILES. TOBRUK . . . BENGHAZI . . . SOUSSE . . . ALL FELL . . .
. . . UNTIL FINALLY TUNIS, THE LAST ENEMY STRONGHOLD, SURRENDERED — AND THE GERMAN ARMY IN NORTH AFRICA HAD BEEN COMPLETELY SMASHED!

TWO MONTHS LATER, AFTER REFITTING, THEY WERE LEADING AN ARMOURED SPEARHEAD IN THE INVASION OF SICILY. . .
NOT MUCH RESISTANCE SO FAR — MAYBE WE'VE CAUGHT JERRY'S DEFENCES ON THE HOP. IF WE CAN KEEP 'EM STAGGERING, WE'LL CHASE 'EM OFF THE ISLAND BEFORE THEY RECOVER!

IT TOOK SEVEN WEEKS OF COUNTLESS SMALL BATTLES TO CONQUER SICILY— AND IMMEDIATELY PLANS WERE MADE FOR THE INVASION OF ITALY. ON SEPTEMBER 3RD, 1943, THE ALLIED ONSLAUGHT BEGAN . . .
ANOTHER TEN MINUTES AND WE'LL HIT THE BEACH!
MAKING A REAL HABIT OF THIS INVASION LARK, AIN'T WE— DOIN' A PROPER TOUR OF THE MED!
TLC 711
AGAIN THE LANDING WAS SUCCESSFUL— AND THE LONG SLOGGING FIGHT UP THE LENGTH OF ITALY BEGAN. ALTHOUGH ITALY SURRENDERED, THE GERMAN FORCES FOUGHT A RELENTLESS WAR OF SLOW RETREAT. . .
STRIKE ME PINK— ANOTHER FLIPPIN' MOUNTAIN BARRIER FOR THEM JERRIES TO SIT ON— AND WE'VE GOT TO KNOCK 'EM OFF!
INDIA

SO THEY CRAWLED NORTHWARDS – AND EVERY INCH OF GROUND WAS A HARD WON VICTORY. THEN, SOUTH OF ROME, THE SHERMAN LOST TWO CREW MEMBERS – BUT NOT IN BATTLE . . .
BYRNE AND WILSON — YOU'RE BOTH APPOINTED LANCE CORPORALS FOR POSTING! BYRNE GOES TO "C" SQUADRON H.Q. AS COMMAND VEHICLE SIGNALLER. WILSON GOES TO "A" SQUADRON AS C.O.'S DRIVER! GET YOUR KIT PACKED, AND MOVE. SERGEANT, REPLACEMENTS FOR THESE TWO WILL BE SENT TO YOU TODAY!
ROMA

WHEN A TEAM OF MEN HAVE LIVED AND FOUGHT TOGETHER THROUGH MANY HAZARDS AND PERILS, A BREAK-UP COMES HARD AND UNPOPULAR . . .
I DIDN'T ASK FOR NO DARNED STRIPE – AND I DON'T BLOOMIN' WELL WANT IT . . . NOR A TRANSFER!
NEITHER DO I, TUG — BUT SOME BRASSHAT SAYS 'JUMP' SO WE 'JUMP'!
I'D BE GLAD TO BE GETTING RID OF YOU TWO DEADBEATS – IF YOU WEREN'T THE BEST DRIVER AND RADIO-OP IN THE REGIMENT!
IL DUCE HA SEMPRE RAGION

SOON AFTER THAT, JOHNNY WAS IN ACTION AGAIN WITH HIS NEW CREW. THEY WERE GOOD MEN — BUT NOT OF THE CALIBRE OF TUG AND KEN. THEN CAME THE NEXT VICTIM OF THE "BRASSHATS" — JOHNNY HIMSELF!
SERGEANT GRAY — YOU'VE BEEN POSTED BY THE WAR OFFICE AS AN INSTRUCTOR TO THE SPECIAL WEAPONS CENTRE IN U.K. A TRANSPORT LEAVES NAPLES AT EIGHTEEN HUNDRED HOURS TONIGHT — BE ON IT!
AN INSTRUCTOR IN ENGLAND? WHAT'S IT ALL ABOUT, SIR?

BUT THE OFFICER COULD TELL HIM NO MORE. HE WAS STILL WONDERING WHEN HE REACHED NAPLES LATE THAT AFTERNOON . . .
TRANSPORT FOR U.K.? THAT'S HER OUT THERE ON THE REAR END OF THE CONVOY. THERE'S A MOTOR LAUNCH FURTHER ALONG THE WHARF TAKING MEN OUT TO HER.
GOOD LUCK, SARGE — WISH I WAS COMING HOME WITH YOU!

THE MOTOR LAUNCH WAS JUST LEAVING THE WHARF WHEN JOHNNY JUMPED ABOARD — AND WITHIN MINUTES, HE WAS CLIMBING ABOARD THE TROOPSHIP... FOR A VERY SPECIAL WELCOME...
I TOLD YOU SO, KEN — I KNEW IT WAS HIM WHEN WE SAW HIM IN THE LAUNCH!
TUG — KEN — WHAT IN HEAVEN'S NAME ARE YOU BOTH DOING HERE?

I BUMPED INTO TUG ON THE QUAYSIDE AN HOUR AGO. WE'VE BEEN POSTED TO . . .
. . . SOME SPECIAL WEAPONS OUTFIT AS INSTRUCTORS. AND IF I'M GUESSING RIGHT . . .
YOU ARE, TUG — I'M FOR THE SAME PLACE! BOYS, THE TEAM'S TOGETHER AGAIN!

MANY TIMES DURING THE THREE WEEK VOYAGE HOME, THEY TRIED WITHOUT SUCCESS TO FATHOM THE CAUSE FOR THEIR POSTINGS. THEY WERE STILL PUZZLED WHEN THEY FINALLY REACHED THE CENTRE . . .
YOU'RE THE NEW LADS FROM THE MIDDLE EAST, EH? RIGHT — THE CHIEF INSTRUCTOR WANTS TO SEE YOU AT ONCE, HE'S IN THE TRAINING HANGAR. LEAVE YOUR KIT, I'LL HAVE IT TAKEN TO YOUR QUARTERS.
SUFFERING CATFISH — WE'RE STARTING WORK BEFORE OUR FEET TOUCH THE GROUND!

AS THEY APPROACHED THE HANGER, THEY SUDDENLY STOPPED, STUNNED WITH STARTLED AMAZEMENT!
BRAND NEW BATTLE WAGONS — NEW DESIGN ANYWAY, BUT SOMEHOW THEY LOOK FAMILIAR!
YOU KNOW WHY, KEN? THEY'RE LIKE OLD GOLIATH — AND THERE IS THE OLD BRUTE ITSELF AT THE FAR END!
WELL I'LL BE . . . LIEUTENANT — NO CAPTAIN CARSON!

RETURNING THEIR SALUTES, CARSON COULDN'T KEEP THE BROAD GRIN OFF HIS STRONG FEATURES. . .
SO THE DESERT CAVALRY HAVE GOT HERE AT LAST! IT'S TAKEN ME THREE MONTHS OF PRODDING TO GET THE WAR OFFICE TO POST YOU UNDER MY COMMAND!
GLAD TO SEE YOU AGAIN, SIR — BUT WHAT'S BEHIND IT?

SIGNING FOR THEM TO FOLLOW, MARK CARSON WALKED TOWARDS THE NEW TANK . . .
USING THE LESSONS WE LEARNED IN GOLIATH'S TRIALS, WE'VE DEVELOPED THESE LATEST IMPROVED VERSIONS — FASTER, HEAVIER ARMOURED AND WITH LONGER RANGE. YOUR JOBS ARE TO TEACH THE CREW HOW TO FIGHT IN 'EM! DRIVING, SIGNALS AND GUNNERY — AND TWO MONTHS TO DO IT!
THAT'S A HECK OF A HURRY, SIR — SO WE'D BETTER GET STARTED RIGHT NOW! LET'S GO GET OUR OVERALLS, LADS!

Chapter 4. BEACH OF DEATH

THEY HAD A BIG TASK TO CARRY OUT — COMPRESSING MONTHS OF EXPERIENCE INTO WEEKS OF INSTRUCTION. THEY WERE HARD AT IT DAY AFTER DAY. TUG WITH HIS DRIVING . . .

. . . WHILE KEN POUNDED THE LATEST SIGNALS TRAINING INTO THE PUPILS . . .

THE WIRELESS SETS ARE THE NERVE CENTRES OF THE TANK FORMATIONS. THEY WELD EVERY SINGLE FIGHTING UNIT INTO A COMBAT TEAM — ENABLING THEM TO CHANGE PLANS ON THE SPOT TO MEET THE ENEMY'S MOVES.

. . . AND JOHNNY GRAY TURNED THEM INTO EXPERT GUNNERS . . .

THERE WAS LITTLE TIME FOR RELAXATION — BUT WHEN THEY HAD ANY, SOMEHOW THEY ALWAYS FOUND THEMSELVES IN THE HANGAR, WITH GOLIATH!
SHE'S IN FIRST CLASS CONDITION — REALLY FIGHTING FIT!
THOSE GEEZERS CAN SAY WHAT THEY LIKE ABOUT THEM NEW JOBS — NOT ONE OF 'EM COULD HOLD A CANDLE TO OLD GOLIATH IN ACTION!

THEIR ALLOCATED TRAINING TIME WAS ALMOST UP, WHEN ONE MORNING, MARK CARSON CALLED THEM ALL TO A MEETING IN THE HANGAR. WITH HIM WAS A TANK CORPS MAJOR...
WELL, CHAPS, THIS IS IT! YOUR TRAINING IS OVER — THE TANKS WILL BE LOADED TONIGHT AND TOMORROW YOU WILL PROCEED TO A SOUTH COAST TOWN, TO AWAIT FURTHER ORDERS!

LEAVING ALDERS TO ISSUE HIS INSTRUCTIONS, CARSON TURNED AWAY— TO MEET THREE BELLIGERENTLY QUESTIONING FACES . . .
THERE'S SOMETHING BIG COMING OFF, ISN'T THERE, SIR? WELL, WHY ARE WE BEING LEFT OUT OF IT?
DO WE HAVE TO STAY HERE TWIDDLING OUR THUMBS WHILE THERE'S A BIG SCRAP ON?
WE WERE ALL POSTED HERE AS INSTRUCTORS! AND THE WAR OFFICE ORDERS ARE THAT ONLY MEN ON ACTIVE DUTY CAN BE IN THE NEW TROOP! THAT KEEPS US RIGHT OUT!

UTTERLY FED UP, THEY GOT ON WITH PREPARING THE TANKS FOR DEPARTURE — AND THEY JUST HAD THEM LOADED WHEN JOHNNY GOT THE FLASH OF INSPIRATION THAT TOOK THEM HOTFOOT TO CARSON'S OFFICE . . .
SIR — PERMISSION REQUESTED TO REVERT TO RANK OF CORPORAL!
RESPECTFULLY REQUEST TO REVERT TO TROOPER, SIR!
ME TOO, CAPTAIN CARSON!

COMPLETELY PUZZLED, CARSON STARED AT THEM— THEN UNDERSTANDING GREW IN HIS EYES . . . A HAND FLASHED TO THE PHONE . . .
SO THAT'S IT! BY LOSING YOUR RANKS, YOU CAN'T STAY AS INSTRUCTORS — AND NOBODY CAN STOP YOU REVERTING! A FIRST CLASS IDEA — AND ONE I CAN USE MYSELF! I'LL START BLISTERING THE WAR OFFICE RIGHT NOW!

THEY WAITED OUTSIDE – AND FOR TEN MINUTES HEARD THE SOMETIMES PERSUASIVE, SOMETIMES FORCEFUL, TONES OF CARSON'S VOICE. THEN AT LAST...
WELL, SIR?
CORPORAL, HELP ME GET THESE THIRD STARS OFF, WHILE YOUR TROOPERS GET GOLIATH READY TO MOVE! LADS– WE'RE GOING AS A CREW WITH THE NEW TROOP!

SO IT WAS, THAT FOUR TANK TRANSPORTERS HEADED SOUTHWARDS THAT NIGHT, MERGING IN THE CLOAKING DARKNESS WITH THE THICK RIVERS OF ARMY VEHICLES FLOWING ON THE SAME ROUTES. BEFORE DAWN THEY HAD PASSED INTO A HEAVILY GUARDED PORT...

IT WAS, IN FACT, ONLY A MATTER OF HOURS— FOR THE FOLLOWING DAY'S DATE WAS TO BECOME WRITTEN IN FIRE IN THE HISTORY OF THE WORLD...
TLC 317
... 6TH JUNE 1944 — AND AT SUNRISE SAW A VAST INVADING ARMADA HEADING FOR THE COAST OF FRANCE — AND THE SECOND FRONT!

ALL NIGHT, BRITISH WARSHIPS HAD HAMMERED THE GERMAN DEFENCES— AND WITH FIRST LIGHT THE LANDING CRAFT WENT IN. AGAINST FURIOUS ENEMY OPPOSITION, THE FIRST BEACHES WERE TAKEN . . .
FIVE MINUTES TO GO, SIR! LOOKS AS IF WE'LL HAVE TO BATTER OUR WAY OFF THE BEACH, TOO!
WE'LL NEVER GET THERE IF THAT JERRY GUN BUNKER ISN'T KNOCKED OUT FIRST— BUT THE NAVY'S SHELLS ARE JUST BOUNCING OFF!
TLC 717

CARSON'S EYES NARROWED— THEN, SNAPPING QUICK ORDERS TO JOHNNY, HE LEAPED TO THE ROYAL MARINE HELMSMAN . . . AND A MOMENT LATER THE ASSAULT CRAFT'S BOWS SWUNG ROUND . . .
STAND BY, CORPORAL! YOU'VE ONLY GOT A SECOND TO AIM AND FIRE— IF YOU MISS, WE'VE HAD IT!

THE GERMAN GUN MUZZLE TRAVERSED A FRACTION INTO PERFECT AIM— THEN THE LANDING CRAFT'S FRONT RAMP FELL A FOOT... AND GOLIATH'S GUN BELCHED FLAME...
... AND A SCREAMING SHELL STREAKED AN INCH CLEAR OVER THE RAMP— RIGHT INTO THE BUNKER'S GUN-SLIT!

THE MASSIVE CONCRETE WALLS EXPLODED OUTWARDS— PUNCHED BY THE SEARING ORANGE BALL OF FIRE WHICH GREW SHATTERINGLY INSIDE...
HEY, HALF THE DARNED CHANNEL IS POURING IN, NOW THE RAMP IS OPEN!
TLC 717
TAKE IT EASY! ANOTHER TWENTY YARDS AND WE'RE THERE!

WITH A GRINDING CRUNCH, THE INVADING CRAFT GROUNDED AND THE RAMP DROPPED. WITH SPLIT SECOND TIMING, GOLIATH ROARED UP THE BEACH...
LOOKS AS IF THE FOOTSLOGGERS HAVE PUSHED JERRY RIGHT OFF THE BEACH! AH, THERE ARE THE OTHER TWO!

AT FULL SPEED, THE TWO STEEL MONSTERS RACED PAST CARSON... AND THE VOICE OF MAJOR ALDERS, THE TROOP C.O., CAME CRACKLING ACROSS THE RADIO...
BUSTER FORCE — GROUND ASSAULT TROOPS PINNED DOWN BY ENEMY OUTPOST A MILE INLAND. WE'RE GOING TO SUPPORT 'EM. FOLLOW ME. OUT.

FIVE RACING, ROARING MINUTES ACROSS SHELL PLUNDERED FIELDS AND THEY FOUND THE INFANTRY— MENACED BY ONE OF THE MOST FIENDISH WEAPONS OF WAR! THE FLAME THROWER!
BUSTER FORCE SUNRAY — THE INFANTRY WOULD TAKE HOURS TO OUTFLANK 'EM — AND THOSE HILLS ARE TOO STEEP, EVEN FOR US! IT MEANS A FRONTAL ATTACK— LET'S GO!

IN TWO PAIRS THE TANKS LUNGED FORWARD— STRAIGHT TOWARDS THE FLAME THROWER! IT WAS A MAD, DEATH-DEFYING CHARGE . . .
AND THEY PAID THE FEARFUL PRICE!
IT'S NO GOOD— WE HAVEN'T GOT A HOPE! GET BACK!

SOMEHOW THE CREW OF THE FLAMING HULK SCRAMBLED SAFELY FROM THE BLAZING FURNACE AS THE THREE SURVIVING TANKS TURNED IN RETREAT. INSIDE GOLIATH, CARSON'S BRAIN WORKED SWIFTLY . . .
GOOD GRIEF, SIR— THAT FLAME THROWER WOULD GET THE LOT OF US IF WE WENT ON!
BUT THERE'S ANOTHER WAY! WE CAN'T GO UP THE HILL FORWARDS, BUT WE'RE LOWER GEARED IN REVERSE— SO WE'LL CLIMB IT BACKWARDS! WILSON, TAKE GOLIATH UP THERE!

WRENCHING HARD ON THE STEERING, TUG SLAMMED THROUGH THE GEARS. GOLIATH SPUN— AND BEGAN TO GRIND UP THE FORTY FIVE DEGREE SLOPE. A LONG FINGER OF FIRE LICKED OUT FROM THE PILL BOX . . .
BY GLORY, CARSON'S GOING TO GET AWAY WITH IT, BECAUSE THE FLAME THROWER CAN'T ELEVATE AND TRAVERSE FAST ENOUGH TO CATCH HIM!

LIKE A GREAT BEETLE STRUGGLING UP A WALL, GOLIATH CHURNED HIGHER AND HIGHER — RIGHT OUT OF THE FLAME-THROWER'S RANGE. THERE WERE GERMAN MACHINE GUN POSTS ON THE HILL TOP . . . BUT CARSON WAS READY . . .
WAITING TO CUT DOWN ANY INFANTRY WHO MANAGED TO CRAWL UP HERE, EH? WELL, TRY US FOR SIZE!

UNDER THAT WITHERING HAIL OF HIGH-POWERED DESTRUCTION, THE ENEMY RESISTANCE WAS BLASTED OUT OF EXISTENCE. ON THE HILL TOP, GOLIATH TURNED ROUND – AND HURTLED DOWN...
COR, STRIKE A LIGHT! IF WE DON'T SMASH THROUGH THAT CONCRETE, WE'LL BE WRAPPED AROUND IT LIKE A MUSTARD PLASTER!

THEN, FLUNG LIKE AN IRRESISTIBLE FORTY TON BATTERING RAM OF CASE-HARDENED STEEL, GOLIATH STRUCK THE GERMAN POST SHATTERINGLY.. CRUSHING AND SPLITTING WIDE THE CONCRETE WALLS LIKE AN EARTHQUAKE!

WITH THAT ONE POWER-PACKED HAMMER BLOW, THE GERMAN MENACE WAS DESTROYED. IN MINUTES BRITISH INFANTRY POURED PAST – AND GOLIATH'S TWO COHORTS WERE PULLING HER FROM THE RUBBLE . . .
FIRST CLASS SHOW, MARK. YOU'RE STILL TEACHING US OUR BATTLE CRAFT!
YOU TAUGHT US THAT ONLY BAD DRIVERS HAD SMASH-UPS, TUG– AND LOOK WHAT YOU'VE DONE TO YOUR OLD WRECK
GARN! GOLIATH CAN STILL TAKE YOUR TWO SCRAP HEAPS ON – AND LICK 'EM!

THE SECURING OF THE ALLIED BRIDGEHEADS WENT ON, AS BRITISH AND AMERICAN TROOPS THRUST INLAND RELENTLESSLY. FOR THREE WEEKS THE SPECIAL TANK TROOP BATTLED FORWARD YARD BY YARD . . . UNTIL . . .
THE ALLIED PERIMETER WILL EXPAND NO FURTHER. THE FRONT HERE WILL BE CONSOLIDATED WHILE SUPPLIES ARE BUILT UP FOR THE BIG BREAK OUT. OUR ORDERS ARE TO TAKE UP POSITION FIVE MILES SOUTH OF HERE BETWEEN GALTAINE TOWN AND THE RIVER MAUNE!

Chapter 5. BATTLE OF GIANTS
WITHIN AN HOUR THEY WERE RUMBLING BETWEEN THE SHELL BATTERED BUILDINGS OF GALTAINE . . .
THE FOLK HERE HAVE HAD A PRETTY ROUGH TIME, SIR!
THEY GAVE AS GOOD AS THEY GOT, THOUGH. THEY SHOT A JERRY BRIGADE TO RIBBONS AS IT RETREATED THROUGH HERE!

THEIR DEFENSIVE POSITION WAS JUST EAST OF THE TOWN — ASTRIDE THE ONLY ROUTE ANY GERMAN ATTACK COULD TAKE BETWEEN TWO THICK WOODS. BEYOND THE WOODS WERE BRITISH INFANTRY . . .
WHAT IS THE LATEST INFORMATION, CAPTAIN?
MY MEN ARE ON THE HIGH GROUND, SIR. JERRY'S ON THE OTHER SIDE OF THE RIVER — AND HE CAN'T CROSS BECAUSE OF THE BLOWN BRIDGES. SO THIS ISN'T A DANGER SPOT, EXCEPT FOR GERMAN SHELL FIRE!

THAT NIGHT QUIETNESS WAS A CLOAK OVER THEIR SECTOR, WHILE TO THE NORTH DUELLING HEAVY GUNS SPLIT THE NIGHT WITH GROWING FURY— UNTIL AN HOUR BEFORE DAWN . . .
CALLING BUSTER FORCE— URGENT! LARGE SCALE ENEMY COUNTER ATTACK FIVE MILES NORTH OF YOU. PROCEED THERE IMMEDIATELY!
I'LL TAKE TWO TANKS, MARK— YOU STAY IN POSITION HERE WITH GOLIATH!
RIGHT, SIR!

IN SECONDS, GOLIATH WAS ALONE— AND AS THE HOURS DRAGGED BY, THE THUNDERING GUNS BUILT UP TO A DEAFENING CRESCENDO...
THEN SUDDENLY, IT HAPPENED!
HALT THERE! — GREAT SCOTT, IT'S ONE OF THE INFANTRY CHAPS!
I THOUGHT I'D NEVER FIND YOU! MESSAGE FROM MY C.O.— THE JERRIES HAVE FLOATED THREE TANKS OVER THE RIVER ON BARGES, AND WE CAN'T HOLD 'EM!

HARD ON THE MESSENGER'S WORDS, AND ABOVE THE ROARING BARRAGE, THEY HEARD THE CLOSE CRACKLE OF RIFLE FIRE FROM THE *EAST!* IN A FLASH, CARSON UNDERSTOOD . . .
I'VE GOT IT! THE NORTHERN ATTACK IS A FEINT TO PULL OUR MAIN DEFENCES UP THERE! THE JERRIES PLAN TO BASH THEIR ARMOUR THROUGH *HERE!* WE'RE THEIR ONLY OBSTACLE – *AND WE'RE GOING TO STOP 'EM! START GOLIATH UP!*
17

RIPPING THE THROTTLE THROUGH TO EMERGENCY SPEED, TUG SENT GOLIATH RACING BETWEEN THE WOODS – INTO THE WIDE OPEN SPACE BEYOND. . . WHERE THREE ARMOUR-CLAD MONSTERS WERE SNARLING ON THE RIVER BANK . . .
THERE THEY ARE – AND, BY GEORGE, THEY'RE PANTHERS. AND MORE WAITING TO COME OVER! LEAVE THE TANKS, CORPORAL – *OPEN UP ON THE BARGES!*

GOLIATH'S GUN SWUNG — AND ROARED DEAFENINGLY. . .
HERE COMES THE PANTHERS' ANSWER— BUT WE'LL GET THAT OTHER BARGE FIRST!

THE NEXT SPLIT SECOND, THE ENEMY TANKS FIRED AS ONE — THREE SHELLS SCREECHED PAST WITHIN INCHES, BUT ONE STRUCK WITH A SHUDDERING PUNCH. THEN GOLIATH BLASTED HER ANGER ANEW. . .
YOU'VE BATTERED IT TO MATCHWOOD! AND WE'LL BE READY FOR THE SALVAGE DUMP IF YOU DON'T GET US OUT FAST, WILSON!

THE AIR WAS A FLAME-RENT TEMPEST OF EXPLOSIVE FURY FLUNG DOWN BY THE ADVANCING PANTHERS AS GOLIATH SPUN— AND RACED BACK THROUGH THE WOODS . . .
WE'RE GOING BACK NO FARTHER! JERRY MUST COME THROUGH ON THE ROAD— AND WE'RE GOING TO FIGHT IT OUT, TO THE DEATH!

EACH MAN FELT THE ICY BREATH OF FEAR TOUCH HIM . . . AND PASS ON . . . LEAVING ONLY A NEW CALM RESOLUTION THAT FORGED THEM INTO A COLD, DEADLY EFFICIENT MACHINE OF WAR. THEN THE FIRST BLACK CROSSED ENEMY CAME . . . AND A BLAZING THUNDERBOLT BURST UNDER ITS TURRET WITH ARMOUR-RIPPING VIOLENCE . . .

TORN OPEN LIKE A TIN FOIL TOY, THE PANTHER SMASHED TO A STOP AND SLEWED HALF ACROSS THE ROAD. BUT FROM BEHIND IT A GUN BELCHED FLAME . . .
EVEN AS THE ENEMY SHOT STRUCK, GOLIATH BELLOWED A SHATTERING ANSWER!

NOW THE TWO WRECKED PANTHERS WERE A SHELL-PROOF BARRICADE ACROSS THE ROAD. FROM BEHIND IT, THE THIRD PANTHER BEGAN TO POUND GOLIATH WITHOUT MERCY...
WE... CAN'T... TAKE... MUCH... MORE, CORPORAL - IF... ONLY... WE... COULD... GET... THE BRUTE!
THERE'S A THOUSAND TO ONE IDEA, SIR— BUT ANYTHING'S WORTH TRYING NOW!

GOLIATH'S GUN DIPPED LOW— AND JOHNNY GRAY JABBED DESPERATELY AT THE FIRING LEVER...
YOU'VE DONE IT, JOHNNY— *BOUNCED IT THROUGH THE GAP, RIGHT BELOW HIS BELT!*

THE RICOCHETTING HIGH EXPLOSIVE SHELL BORED UP THROUGH THE PANTHER'S THIN UNDERSKIN – *THEN THE WHOLE TANK DISINTEGRATED INTO A VOLCANO OF DESTRUCTION*. . . AND ONE MASSIVE PIECE OF ARMOURED STEEL WAS HURLED BACK– *SMASHING INTO THE LAST PANTHER!*

THEN FROM BEHIND THEM CAME ANOTHER VOICE, HEAVY WITH A FRENCH ACCENT AND LIGHT WITH ADMIRATION . . .
OUI, M'SIEUR– AND, YOU SAVED GALTAINE, ALSO! LES SALS BOCHES WOULD HAVE DESTROYED THE TOWN– AND MASSACRED THE PEOPLE IN REVENGE FOR WHAT WE FIGHTERS OF THE RESISTANCE DID TO THEM! THIS BATTLE, AND THE BRAVE ENGLISH WHO CRUSHED THE PANZERS, WILL NEVER BE FORGOTTEN IN GALTAINE!

THE NEXT INSTANT THE SKY WAS SLASHED TO SHREDS AS THE BRITISH ARTILLERY OPENED UP ON THE PANZER CONCENTRATION EAST OF THE RIVER. FOR TWO HOURS THE OBLITERATING HAIL OF SHELLS WENT ON. THEN, AS IT ENDED, BUSTER FORCE TANKS ROARED UP. . .
WHILE WE WERE ON THAT WILD GOOSE CHASE, WE HEARD OF YOUR FANTASTIC BATTLE BY RADIO! BY HEAVENS, IT'S A MIRACLE YOU'RE STILL ALIVE!
WE'RE STILL WONDERING TOO, SIR! 'FRAID OUR BATTLE WAGON IS A COMPLETE WRITE-OFF– WE'LL HAVE TO GET A NEW BUS FROM THE NEAREST ARMOURED DIV.
IT'LL BE JUST LIKE LEAVING THE FIFTH MEMBER OF THE TEAM– AND THE BEST!

THE SPECIAL TANK TROOP'S SUCCESS HAD BEEN PROVED— AND TOP PRIORITY ORDERS WERE ISSUED FOR THE MANUFACTURING OF SCORES OF THE NEW TANKS. MEANWHILE, MARK CARSON AND HIS SPLENDID CREW FOUGHT ON IN THE BATTLES THAT WERE TO LIBERATE EUROPE AND FINALLY CRUSH THE EVIL POWER OF NAZI GERMANY. BUT EVEN THOUGH THE TANKS THEY FOUGHT IN WERE SUPERB WEAPONS . . .
SOMEHOW NONE WERE THE SAME AS GOLIATH!
. . . AND GOLIATH? THE GREAT TANK WAS LEFT WHERE SHE HAD WON HER GREATEST VICTORY — BUT NOT AS A USELESS, RUSTING HULK! FOR, TO THE PEOPLE OF GALTAINE, GOLIATH HAD SAVED THEM FROM ANNIHILATION. HER ARMOURED SHELL WAS CLEANED AND POLISHED, FOREVER TO BE A SHINING SYMBOL OF THE FRENCH PEOPLE'S RESPECT FOR THE BRAVE MEN WHO HAD FOUGHT TO FREE THEIR COUNTRY.
GOLIATH IS THERE TO THIS DAY!

LONE COMMANDO
IT WAS ON APRIL 9TH., 1940, THAT WAR SUDDENLY STRUCK NORWAY. IN THE HALF LIGHT OF THE EARLY MORNING, SMALL FORCES OF GERMAN SHOCK TROOPS SEIZED THE NORWEGIAN PORTS. AT THE SAME TIME, GERMAN TROOPSHIPS AND CRUISERS WERE MOVING IN TOWARDS OSLO. BY THE LATE AFTERNOON OF THAT FATEFUL DAY, OSLO WAS IN GERMAN HANDS...
DESPERATE APPEALS FROM THE NORWEGIANS BROUGHT AN ILL-SPARED FORCE OF BRITISH TROOPS TO THEIR AID, BUT THEY COULD DO LITTLE AGAINST THE MIGHT OF THE WEHRMACHT AND THE LUFTWAFFE. BY THE END OF APRIL, 1940 — THE WHOLE OF NORWAY FELL UNDER THE HEEL OF THE NAZI JACKBOOT...

Chapter 1. PERILOUS REHEARSAL

ALTHOUGH THE BRITISH ARMY WERE DRIVEN OUT OF EUROPE, THIS DID NOT MEAN THAT BRITAIN WAS DEFEATED. WHILE HER ARMIES WERE BEING REBUILT, THE COMMANDO FORCES WERE FORMED—SMALL UNITS OF TOUGH AND DARING MEN, SKILLED IN ALL THE ARTS OF WAR, AND TRAINED TO STRIKE SWIFTLY WHERE THEY WERE LEAST EXPECTED...

IT WAS EARLY 1942 WHEN PLANS WERE LAID FOR A COMMANDO ATTACK ON NORWAY. THIS ATTACK WAS TO SERVE TWO PURPOSES— TO TEST THE STRENGTH OF GERMAN DEFENCES, AND ALSO TO ANNIHILATE A CERTAIN RADAR POST WHICH WAS AN IMPORTANT LINK IN THE ENEMIES' NORTH ATLANTIC RADAR SYSTEM...

LET ME INTRODUCE YOU TO MAJOR JANSEN, KINDLY LOANED TO US BY THE FREE NORWEGIAN FORCES! HE WILL COMMAND THE OPERATION — AND AS HE HAS ALREADY TOLD ME, HE KNOWS THAT SECTOR OF THE COAST INTIMATELY!
I UNDERSTAND, MAJOR JANSEN, THAT YOU HAVE ONLY RECENTLY ESCAPED FROM NORWAY?
THAT IS SO — I WAS ONE OF THE LUCKY FEW!

JANSEN WAS INTRODUCED TO HIS SECOND-IN-COMMAND — A YOUNG COMMANDO OFFICER ALREADY EXPERIENCED IN THIS TOUGH AND UNUSUAL KIND OF WARFARE...
MAJOR JANSEN — THIS IS CAPTAIN FAIRWEATHER! LIKE YOURSELF, HE KNOWS THIS PART OF THE NORWEGIAN COAST.
BUT, SIR — I UNDERSTOOD THAT NONE OF YOUR COMMANDOS HAD KNOWLEDGE OF MY COUNTRY...
I DON'T KNOW THE PLACE THAT WELL — I SPENT A FEW SEASONS BEFORE THE WAR SAILING IN THE FIORDS IN THIS AREA!

AFTER THE CONFERENCE, BRIGADIER JOHNSON HAD AN INFORMAL CHAT WITH JANSEN AND FAIRWEATHER...
ALTHOUGH I DIDN'T SAY THIS AT THE CONFERENCE, GENTLEMEN, INTELLIGENCE REPORTS LEAD ME TO BELIEVE THAT THIS SECTOR OF THE NORWEGIAN COAST IS ENTIRELY UNDEFENDED—SO THE OPERATION SHOULD BE A WALKOVER—PROVIDED, OF COURSE, THAT THERE IS NO SECURITY LEAKAGE...
YOU CAN DEPEND ON US, SIR!

ENCOURAGED BY THE BRIGADIER, JANSEN GAVE A DETAILED ACCOUNT OF HIS ESCAPE FROM OCCUPIED NORWAY...
I STILL CAN'T IMAGINE HOW YOU GOT OUT OF THAT SITUATION ALIVE, JANSEN!
IT WAS NOTHING AT ALL—ANY GOOD SWIMMER COULD HAVE DONE WHAT I DID!

JANSEN TOLD HOW HE AND A SMALL BAND OF FREE NORWEGIANS, AFTER FIGHTING A DESPERATE REARGUARD ACTION AGAINST THE ADVANCING GERMAN ARMY, WERE PINNED DOWN AT THE HEAD OF HJORL FIORD...
WE'RE BEATEN, CYCLOPS—THEY'RE ON EVERY SIDE!
WE'VE **GOT** TO GET TO THAT FIORD!

A SMALL BOAT SHOULD HAVE BEEN WAITING FOR THEM BUT THEY FOUND THAT IT HAD SLIPPED ITS MOORINGS AND WAS DRIFTING FAR OUT IN THE ICY WATERS. SO JANSEN AND HIS MEN, THEIR ESCAPE CUT OFF, FOUGHT THEIR LAST ACTION...

ONLY JANSEN SURVIVED. SHAMMING DEATH, HE LAY, WOUNDED IN THE SHOULDER, AMONG THE BODIES OF HIS COMRADES UNTIL THE GERMAN PATROL HAD WITHDRAWN. THEN, PLUNGING INTO THE BITTERLY COLD WATERS, HE STRUCK OUT TOWARDS THE OPPOSITE SHORE, WHERE THE BOAT HAD NOW GROUNDED...

WOUNDED AND ALONE, JANSEN MANAGED TO SAIL THE BOAT UNDER COVER OF DARKNESS OUT OF THE FIORD INTO THE OPEN SEA. FIVE DAYS LATER, KEPT ALIVE ONLY BY HIS INDOMITABLE WILL TO SURVIVE, HE REACHED THE THE SHORES OF SCOTLAND—AND FREEDOM...

MIKE FAIRWEATHER HAD BEEN LISTENING WITH GREAT INTEREST AS THE NORWEGIAN TOLD THE STORY OF HIS GREAT ESCAPE...
YOU KNOW, MAJOR JANSEN, YOU MUST BE A TREMENDOUSLY POWERFUL SWIMMER! THE LAST TIME I WAS IN HJORL FIORD, I HAD THE DICKENS OF A JOB CUTTING ACROSS THE CURRENT, EVEN IN A BOAT! THE CURRENT WAS OFFSHORE, AND MUST HAVE BEEN RUNNING AT ABOUT TEN KNOTS!
WHEN YOU ARE DESPERATE, CAPTAIN, YOU WILL DO ANYTHING TO SURVIVE!

THE CONVERSATION TURNED BACK TO THE DETAILS OF THE COMING OPERATION. IT WAS AGREED THAT JANSEN WOULD ARRIVE AT THE COMMANDO·TRAINING CAMP IN THREE DAYS' TIME TO SUPERVISE THE FINAL REHEARSAL. AS MIKE FAIRWEATHER DROVE AWAY FROM STAFF H.Q. HE FOUND HIS MIND RETURNING TO THE NORWEGIAN'S STORY.
THERE'S NO DOUBT JANSEN'S A TOUGH ONE —YET I JUST CAN'T BELIEVE THAT A MAN WITH A SHOULDER WOUND COULD SWIM ACROSS A TEN-KNOT CURRENT IN ICY WATER ! IT DOESN'T FIT IN WITH **MY** PICTURE OF HJORL FIORD...
MP

LATER, JANSEN TOOK LEAVE OF BRIGADIER JOHNSON...
ARE YOU QUITE SATISFIED WITH CAPTAIN FAIRWEATHER'S QUALIFICATIONS AS MY JUNIOR OFFICER ? HIS KNOWLEDGE OF THE NORWEGIAN COAST IS NOT ALL HE SAYS IT IS —HE STRIKES ME AS AN IMAGINATIVE YOUNG MAN...
DON'T WORRY ABOUT FAIRWEATHER — HE'S VERY RELIABLE, GOOD MAN FOR DETAIL. YOU'LL GET ON GREAT GUNS TOGETHER...

THE COMMANDO BASE WAS SITUATED ON A DESOLATE PART OF THE NORTH-EAST SCOTTISH COAST. WHEN JANSEN TURNED UP THERE FOR THE DRESS-REHEARSAL OF OPERATION 'VIKING' HE FOUND FAIRWEATHER WAITING...
WELL, SIR—EVERYTHING SET! SUBJECT TO YOUR APPROVAL, I WILL COMMAND THE FIRST WAVE IN LANDING-CRAFT 'A' AND YOU WILL FOLLOW ME UP IN 'B'. THE CLIFFS AT KINEFF, A FEW MILES FROM HERE, ARE AS NEAR AS WE CAN GET TO THE REAL THING...
YOU SEEM TO HAVE IT ALL CUT AND DRIED, CAPTAIN—WE'LL SEE HOW IT WORKS OUT!
TWO HOURS LATER, THE DESTROYER APPROACHED THE COASTAL SECTOR CHOSEN FOR THE EXERCISE...
THOSE ARE THE BEACHES ON EITHER SIDE OF THE CLIFF—I THINK YOU'LL AGREE THAT IT'S VERY LIKE THE SET-UP IN HJORL FIORD! WITH YOUR PERMISSION, SIR, I'LL GO IN ON THE LEFT, AND YOU ON THE RIGHT...
I THINK THAT WILL DO, CAPTAIN FAIRWEATHER—BUT FROM NOW ON, YOU'D BETTER LEAVE THE REST OF THE PLANNING TO ME...

MIKE'S LANDING CRAFT WAS THE FIRST TO GO IN . . .
THIS IS GOING TO BE AS NEAR THE REAL THING AS WE CAN POSSIBLY MAKE IT! WE'VE BUILT A HUT ON THE CLIFF TOPS WHICH IS A REPLICA OF THE GERMAN RADAR STATION—AND THE 'ENEMY' WHO ARE DEFENDING IT WILL BE USING LIVE AMMUNITION—SO YOU KNOW WHAT TO EXPECT WHEN YOU GET UP THERE!
DON'T YOU WORRY, SIR—AFTER OUR USUAL ASSAULT COURSE THIS SORT OF THING IS A PIECE OF CAKE!
COMMANDO

WITH MIKE IN THE LEAD, THE FIRST COMMANDO FORCE WAS ALREADY ASHORE AND CRAWLING LIKE FLIES UP THE DANGEROUS CLIFF FACE AS JANSEN'S LANDING CRAFT GROUNDED ON THE OTHER BEACH.
CAPTAIN FAIRWEATHER'S MEN AREN'T WASTING ANY TIME, SIR!
KEEP YOUR MIND ON YOUR JOB, SERGEANT—AND GET OVER TO THAT CLIFF-FACE DOUBLE-QUICK! THIS IS WAR—NOT A GAME!

AS FAIRWEATHER AND HIS SERGEANT CLIMBED OVER THE CLIFF TOP, THEY WERE IMMEDIATELY PINNED DOWN BY 'HOSTILE' FIRE . . .
THESE BLIGHTERS MEAN BUSINESS, SIR . . .
WE'RE NOT HERE FOR OUR HEALTH, SERGEANT — COVER ME WITH SMALL ARMS FIRE WHILE I GO AHEAD TO SET UP A MORTAR!

FARTHER ALONG THE CLIFF FACE JANSEN AND HIS MEN WERE COMING OVER THE TOP. WITH PRACTISED SKILL, MIKE SLITHERED FORWARD THROUGH THE WIRY GRASS, LUGGING A MORTAR WITH HIM. HE WAS WITHIN FIFTY YARDS OF THE 'ENEMY' EMPLACEMENT WHEN . . .
A GRENADE!

WITH LIGHTNING PRESENCE OF MIND, MIKE WHIPPED OFF HIS STEEL HELMET AND SLAMMED IT OVER THE GRENADE, THEN FLUNG HIS FULL WEIGHT ON TOP...
UUUGH!

BY HIS SWIFT ACTION THE COMMANDO CAPTAIN HAD SAVED HIMSELF FROM INSTANT DEATH. HE WAS STILL RECOVERING FROM CONCUSSION WHEN A FIGURE SUDDENLY APPEARED AT THE POINT FROM WHICH THE GRENADE HAD COME.
JANSEN! YOU!
YOU'RE A LUCKY MAN, FAIRWEATHER... WHEN I SAW THAT GRENADE LAND, I THOUGHT YOU'D HAD IT!

THE CONCERN IN JANSEN'S VOICE WEAKENED MIKE FAIRWEATHER'S IMMEDIATE ASSUMPTION THAT THE NORWEGIAN HAD FLUNG THE GRENADE. LATER...
DRINK THIS UP, FAIRWEATHER — YOU'LL FEEL BETTER FOR IT! IT'S BEEN A FINE SHOW — IF THE MEN CAN DO AS WELL IN NORWAY, THE OPERATION WILL BE A WALKOVER!
I'D LIKE TO GET THE MAN WHO THREW THAT GRENADE...

JANSEN MOVED AWAY TO ORGANISE THE WITHDRAWAL...
AND I'M ALMOST CERTAIN IT WAS YOU, JANSEN! WHAT I CAN'T FATHOM IS — WHY YOU SHOULD WANT TO KILL ME....?

NEXT DAY, JANSEN AND FAIRWEATHER WERE CALLED TO EDINBURGH, WHERE BRIGADIER JOHNSON WENT INTO CONFERENCE WITH THEM OVER THE FINAL DETAILS FOR OPERATION 'VIKING'....
THE DESTROYER WILL BE STANDING OFFSHORE UNTIL ONE HOUR BEFORE DAWN — SO THAT GIVES YOU THREE HOURS TO CARRY OUT OPERATION 'VIKING.' YOU MUST BE ON THE WAY BACK IN YOUR LANDING CRAFT BEFORE 0-FOUR HUNDRED, OTHERWISE YOU'LL BE LEFT BEHIND...
NORWAY
SWEDEN
APART FROM ACCIDENTS TO LANDING-CRAFT, IT SHOULD BE QUITE STRAIGHTFORWARD, SIR!
FAIRWEATHER AND I WILL BE IN CONSTANT TOUCH WITH OUR WIRELESS, SIR — AND IN AN EMERGENCY WE CAN CALL UP THE DESTROYER DIRECT!

Chapter 2. OPERATION VIKING

JANSEN HAD A LAST WORD FOR MIKE BEFORE EMBARKING:..
GET THIS QUITE STRAIGHT, FAIRWEATHER—I AM IN COMMAND OF THIS OPERATION! YOU WILL OBEY MY ORDERS, NO MATTER WHAT THEY ARE!
BUT OF COURSE, SIR—I DON'T QUESTION YOUR AUTHORITY...

MINUTES LATER, FAIRWEATHER'S CRAFT WAS STEADILY PULLING AWAY INTO THE DARKNESS THROUGH CHOPPY MINE-INFESTED WATERS.
THIS IS THE BIT I HATE, SIR—THE WAITING!
EVERYTHING'S IN OUR FAVOUR, SERGEANT—THE WEATHER—THE DARKNESS—THE ELEMENT OF SURPRISE!

MIKE'S LANDING CRAFT APPROACHED THE MOUTH OF THE FIORD...
TAKE THIS DEAD SLOW, HELMSMAN—WE'LL BE MOVING IN BETWEEN SHEER CLIFFS, AND THE LEAST SOUND WILL ECHO LIKE THUNDER!
AYE, AYE, SIR—ENGINES DEAD SLOW!

ROLLING GENTLY ON THE SLOW SWELL, THE CLUMSY LANDING CRAFT PLOUGHED CAUTIOUSLY ON THROUGH THE STARLESS DARKNESS, WITH NO SOUND BUT THE MUFFLED THROB OF THE ENGINES AND THE LAPPING OF WAVES AGAINST THE STEEL HULL...
HULLO, REDHEAD— THIS IS ROLF! WHAT IS YOUR POSITION ...OVER!
NO LIGHTS ANYWHERE, SIR— THAT'S A GOOD SIGN!
THAT'S MAJOR JANSEN CALLING, SERGEANT....HULLO, ROLF, THIS IS REDHEAD! I TOOK A COURSE FROM THE FIORD ENTRANCE— IF MY GUESS IS RIGHT WE'VE COME ABOUT TWO MILES, AND THE BEACH SHOULD BE FIVE HUNDRED YARDS TWO POINTS OVER ON THE PORT BOW—OVER!

THE CRACKLING OF MIKE'S RADIO REPLY HAD JUST DIED ON THE ETHER WHEN SUDDENLY A SEARCHLIGHT BEAM CUT THE DARKNESS LIKE A KNIFE. IN AN INSTANT, FAIRWEATHER'S CRAFT WAS CAUGHT IN ITS GLARE...
HELMSMAN— FULL SPEED AHEAD!
LC

STANDING UPRIGHT IN THE STERN WITH LEVELLED BREN GUN, MIKE FAIRWEATHER SENT A CHATTERING BURST OF FIRE UP THE SEARCHLIGHT BEAM . . .
HELMSMAN— ZIGZAG LIKE FURY BEFORE THEY FIND OUR RANGE !
AYE, AYE, SIR !

AS THE BULLETS RIPPED ALONG THE BEAM, THE SEARCHLIGHT WINKED OUT. BUT THE GERMAN DEFENCES HAD MARKED THEIR TARGET— AND MACHINE GUNS HAMMERED FROM THE FIORD CLIFFSIDES, BEATING A STACCATO TATTOO ON THE ARMOURED HULL. NEW SEARCHLIGHT BEAMS SPRUNG INTO LIFE FROM SEVERAL POINTS. . .
SERGEANT— WE'VE WALKED INTO A RECEPTION PARTY—SO WE'RE NOT GOING WHERE WE'RE EXPECTED — WE'RE CHANGING COURSE! CALL UP ROLF AND WARN HIM !
OKAY, SIR— REDHEAD TO ROLF, REDHEAD TO ROLF. . .

CUTTING SHARPLY ACROSS THE FIORD, MIKE RAN THE LANDING CRAFT AGROUND ON A SHINGLE BEACH. BEHIND THEM, SEARCHLIGHTS AND MACHINE-GUN FIRE LACED TO AND FRO ACROSS THE WATER...
THE HUN'S USING FLARES NOW— WE'LL BE PICKED OFF LIKE SITTING DUCKS! EVERYBODY UP THAT CLIFF-FACE DOUBLE-QUICK!
NO ANSWER FROM ROLF, SIR...

SHELTERED BY THE GULLIES OF THE CLIFF, MIKE AND HIS MEN CLAMBERED UP THE ROCK FACE, WHILE RANDOM MORTAR FIRE SOUGHT OUT THEIR POSITION...

SCRAMBLING OVER THE CLIFF EDGE, FAIRWEATHER LOOKED BACK ACROSS THE FIORD—AND SAW SEARCHLIGHTS SUDDENLY CONE JANSEN'S CRAFT AS IT DROVE IN TO THE BEACH.
LOOK, SIR—IT'S ROLF! THEY'VE PINNED HIM FAIR AND SQUARE!
BY THE SIZE OF THOSE SHELL-BURSTS, JERRY'S USING BIGGER STUFF THAN MORTARS! INTELLIGENCE SAID THE AREA WAS CLEAR! THEY'VE BOOBED BADLY—OR THERE'S BEEN A SECURITY LEAK! GIVE ROLF EVERY OUNCE OF COVERING FIRE WE CAN MUSTER!

MEANWHILE, ON THE BEACH-HEAD, JANSEN'S COMMANDO FORCE WAS RUNNING THE GAUNTLET...
TAKE THOSE MEN UP THAT CLIFF, SERGEANT!
RIGHT, SIR — AAAAGH!

FROM THEIR VANTAGE POINT ON THE CLIFF TOP, MIKE'S FORCE DIRECTED ACCURATE FIRE WITH BREN GUNS AND MORTARS ON TO THE BRIEF FLASHES OF LIGHT WHICH MARKED THE GERMAN STRONGPOINTS ON THE OPPOSING CLIFF TOPS...
WE'LL GIVE ROLF ANOTHER TWO MINUTES TO GET UNDER COVER — THEN WE'LL MOVE OUT OF HERE BEFORE JERRY FINDS OUR RANGE WITH THE HEAVY STUFF!
I'VE BEEN COUNTING THE FLASHES, SIR! IT LOOKS AS IF JERRY'S GOT HALF A DIVISION UP HERE — WE'VE WALKED INTO A HORNET'S NEST!

MEANWHILE, JANSEN'S FORCE HAD ASSAILED THE FIRST OBSTACLE — THE CLIFFS — ONLY TO BE CUT DOWN AS THEY EMERGED OVER THE TOP OF THE PRECIPICE. SHELTERING IN A GULLY, JANSEN AND TWO WOUNDED MEN LAY LOW...
HULLO, REDHEAD! WHAT IS YOUR POSITION? OVER!
HULLO, ROLF! WE'RE DOING OUR BEST TO COVER YOU FROM THE OPPOSING CLIFFS! WE'RE ON A CLIFF TOP APPROXIMATELY EIGHT HUNDRED YARDS DUE EAST OF YOUR LANDING BEACH! OVER!

BEFORE JANSEN COULD REPLY, THE GERMAN MORTARS HAD FOUND MIKE'S POSITION —AND THE COMMANDO CAPTAIN ORDERED HIS MEN FORWARD TOWARDS THE HILL, ON THE OTHER SIDE OF WHICH LAY TARGET 'VIKING' —THE GERMAN RADAR STATION.
COME ON, LADS! SERGEANT — GET THE MEN MOVING! WE'LL HALT BEFORE THE BROW OF THE HILL, AND CALL MAJOR JANSEN AGAIN, SO THAT WE CAN SYNCHRONIZE OUR ATTACK!

BUT JANSEN WAS CALLING OFF THE ATTACK.
CORPORAL — GET THOSE MEN DOWN THE CLIFF, WHILE I CALL UP FAIRWEATHER! HULLO, REDHEAD-RETREAT BACK TO THE LANDING CRAFT, AND DON'T LOSE ANY TIME — OVER!
HULLO, ROLF! RETREAT BLAZES! WE'RE JUST ABOVE THE RADAR STATION NOW, SO WE'RE GOING IN TO ATTACK!
THE THICK-HEADED, STUBBORN IDIOT!

MIKE FAIRWEATHER, BELIEVING HIS COMMANDING OFFICER TO BE A COWARD, SHOOK WITH RAGE, AND WAS SEIZED WITH A DETERMINATION TO CARRY OUT THE OPERATION AT ALL COSTS...
HULLO, REDHEAD I SAID RETREAT TO THE BOAT — AND THAT IS AN ORDER — REPEAT ORDER! OVER...
HULLO, ROLF! RETREAT IF YOU LIKE — BUT WE'RE GOING ON, ORDERS OR NO ORDERS — OVER!

MIKE FAIRWEATHER SENT HIS SERGEANT AND TWO MEN TO RECONNOITRE FROM THE BROW OF THE HILL, WHILE HE TRAINED HIS NIGHT BINOCULARS ON JANSEN'S LANDING BEACH. HE SAW JANSEN AND HIS REMAINING MEN STAGGER INTO THEIR LANDING CRAFT UNDER A HAIL OF FIRE...
GREAT SCOTT— THERE'S ONLY FOUR OF THEM! THE REST HAVE BEEN WIPED OUT!
YOU'D BETTER COME UP, SIR— THERE'S TROUBLE OVER THE HILL— BIG TROUBLE!

THE SERGEANT WAS RIGHT ABOUT TROUBLE—A STRONG GERMAN PATROL WAS ADVANCING UP THE HILLSIDE, AND IN THE LIGHT OF FLARES, MIKE SAW THE FIGURES FLIT FROM COVER TO COVER AS THEY MOVED INEXORABLY IN FOR THE KILL...

THERE'S ONLY ONE WAY OUT OF THIS SITUATION, AND THAT'S TO ATTACK! UP AND AT 'EM, LADS!

CHARGING DOWN THE DARK HILLSIDE, THE COMMANDOS WENT INTO THE ATTACK—AND THEY WERE MASTERS AT HAND-TO-HAND FIGHTING...

SUCH WAS THE FURY OF THE COMMANDO ONSLAUGHT THAT THE GERMAN PATROL SCATTERED IN DISORDER. MIKE, FOLLOWED CLOSELY BY HIS SERGEANT, FOUND HIMSELF WITHIN FIFTY YARDS OF THE RADAR POST...
WE WON'T HAVE TIME TO KNOCK THE POST OUT THOROUGHLY, SERGEANT —BUT WE'RE GOING TO DO SOME DAMAGE! USE YOUR GRENADES!
RIGHT, SIR!

WITH A MIGHTY SWING OF HIS ARM, MIKE HURLED A MILLS BOMB FIFTY YARDS ON TO THE ROOF OF THE RADAR POST. AS THE FLASH OF THE EXPLOSION SEARED THE DARKNESS, THE OTHER COMMANDOS FOLLOWED SUIT — AND THE GERMAN DETECTOR STATION ERUPTED IN A SEA OF FLAME...
WE'VE DONE THE JOB WE CAME TO DO — NOW LET'S GET OUT OF HERE!

BUT THEIR ESCAPE WAS NOW CUT OFF ON ALL SIDES.
WE'LL NEVER MAKE IT BACK TO THE LANDING CRAFT, SIR — I RECKON THE JERRIES HAVE NOW GOT AT LEAST TWO HUNDRED MEN ON THE HILLTOP — WE CAN'T FIGHT OUR WAY THROUGH THAT!
THEN THERE'S NOTHING FOR IT, SERGEANT, WE'VE GOT TO GO INLAND! THAT'S THE LAST DIRECTION THE HUN WILL EXPECT US TO TAKE!

CRAWLING ACROSS THE BULLET-SCARRED ROCKS, THE COMMANDOS EDGED THEIR WAY ROUND THE RADAR POST WHILE THE GERMAN NET CLOSED IN...
SEE THE DARK MASS IN THE BACKGROUND, SERGEANT? IF I'M NOT MISTAKEN, THAT'S ONE OF THE FOOTHILLS OF A MOUNTAIN CHAIN WHICH LEADS TO THE INTERIOR! WE'RE GOING UP THAT CLIFF FACE—IT'S THE ONLY WAY OUT...
IT MAY BE THE ONLY WAY OUT, SIR—BUT I THINK WE'RE BUYING A ONE-WAY TICKET!

IN THE CONFUSED FLARE-STUDDED DARKNESS, THE COMMANDOS SLID LIKE WRAITHS FROM ONE SHELTERED SPOT TO ANOTHER—UNTIL THE CEASELESS CRACKLE OF THE GERMAN SMALL ARMS FIRE FELL GRADUALLY BEHIND. AT LAST THE CLIFF FACE ROSE BEFORE THEM LIKE A WALL...
IF A SEARCHLIGHT PICKS US OUT NOW, WE'LL BE CAUGHT LIKE FLIES ON A FLYPAPER!
THE JERRIES DON'T KNOW WE'VE SLIPPED THEM—THEY'LL SHOOT AT EACH OTHER FOR HOURS, THINKING IT'S US...

DAWN FOUND MIKE FAIRWEATHER AND HIS SMALL COMMANDO FORCE HIGH ON THE MOUNTAIN...
THE MEN ARE FAIR DONE, SIR—EVEN FOR COMMANDOS THAT WAS A GRIM BIT OF MOUNTAINEERING!
WE'LL HAVE A TEN MINUTE REST—I'LL MAKE A QUICK RECONNOITRE TO ENSURE THE COAST'S CLEAR!

BUT THE GERMANS HAD PICKED UP THE TRAIL. FROM A VANTAGE POINT ON A SLAB OF ROCK OVERLOOKING THE PRECIPICE, THE COMMANDO SAW A PATROL FAR BELOW ON THE LOWER SLOPES...
THEY'RE NOT WASTING MUCH TIME— BUT I RECKON WE'VE GOT A TWO-HOUR START ON THEM... IF WE KEEP IT UP WE MAY SHAKE THEM OFF...

IT WAS NOT A SINGLE PATROL, HOWEVER, BUT THE RESOURCES OF THE WEHRMACHT —AND AS FAIRWEATHER LED HIS MEN ON UP THE TRACKLESS SLOPES...
LOOK, SIR — A JERRY SPOTTER PLANE!
DISPERSE! —AND KEEP YOUR HEADS DOWN!

BUT THE FEISELER STORCH CIRCLED — AND FAIRWEATHER KNEW THEY HAD BEEN SEEN...
IT'S NO GOOD, SIR — WE MAY AS WELL STAND AND FIGHT IT OUT!
USE YOUR HEAD, SERGEANT! JERRY'S FINDING IT AS DIFFICULT AS WE ARE! IT DOESN'T MATTER HOW MANY SPOTTER PLANES PICK US OUT — THEIR PATROLS HAVE STILL GOT TO GET HERE!

WITH THEIR OFFICER URGING THEM ON, THE COMMANDOS PLODDED UPWARD — AND THEN SUDDENLY...
LOOK — THEY'VE GOT IN FRONT OF US! WHAT DID I TELL YOU, SIR?
WAIT — THAT ISN'T A JERRY!

Chapter 3. MYSTERY OF CYCLOPS

AN HOUR LATER, IN A MOUNTAIN HIDEOUT, THE COMMANDOS MET THE RESISTANCE LEADER...
...MY NAME IS PIET! YOU MAY THINK IT STRANGE—BUT WE KNEW YOU WERE COMING LONG BEFORE YOU ARRIVED! THE GERMANS HAVE BEEN MOVING TROOPS INTO THIS AREA FOR THE PAST TEN DAYS...
I SEE...SO THERE WAS A SECURITY LEAKAGE...

MEANWHILE, IN THE GERMAN WEHRMACHT H.Q., THE SITUATION WAS ALSO BEING DISCUSSED....
THEY SHOULD NOT HAVE ESCAPED! WE HAD HALF A DIVISION IN THIS AREA WAITING FOR THEM!
BUT, HERR OBERST, THE INFORMATION WE HAD FROM INTELLIGENCE TOLD US THAT THEY WOULD LAND ON THE TWO BEACHES A AND B! HAD THEY KEPT TO THEIR PLAN WE WOULD HAVE WIPED THEM OUT!

IN THE MOUNTAINS, GERMAN PATROLS SOUGHT VAINLY FOR TRACES OF THE VANISHED BRITISH FORCE . . .
ACH—IT IS IMPOSSIBLE! THEY CANNOT BE SEEN BY SPOTTER AIRCRAFT—SO HOW CAN THEY EXPECT US TO FIND THEM!
AND THE BRITISH MAY BE UNDER COVER—WATCHING US. IT WOULD BE EASY TO AMBUSH US IN ANY OF THESE GULLIES!
SAFE IN A MOUNTAIN CAVE, WELL HIDDEN FROM THE EYES OF THE GERMAN SPOTTERS, THE COMMANDOS RESTED. AFTER THREE DAYS, PIET REAPPEARED...
...I HAVE BEEN IN TOUCH WITH THE RESISTANCE AT A COASTAL VILLAGE. I THINK WE MAY GET YOU OUT OF NORWAY BY FISHING BOAT—BUT FIRST YOU MUST GET TO THAT VILLAGE. THERE IS ONE POSSIBLE ROUTE WHICH THE GERMANS CANNOT FOLLOW—BUT IT IS DANGEROUS...
WHEREVER YOU CAN GO—SO CAN WE!
THAT'S RIGHT, SIR—AND THE SOONER THE BETTER!

THEY SET OUT AT DAWN NEXT DAY — AND BY MIDDAY, HAD CLIMBED HIGH INTO THE NORWEGIAN MOUNTAIN FASTNESSES...
I THINK WE'VE BEEN SPOTTED, PIET!
D-IKVN
WHAT DOES IT MATTER? THE HUN WOULD HAVE TO SEND IN PARATROOPS TO REACH US. NO — WE ARE SAFE FROM PURSUIT FOR THE TIME BEING — AND WE WILL SOON BE LOST FROM SIGHT IN THE GREAT HILLS...

AND SO THE FUGITIVES PRESSED ON TOWARDS THE NORTH, THROUGH HAZARD AFTER HAZARD...
THIS MAKES THE COMMANDO COURSE LOOK LIKE A TEDDY BEAR'S PICNIC!
THINK OF THE LINE YOU CAN SHOOT WHEN YOU GET HOME, SERGEANT!

FINALLY, AFTER FOUR DAYS, THEY STOOD ON THE SUMMIT OF A GREAT ESCARPMENT...
WELL, CAPTAIN — THE WORST IS OVER! FROM HERE YOU CAN SEE THE COAST! OUR FISHING PORT IS ONLY TWENTY MILES AWAY THROUGH RELATIVELY EASY COUNTRY — WITH LUCK WE'LL HAVE YOU ABOARD YOUR FISHING BOAT IN TWO DAYS!
THIS IS QUITE A ROUTE — WHEN I GET BACK I'LL BE ABLE TO TELL JANSEN SOMETHING ABOUT NORWAY HE DOESN'T KNOW!

AS THE MEN ATE A HASTY MEAL, PIET AND MIKE RECONNOITRED AHEAD...
YOU MENTIONED THE NAME JANSEN! I KNEW A MAN CALLED JANSEN ONCE — HE WAS ONE OF OUR RESISTANCE LEADERS EARLY IN THE WAR! I REMEMBER HIM WELL BECAUSE HIS CODE NAME WAS CYCLOPS. YOU SEE, HE ONLY HAD ONE EYE. BUT HE WAS CAUGHT BY THE GESTAPO — WE NEVER SAW HIM AGAIN!
WELL, IT'S NOT LIKELY THAT THERE CAN BE TWO JANSENS WITH ONLY ONE EYE — SO YOU MAY BE INTERESTED TO LEARN THAT YOUR CYCLOPS ESCAPED FROM THE GESTAPO AND REACHED ENGLAND! IN FACT, HE WAS MY COMMANDING OFFICER IN THE RAID ON HJORL FIORD...

PIET TOOK A SURPRISING ATTITUDE TO FAIRWEATHER'S DISCLOSURE....
BUT THIS CANNOT BE, CAPTAIN — I **KNOW** THAT CYCLOPS JANSEN IS STILL IN GESTAPO HANDS — HE IS BEING HELD AS A HOSTAGE!
BUT HOW DO YOU KNOW THIS?
BECAUSE CYCLOPS JANSEN'S FAMILY WERE FORCED TO BETRAY THEIR COUNTRY ON HIS ACCOUNT — HIS BROTHER NILS HAS BECOME ONE OF THE MOST NOTORIOUS QUISLINGS IN OSLO, AND MUST DO AS THE GESTAPO ASK — OR CYCLOPS DIES!

AS THE REST OF THE MEN JOINED THEM AND SET OUT ONCE MORE ON THEIR LONG MARCH TO THE COAST, PIET WENT ON...
WHEN CYCLOPS WAS CAPTURED, HIS BROTHER NILS CAME TO US AND ASKED US TO RESCUE HIM — BUT WE COULD DO NOTHING! NILS BARTERED WITH THE GESTAPO — AND BECAME A QUISLING — SO CYCLOPS MUST STILL BE IN THE HANDS OF THE GESTAPO!

SUDDENLY, A GREAT MANY THINGS BECAME CLEAR TO THE COMMANDO CAPTAIN...
IT MAKES SENSE! THERE'S BEEN SOMETHING WRONG ABOUT JANSEN FROM THE BEGINNING! I KNEW HIS STORY ABOUT SWIMMING THE FIORD COULDN'T BE TRUE — AND NOW THIS CLINCHES IT! HE'S BEEN IN THE HANDS OF THE GESTAPO — HE TURNS UP IN BRITAIN TELLING A FALSE STORY — AND THERE'S A SECURITY LEAKAGE OVER A RAID WHICH HE COMMANDS! YES — HE'S IN THE HANDS OF THE GESTAPO, ALL RIGHT — ***AS ONE OF THEIR AGENTS!***

FOR THE NEXT TWENTY FOUR HOURS MIKE AND HIS MEN FOLLOWED PIET AS THEY NEGOTIATED THE LAST FEW MILES OF MOUNTAINOUS COUNTRY. AT LAST THEY NEARED THE COAST, AND AT MIDNIGHT THEY WERE CREEPING THROUGH THE DESERTED FISHING VILLAGE WHICH WAS THEIR DESTINATION...
THERE AREN'T MANY GERMANS IN THIS AREA — IT'S TOO FAR NORTH TO BE OF ANY USE TO THEM! BUT WE MUST GO WITH CARE...

BUT THERE WERE NO PATROLS AND NO OPPOSITION — AND SOON THE COMMANDOS WERE ON BOARD THE SMALL BOAT WHICH WAS TO TAKE THEM ACROSS THE NORTH SEA...
WELL, IT'S BEEN A PIECE OF CAKE, SIR — ALL WE'VE GOT TO WORRY ABOUT NOW ARE U-BOATS!
THAT'S YOUR WORRY, SERGEANT — I WON'T BE COMING!

MIKE FAIRWEATHER EXPLAINED EXACTLY WHAT WAS IN HIS MIND.....
WHEN YOU REACH SCOTLAND, REPORT TO BRIGADIER JOHNSON. TELL HIM I'VE STAYED BEHIND TO DO A CERTAIN JOB FOR INTELLIGENCE! THERE'S BEEN A DEFINITE LEAKAGE OF INFORMATION ABOUT OUR RAID, AND I THINK I KNOW WHERE IT'S COME FROM! ON NO ACCOUNT MUST MAJOR JANSEN LEARN WHY I AM STAYING BEHIND!
VERY WELL, SIR...

THE FISHING BOAT DREW AWAY INTO THE DARKNESS— AND THE COMMANDO CAPTAIN STOOD WITH THE RESISTANCE LEADER WATCHING IT GO...
THERE GOES YOUR PASSPORT TO FREEDOM, CAPTAIN— YOU MAY NOT GET ANOTHER SO EASILY!
I'LL WORRY ABOUT THAT, PIET, WHEN THE TIME COMES! THE IMPORTANT QUESTION NOW IS—HOW SOON CAN YOU GET ME TO OSLO?

A FEW DAYS LATER, THE BATTERED LITTLE TRAWLER PITCHED SLOWLY IN TOWARDS THE HARBOUR OF OSLO...

ONE OF MY MEN'S SHORE PASSES WILL GET YOU PAST THE SENTRIES AT THE HARBOUR GATES, AND THEN WE WILL GO TO A CERTAIN TAVERN!

YOU ARE TAKING A TERRIBLE RISK! IF YOU ARE CAUGHT, IT WILL MEAN DEATH! YOU ARE A BRAVE MAN...

SAFELY OUT OF THE DOCKS, THE CAPTAIN LED FAIRWEATHER TO A SMALL TAVERN, AND IN THE CELLAR HE MET THE LEADERS OF THE LOCAL RESISTANCE GROUP. . . .
. . . IT IS AN INCREDIBLE STORY YOU TELL US, CAPTAIN FAIRWEATHER! WE HAVE KNOWN FOR SOME TIME THAT NILS JANSEN IS A QUISLING—BUT CYCLOPS JANSEN HIMSELF IS A BRAVE MAN AND A PATRIOT, HE FELL INTO GESTAPO HANDS FIGHTING FOR HIS COUNTRY!
I AM AFRAID, GENTLEMEN, THAT I SPEAK THE TRUTH! EVERY MAN HAS HIS PRICE—AND JANSEN'S PRICE WAS THE SAFETY OF HIS FAMILY!

AS I SEE IT, IT'S A PERFECT GESTAPO DOUBLE CROSS! WHEN CYCLOPS JANSEN WAS CAUGHT, THE GESTAPO USED HIM AS A HOSTAGE TO FORCE HIS BROTHER TO TURN QUISLING! THEN THEY FORCED CYCLOPS TO WORK FOR THEM BY THREATENING TO TORTURE HIS FAMILY AND HIS BROTHER NILS IF HE DID NOT DO SO. IN FACT, GENTLEMEN, CYCLOPS **DOES NOT KNOW** HIS BROTHER NILS IS A QUISLING AND NILS DOES NOT KNOW THAT CYCLOPS IS IN BRITAIN —ALSO WORKING FOR THE GESTAPO.

THE RESISTANCE LEADERS WERE ASTONISHED . . . .
WHAT YOU SAY MAY WELL BE TRUE, CAPTAIN—BUT WHAT CAN WE DO?
WE CAN DO TWO THINGS! IF NILS JANSEN CAN BE MADE TO REALISE THAT HIS BROTHER IS SAFE IN BRITAIN, HE MAY JOIN THE RESISTANCE—AND THAT WILL BE A BLOW STRUCK FOR FREE NORWAY! ALSO, IF THEIR FAMILY CAN BE TAKEN OUT OF REACH OF THE GESTAPO, CYCLOPS MAY DIVULGE THE SPY CHANNEL THROUGH WHICH SECURITY SECRETS ARE LEAKING OUT OF BRITAIN . . .

NILS JANSEN WAS ONE OF THE MOST HATED MEN IN OSLO. AT THE BEGINNING OF THE WAR HE HAD BEEN A STAUNCH SUPPORTER OF FREE NORWAY—BUT AFTER THE CAPTURE OF HIS BROTHER HE HAD WORKED HARD FOR THE GERMANS AS THE MANAGER OF A POWER STATION. WITH TWO RESISTANCE MEN, MIKE WENT TO SEE THE NORWEGIAN...
IT IS IMPOSSIBLE—THEY CANNOT HAVE NEWS OF MY BROTHER ...!
THESE MEN HAVE FORCED THEIR WAY IN, SIR—THEY SAY THEY HAVE SOME INFORMATION ABOUT SOMEONE CALLED 'CYCLOPS'...
SHOW THEM IN—AND LEAVE US ALONE!

THE THREE GRIM-LOOKING MEN WERE USHERED INTO THE LUXURIOUS OFFICE. JANSEN SAT WATCHING THEM WITH NARROWED EYES, HIS FINGERS HOVERING OVER A BELLPUSH ON THE DESK. SUDDENLY HE SAW HIMSELF GAZING INTO THE MUZZLE OF A REVOLVER...
KEEP YOUR FINGERS AWAY FROM THAT BUTTON, JANSEN! I'M A BRITISH COMMANDO OFFICER—AND THESE MEN ARE RESISTANCE LEADERS! BETRAY US—AND YOU WILL NOT LEAVE HERE ALIVE!
WHAT—!

TERSELY, MIKE TOLD THE QUISLING THE TRUTH ABOUT HIS BROTHER...
I CANNOT BELIEVE THIS! IT IS A GESTAPO TRICK....
JANSEN— DON'T YOU SEE WHAT A FOOL YOU ARE! THE HUN HAS BEEN DOUBLE-CROSSING YOU AND YOUR BROTHER ALL THE TIME!
I'M AFRAID YOU WILL HAVE TO BELIEVE US, MISTER JANSEN!

GAZING SEARCHINGLY AT THE TIGHT-LIPPED MEN WHO STOOD BEFORE HIM, NILS JANSEN REALISED THAT THEY WERE SPEAKING THE TRUTH — AND HE BURIED HIS FACE IN HIS HANDS...
WHAT DIFFERENCE CAN THAT MAKE TO ME NOW! THERE IS NO TURNING BACK FOR ME — I HAVE SERVED THE GESTAPO TOO WELL — EVERY LOYAL NORWEGIAN IS MY ENEMY...
YESTERDAY, JANSEN, THAT MAY HAVE BEEN TRUE — BUT IF YOU JOIN FORCES WITH US NOW, YOU CAN WIPE OUT THE PAST! YOU HAVE BEEN TORN BETWEEN TWO LOYALTIES — YOUR FAMILY AND YOUR COUNTRY. IT WAS A STRAIN FEW MEN COULD HAVE WITHSTOOD...

GREY-FACED, NILS JANSEN ROSE TO HIS FEET....
COME, LET US GET AWAY FROM HERE QUICKLY — EVEN NOW MY CLERK MAY BE REPORTING YOUR PRESENCE HERE TO THE GESTAPO!

LEAVING THE POWER STATION BY A BACK ENTRANCE, JANSEN TOOK THEM TO HIS CAR PARKED IN A SIDE STREET. THEY DROVE SLOWLY THROUGH THE DRAB CENTRE OF OSLO, TALKING URGENTLY...
I WILL JOIN YOU — ON THE CONDITION THAT MY FAMILY ARE TAKEN TO A PLACE OF SAFETY! I AM SACRIFICING MUCH IN DOING THIS...
STEK
MANY HAVE SACRIFICED MORE, JANSEN — AND IN TIME TO COME YOU WILL BE GLAD YOU HAVE MADE THIS DECISION! WE WILL COME FOR YOUR FAMILY TONIGHT!

DROPPING MIKE AND THE RESISTANCE LEADERS NEAR THE DOCKS, NILS JANSEN DROVE QUICKLY AWAY...
CAN THE LEOPARD CHANGE IT'S SPOTS? IF HE BETRAYS US NOW —
WE'RE TAKING A RISK — BUT NOW THAT HE KNOWS HIS BROTHER IS SAFE, HE'LL HAVE NO REASON TO PARLEY WITH THE GESTAPO! IN FACT, HE'S GOT A LOT TO GET EVEN WITH THEM FOR....

THAT NIGHT, AS ARRANGED, RESISTANCE MEN WENT TO NILS JANSEN'S HOUSE. THEY WERE STILL READY FOR TREACHERY—BUT NO GESTAPO AWAITED THEM—ONLY NILS, HIS MOTHER AND FATHER, AND UNCLE...
I HAVE TOLD THEM THEY ARE GOING TO SAFETY—THEY NOW KNOW THE TRUTH ABOUT MY BROTHER.
WE HAVE A CAR WAITING—LET US GET OUT OF HERE QUICKLY IN CASE THE GERMANS ARE WATCHING YOUR HOUSE!

THAT SAME NIGHT, IN A HIDEOUT IN THE MOUNTAINS.....
I CAN SERVE THE CAUSE BEST BY REMAINING IN CHARGE OF THE POWER STATION—MUCH SECRET INFORMATION PASSES THROUGH MY HANDS. BUT IF I FALL INTO THE CLUTCHES OF THE GESTAPO, HERE IS HOW THE POWER STATION CAN BE SABOTAGED...

BEFORE NILS RETURNED TO OSLO, LEAVING HIS FAMILY IN THE SAFETY OF THE MOUNTAIN HIDEOUT, HE HAD ONE LAST REQUEST TO MAKE OF FAIRWEATHER...
I AM WRITING THIS LETTER TO MY BROTHER EXPLAINING THAT I HAVE JOINED THE RESISTANCE MOVEMENT! I HOPE THAT YOU, CAPTAIN FAIRWEATHER, CAN TAKE IT TO HIM!
IF I AM LUCKY ENOUGH TO REACH MY OWN COUNTRY AGAIN, I WILL DELIVER IT IN PERSON — BE ASSURED OF THAT!

NILS RETURNED TO OSLO AND WENT STRAIGHT TO HIS OFFICE IN THE POWER STATION. THE GESTAPO WERE WAITING FOR HIM...
JANSEN — THE GAME IS UP! IT IS UNLUCKY FOR YOU THAT WE HAD MICROPHONES HIDDEN IN YOUR OFFICE!
YOU CAN TELL US THE NAMES OF YOUR ACCOMPLICES NOW — OR WE WILL EXTRACT THEM FROM YOU BY TORTURE!
WHAT HAPPENS TO ME NOW DOES NOT MATTER...

THE NEWS OF JANSEN'S CAPTURE REACHED THE RESISTANCE — AND ALTHOUGH IT WAS TOO LATE TO DO ANYTHING TO SAVE HIM, HIS SABOTAGE PLAN COULD STILL BE CARRIED OUT. TWENTY FOUR HOURS LATER, THE RESISTANCE STRUCK — DEVASTATINGLY.
THE MAIN GENERATORS HAVE BEEN DESTROYED — THE DAMAGE WILL TAKE MONTHS TO REPAIR...

MIKE FAIRWEATHER'S TASK IN OSLO WAS FINISHED. WITH THE HELP OF THE RESISTANCE HE WAS SMUGGLED ACROSS NORWAY TO A SMALL FISHING VILLAGE IN THE NORTH – FROM WHERE HE WAS TO SET SAIL FOR SCOTLAND....
WHEN YOU REACH BRITAIN, AND YOUR MISSION IS COMPLETED, CONTACT THE NORWEGIAN FREEDOM RADIO — AND GET THEM TO BROADCAST THE MESSAGE – 'THE HARE HAS LEFT THE MOUNTAINS'! THEN WE WILL KNOW THAT OUR WORK HAS NOT BEEN IN VAIN!
DON'T WORRY, MY FRIEND — I WILL PERSUADE CYCLOPS JANSEN — SOMEHOW!

Chapter 4. THE PRICE OF HONOUR

MIKE WATCHED WITH THANKFUL RELIEF AS A NAVAL CORVETTE SPED TOWARDS HIM.
KEEP HER STRAIGHT ON THE TILLER—AND WE'LL SOON HAVE YOU IN!
F44

TAKEN ASHORE, THE EXHAUSTED COMMANDO CAPTAIN SLEPT AS IF DRUGGED IN THE LOCAL POLICE STATION. BRIGADIER JOHNSON WAS CALLED IN TO IDENTIFY HIM.
YES, THAT'S CAPTAIN FAIRWEATHER! WHEN HE AWAKES, TELL HIM TO REPORT TO ME.
VERY GOOD, SIR!

EIGHT HOURS LATER....
I'LL SEND YOU UP TO CAMP IN MY CAR AS SOON AS YOU'VE EATEN YOUR BREAKFAST, CAPTAIN!
THIS IS A BIT TRICKY—I MUST SEE JANSEN ALONE FIRST....
THANKS, INSPECTOR—THIS IS THE FINEST HAM AND EGGS I'VE EVER TASTED.

ARRIVING AT THE CAMP, ALMOST THE FIRST PERSON MIKE SAW WAS HIS SERGEANT....
GREAT SCOTT, SIR—YOU MADE IT!
QUICK, SERGEANT—I MUST FIND MAJOR JANSEN RIGHT AWAY! IS HE STILL ON THE CAMP?
YOU BET HE IS, SIR—I'LL TAKE YOU TO HIS OFFICE!

GOOD AFTERNOON, MAJOR JANSEN—OR SHOULD I SAY, 'CYCLOPS'?
NORWAY
YOU...!

AT THE MENTION OF HIS OLD RESISTANCE NAME, JANSEN RECOILED AS IF STRUCK BY A WHIP. THEN QUICKLY HE RALLIED, AND GAZED UP INTO THE BLEAK EYES OF HIS SUBORDINATE WITH COLD DEFIANCE...
WELL, WELL — THE WANDERING CAPTAIN! YOU SHOULD HAVE STAYED IN NORWAY, YOU KNOW! YOU REALISE OF COURSE, THAT YOU WILL BE CHARGED WITH DISOBEYING ORDERS...
BEFORE WE TALK ABOUT MY TROUBLES, WE'D BETTER DISCUSS YOURS, MAJOR! THE CHARGE IN YOUR CASE CARRIES A DEATH SENTENCE... ESPIONAGE!

BRIEFLY, MIKE FAIRWEATHER TOLD HIS STORY, AND AS IT UNFOLDED, EVERY VESTIGE OF DEFIANCE WAS STRIPPED FROM JANSEN...
YOU SAY MY FAMILY IS SAFE, AND MY BROTHER HAS BEEN CAPTURED BY THE GESTAPO? WHAT PROOF HAVE YOU OF ALL THIS?

WITHOUT A WORD, MIKE PRODUCED NILS JANSEN'S LETTER TO HIS BROTHER. AS CYCLOPS READ, HIS LAST PRETENCE FELL AWAY...
"SO, BROTHER, OUR FAMILY IS SAFE, I DO NOT THINK I SHALL BE ALIVE TO SEE YOU WHEN ALL THIS IS OVER — BUT I KNOW THAT NOW YOU ARE FREE FROM THE GESTAPO, YOU WILL REINSTATE THE HONOUR OF OUR FAMILY... YOUR BROTHER... NILS."

AFTER A LONG SILENCE, THE NORWEGIAN SPOKE, AND HIS VOICE WAS QUIET AND CALM...
WELL, CAPTAIN FAIRWEATHER, I AM READY — WHAT DO YOU PROPOSE TO DO ABOUT ME?
YOU BETRAYED YOUR COUNTRY AND YOUR OWN MEN, AND YOU TRIED TO KILL A BROTHER OFFICER — FOR IT WAS YOU WHO FLUNG THAT GRENADE AT ME, WASN'T IT? WHATEVER YOUR REASONS FOR DOING THESE THINGS, YOU ARE LIABLE TO PAY THE PENALTY — AND YOU KNOW WHAT THAT IS!

JANSEN LEANED FORWARD URGENTLY...
LISTEN, FAIRWEATHER! I ADMIT EVERYTHING! I WILL UNCOVER THE WHOLE SPY RING WHICH ENTANGLED ME — BUT I ASK ONE THING OF YOU — LET ME GO ON ONE MORE RAID, AND I PROMISE I'LL COME BACK AND STAND MY TRIAL!
HOW DO I KNOW THAT YOU WON'T BETRAY US AGAIN?
THE ANSWER TO THAT IS IN MY BROTHER'S LETTER — WHICH YOU MAY READ, CAPTAIN FAIRWEATHER.

AS MIKE READ NILS JANSEN'S LETTER..."I KNOW THAT YOU WILL REINSTATE THE HONOUR OF OUR FAMILY...." HE KNEW THAT JANSEN WOULD KEEP HIS WORD...
OKAY, JANSEN! I AGREE—ON THE CONDITION THAT YOU WRITE OUT ALL THE PARTICULARS OF THIS BUSINESS, AND DEPOSIT THE DOCUMENT IN THE GUARD ROOM AGAINST YOUR RETURN!
THAT'S A DEAL, CAPTAIN FAIRWEATHER.
NORWAY

MIKE REALISED THAT IT WAS NOT GOING TO BE EASY TO WITHHOLD HIS REPORT ON HIS ACTIVITIES IN NORWAY UNTIL AFTER THE NEXT RAID. HE MADE HIS WAY UNEASILY TOWARDS THE BRIGADIER'S OFFICE.
WELL, WELL, FAIRWEATHER! I MUST SAY I'D GIVEN YOU UP AS A GONNER! WHAT HAVE YOU BEEN UP TO—EH?
FOR SECURITY REASONS, SIR—THE LIVES OF MANY PEOPLE ARE AT STAKE—I WILL NOT BE ABLE TO MAKE A FULL REPORT FOR AT LEAST A WEEK! I WILL, HOWEVER, LET YOU KNOW BROADLY WHAT I'VE BEEN DOING, SO THAT YOU'LL KNOW THAT I HAVEN'T BEEN IN NORWAY JUST FOR MY HEALTH!

A FORTHCOMING RAID WAS SO MUCH IN THE SENIOR OFFICER'S MIND THAT HE DIDNOT PRESS THE MATTER. HE CALLED JANSEN TO HIS OFFICE....
GENTLEMEN, WE'VE BEEN ORDERED TO RAID A FACTORY IN NORWAY! THIS FACTORY MUST BE DESTROYED—IT IS PRODUCING THE 'HEAVY WATER' ESSENTIAL TO THE GERMAN RESEARCH IN NUCLEAR WARFARE. YOU WILL WORK IN CLOSE CO-OPERATION WITH THE NORWEGIAN RESISTANCE...

THE FACTORY IS AT THE END OF THIS FIORD—NESTLING AMONG VERY HIGH AND PRECIPITOUS MOUNTAINS, THE ONLY APPROACH BEING THROUGH A NARROW BOTTLENECK. WHEN YOU LAND, THE RESISTANCE CHAPS WILL GIVE YOU COVERING FIRE SO THAT YOU CAN DEMOLISH ALL THE KEY POINTS WITH HIGH EXPLOSIVES!
NORWAY

JANSEN AND MIKE FAIRWEATHER FORGOT FOR THE PRESENT THE DRAMA IN WHICH THEY WERE INVOLVED, AND INSTEAD CONCENTRATED ON THE COMING DANGEROUS OPERATION.
I KNOW THAT PLACE WELL, FAIRWEATHER! IF WE CAN MANOEUVRE THE LANDING-CRAFT PAST THE NARROW ENTRANCE, WE'LL HAVE A CHANCE, BUT IT'S ALMOST CERTAIN THAT THE JERRIES KEEP A CONTINUOUS WATCH ON IT!
I SUGGEST THAT WE LET THE LANDING-CRAFT TAKE US TO A POINT ABOUT HALF A MILE FROM THE BOTTLENECK—AND THEN GO IN BY RAFT...
GOOD IDEA, CAPTAIN!
TWENTY MEN UNDER FAIRWEATHER AND JANSEN WOULD MAKE THE ATTACK—AND THE NORWEGIAN RESISTANCE WAS IMMEDIATELY INFORMED.
LIEF— LISTEN TO THIS! 'TWENTY BRITISH COMMANDOS WILL ATTACK TARGET ALPHA ON THE NIGHT OF THE FIFTEENTH — NEED COVERING FIRE RESISTANCE—INSTRUCTIONS ON THE NEXT BROADCAST SCHEDULE—CONFIRM...'
ONLY TWENTY MEN! THAT MEANS WE'LL NEED A BIG FORCE!
AND WE'LL HAVE TO MOVE QUICKLY—IT'S THE TWELFTH, TODAY!

IN BRITAIN, THE TWENTY MEN ASSEMBLED FOR BRIEFING BEFORE EMBARKING ON THE DESTROYER THAT WAS TO TAKE THEM TO NORWAY....
WHEN WE HAVE GAINED ENTRANCE TO THE FACTORY, YOU WILL COVER THE CAPTAIN AND MYSELF AS WE SET THE CHARGES! WHEN ONE OF US BLOWS THE WHISTLE THREE TIMES, YOU WILL CLEAR OFF—QUICKLY—BEFORE THE BALLOON GOES UP!

THE DESTROYER CARRYING THE COMMANDO FORCE GLIDED SWIFTLY INTO THE DARKENING WATERS OF THE NORTH SEA.
CAPTAIN FAIRWEATHER—WILL YOU SUPERVISE THE ASSEMBLY OF THE COLLAPSIBLE CANOES AND INSPECT EACH MAN? WHEN YOU'VE DONE THAT, REPORT TO ME ON THE BRIDGE!

HALF AN HOUR LATER, MIKE FOUND JANSEN PORING OVER THE DIAGRAMS OF THE FACTORY.
THE VITAL MACHINERY OF THE PLANT IS SEALED IN THIS CONCRETE STRUCTURE AND TO DO THE JOB PROPERLY, I'LL HAVE TO GET INSIDE—*BUT THERE IS NO ENTRANCE!* OUR ONLY HOPE IS THIS POINT HERE—IT LOOKS LIKE AN INSPECTION SHAFT.

MEANWHILE, CREEPING SILENTLY FROM CRAG TO CRAG, TREADING CAT-FOOTED AS THEY PADDED PAST THE VIGILANT SENTRIES, THE RESISTANCE MEN TOOK THEIR POSITIONS. IF ONE MAN WAS DISCOVERED AT THIS STAGE, THE OPERATION WOULD BE DOOMED...

ALL ARE IN POSITION!

GOOD—NOW WE MUST WATCH THE FIORD ENTRANCE FOR THE BRITISH!

AFTER HALF AN HOUR'S STEADY PADDLING THE DIM BLACK MOUTH OF THE FIORD LOOMED AHEAD. THE CRASHING SPRAY GUIDED THE COMMANDOS IN, AS THEY KEPT CLOSE TO THE OVERHANGING CLIFFS.
HOLD YOUR BREATH, NOW, FAIRWEATHER —WE'RE RIGHT UNDER THEIR NOSES!
THIS IS ONE BIT OF NORWAY I DON'T KNOW, JANSEN —SO I'M TRUSTING TO YOU!

THE TURBULENT SEA AND THE DARKNESS OF THE NIGHT CLOAKED THEM AS THEY PASSED SAFELY INTO THE COMPARATIVE CALM OF THE SMALL FIORD.
THIS IS IT, FAIRWEATHER— IN THREE MINUTES THE FUN WILL START!
I DON'T THINK YOU'LL RAT ON US THIS TIME, MAJOR JANSEN —BUT IF YOU THINK ABOUT IT, REMEMBER I'LL BE WATCHING YOU—AND ONE FALSE MOVE FROM YOU AND I'LL SHOOT!

IT WAS A LONE SENTRY HALF ASLEEP AT HIS POST WHO FIRST SAW THE INVADERS...
HILFE! HILFE! ACHTUNG —AAAAGH!
QUIET, JERRY!
COME ON, YOU FELLERS— HE'S GIVEN THE ALARM!

THE FIRST WARNING THE RESISTANCE MEN HAD OF THE COMMANDOS' APPROACH WAS THE GUTTURAL SOUNDS OF STARTLED GERMANS AS THEY CALLED OUT THE GUARD AT THE FACTORY...
THE BRITISH ARE HERE! CONCENTRATE ON THE GERMAN GUARDHOUSE! FIRE!

THE RESISTANCE MEN MOVED FORWARD FROM THEIR POSITIONS, FIRING STEADILY INTO THE DISORGANISED GERMAN GARRISON. THE FIRST MORTAR SHELLS FELL, AS ARRANGED, INTO THE BARBED WIRE PERIMETER OF THE FACTORY FENCE. THE ENEMY WAS CAUGHT UNAWARES...

AS THE DARKNESS CAME ALIVE WITH THE BURSTS OF MORTAR BOMBS AND THE ANGRY TONGUES OF RIFLE AND TOMMY-GUN FIRE, THE COMMANDOS MOVED SILENTLY AND SWIFTLY IN...
OKAY, FAIRWEATHER — HERE WE GO! BEST OF LUCK — AND REMEMBER WE'VE GOT TO FIND THE ENTRANCE TO THE MAIN BUILDING! WE'LL LAY THE OTHER CHARGES FIRST!
RIGHT, MAJOR!

BUT ALTHOUGH THE GERMANS SEEMED TO BE DISORGANISED, TWO PLATOONS OF THE GARRISON HAD BROKEN AWAY IN THE DARKNESS AND HAD CREPT ROUND THE FLANK OF THE ATTACKING COMMANDOS. THEY HELD THEIR FIRE UNTIL THE RESISTANCE MEN, WHO IN THEIR ENTHUSIASM HAD MOVED TOO FAR FORWARD WERE ALSO CAUGHT UNAWARES...
THEY'VE OUTFLANKED US!
SERGEANT — TAKE NUMBER TWO SECTION TO THE LEFT! CORPORAL JONES — YOU TAKE SIX MEN AND MOVE IN ON THE RIGHT WITH GRENADES!

THE GERMANS WERE ENTIRELY SURPRISED BY THE VIGOROUS COUNTER-ATTACK, AND RETREATED UP THE HILL INTO THE CRAGS.
LEUTNANT HORSCH! THE TELEPHONE WIRES ARE BROKEN! TAKE MY CAR AND DRIVE TO H.Q. FOR REINFORCEMENTS — BE QUICK! THERE IS NO TIME TO LOSE! THESE SCHWEIN WILL DESTROY THE FACTORY!
JAWOHL, HERR HAUPTMANN!

JANSEN AND FAIRWEATHER, COVERED BY THE FIRE OF THE RESISTANCE MEN, CROSSED THE BROKEN PERIMETER WIRE OF THE FACTORY...
YOU TAKE THOSE BUILDINGS ON THE LEFT, — FAIRWEATHER, I'LL GO OVER TO THOSE ON THE RIGHT! WE'LL MEET AT THE MAIN BUILDING!

PLACING DEMOLITION CHARGES REQUIRES CONCENTRATION. UNDER SPORADIC FIRE FROM THE GERMANS, JANSEN AND MIKE FAIRWEATHER HAD A NERVE-RACKING TASK...
ONLY TWO MORE SHEDS TO DEAL WITH — AND BY GOLLY, THE ENEMY FIRE IS GETTING CLOSER!

THE GERMAN TROOPS HAD REORGANISED AND WERE CREEPING SLOWLY BACK. AT THE SAME TIME, GERMAN REINFORCEMENTS WERE ON THE WAY...

JANSEN AND FAIRWEATHER, THEIR CHARGES LAID, MET AT THE MAIN PLANT. THE ONLY ENTRANCE WAS AN INSPECTION SHAFT, COVERED BY A HUGE GRID. THE GERMANS WERE NOW RAPIDLY CLOSING IN, DESPITE THE DETERMINED EFFORTS OF THE COMMANDOS AND RESISTANCE MEN...
STAND BACK, FAIRWEATHER— I'M GOING TO OPEN THE GRID WITH THIS GRENADE!
WE'LL HAVE TO HURRY, JANSEN!

THE GRID OVER THE SHAFT DISINTEGRATED INTO WHINING FRAGMENTS ON THE EXPLOSION OF THE GRENADE. THE WAY INTO THE VITAL CORE OF THE PLANT WAS OPEN...
YOU COVER ME, FAIRWEATHER— I'M GOING IN! IF I'M NOT OUT IN FIVE MINUTES, WITHDRAW AND EXPLODE THE CHARGES! THEN TAKE THE MEN WITH YOU!
BUT, SIR—!
THAT'S AN ORDER, FAIRWEATHER!

JANSEN HOISTED HIMSELF UP INTO THE INSPECTION SHAFT, AND SLID OUT OF SIGHT INTO THE DEPTHS OF THE PLANT MIKE FAIRWEATHER CROUCHED IN THE SHADOWS CLOSE BY AND SAW HIS SERGEANT RUNNING TOWARDS HIM...
SIR! WE MUST GET OUT! JERRY REINFORCEMENTS ARE ON THE WAY—HALF A DIVISION, I SHOULD SAY! HAVE YOU FINISHED THE JOB?
FOLLOW THE WIRE TO THE DETONATOR AND STAND BY. MAJOR JANSEN HAS GONE IN HERE TO LAY A CHARGE!

A MOMENT LATER, GERMAN TROOP CARRIERS CLATTERED INTO THE FACTORY COURTYARD— THE TIME HAD COME FOR THE COMMANDOS TO GET OUT!
JANSEN—HURRY! JERRY REINFORCEMENTS HAVE ARRIVED!

IN THE HEART OF THE HEAVY WATER PLANT, JANSEN WAS SETTING HIS FUSES...
THERE S ENOUGH EXPLOSIVE IN THIS LITTLE PACKET.TO TURN THE PLANT INTO A VOLCANO! THIS FUSE OUGHT TO BURN FOR FOUR MINUTES—WHICH GIVES ME JUST ENOUGH TIME TO GET BACK UP THE SHAFT!

THE FUSE SPLUTTERED INTO LIFE—AND JANSEN HURRIED ACROSS TO THE VENTILATOR. BUT AS HIS NAILED BOOTS SLITHERED VAINLY FOR A HOLD ON THE SLIPPERY METAL SHAFT, HE REALISED THAT HE WOULD NEVER BE ABLE TO GET OUT THE WAY HE HAD COME IN—AND THERE WAS NO OTHER WAY OF ESCAPE.
I'VE HAD IT—THE SHAFT IS TOO WIDE FOR ME TO ELBOW MY WAY UP—AND IT WOULD TAKE AT LEAST HALF AN HOUR TO DO IT INCH BY INCH...

THERE WAS ONLY ONE ALTERNATIVE LEFT TO JANSEN—AND THAT WAS TO PULL THE FUSE AWAY FROM THE EXPLOSIVE CHARGE, AND SO SAVE HIMSELF. BUT THE COURAGE THAT HAD MADE CYCLOPS' JANSEN ONE OF THE TOUGHEST RESISTANCE FIGHTERS NOW SHOWED ITSELF—AND TURNING ON HIS HEEL HE WALKED AWAY FROM THE VENTILATOR—BACK TOWARDS THE CENTRE OF THE PLANT...
IT'S A CASE OF ONE LIFE AGAINST THE SUCCESS OF THE MISSION—AND THE MISSION MUST SUCCEED AT ALL COSTS! SO THE TIME HAS COME TO PROVE MYSELF WORTHY OF MY BROTHER'S TRUST...

OUTSIDE THE PLANT, MIKE WAITED ANXIOUSLY, HIS HAND ON THE PLUNGER WHICH WOULD DETONATE THE CHARGES PLACED AROUND THE OUTER BUILDINGS...
WHAT'S HAPPENED TO MAJOR JANSEN, SIR? HE SHOULD BE OUT OF THERE BY NOW—IT'S EXACTLY THIRTY SECONDS TO HIS OWN DEADLINE!
HE'S PROBABLY STRUCK SOME SNAG—I'LL HOLD IT FOR ANOTHER FIVE MINUTES...

THE SECOND HAND OF THE WATCH WAS FLICKING PAST THE DEADLINE WHEN SUDDENLY THE GROUND SHOOK AND THE MAIN PLANT ERUPTED INTO A HOLOCAUST OF FLAME....
BY THUNDER! JANSEN'S IN THERE!

JANSEN HAD PAID THE ULTIMATE PRICE—AND IN THE SPLIT SECOND OF THIS REALISATION, MIKE FAIRWEATHER KNEW THAT THERE WAS ONLY ONE THING FOR HIM TO DO—OBEY HIS ORDERS TO THE BITTER END...
YOU GAVE YOUR LIFE FOR THIS MISSION, JANSEN — SO WE'RE GOING TO STICK TO YOUR SCHEDULE — HERE GOES!

THE PLUNGER SHAFT SANK INTO ITS BOX—AND GREAT GOUTS OF RUBBLE WERE HURLED INTO THE AIR AS THE SECONDARY CHARGES DETONATED...
COR—EVERYTHING BUT THE KITCHEN SINK!

AND SO THE OPERATION WAS CARRIED THROUGH. THE COMMANDO FORCE, UNDER MIKE'S LEADERSHIP, RETREATED THROUGH VENGEFUL ENEMY FIRE TOWARDS THE WAITING DESTROYER...
NOT FAR TO GO NOW, SIR — PITY THE MAJOR DIDN'T MAKE IT!
HE DID A GOOD JOB, SARGE — WE OWE A LOT TO HIM!
...IF JANSEN HAD SURVIVED, HE WOULD HAVE HAD TO STAND TRIAL — AND I WOULDN'T HAVE LIKED TO SEE THAT HAPPEN. HE MAY HAVE BEEN A TRAITOR — BUT TO THE END HE WAS A MAN...

THE FINAL IRONY WAS TO COME ONE WEEK LATER, WHEN BRIGADIER JOHNSON SUMMONED MIKE FAIRWEATHER TO EDINBURGH TO MEET A CIRCLE OF PROMINENT STAFF OFFICERS...
CAPTAIN FAIRWEATHER — I AM PROUD TO INFORM YOU THAT YOU HAVE BEEN AWARDED THE MILITARY CROSS FOR OUTSTANDING GALLANTRY — AND YOU WILL NO DOUBT BE PLEASED TO LEARN THAT MAJOR JANSEN HAS BEEN POSTHUMOUSLY AWARDED THE D.S.O.!
I AM DEEPLY HONOURED, SIR!
YES — PERHAPS IT IS BETTER THAT JANSEN SHOULD GO DOWN IN THE HISTORY BOOKS AS A HERO — FOR BY HIS LAST GREAT SACRIFICE HE CLEARED HIS SLATE...

THAT SAME NIGHT, THE VOICE OF THE FREE NORWEGIAN RADIO SENT OUT A STRANGE MESSAGE WHICH WAS UNDERSTOOD ONLY BY THOSE WHO HAD ONCE KNOWN A MAN CALLED 'CYCLOPS...
...THE HARE HAS LEFT THE MOUNTAINS!

THE BLACK ACE
THE THROTTLES OF THE LANCASTER WERE SLAMMED WIDE OPEN. HER ENGINES WERE IN FINE PITCH~ MAKING A NOISE LIKE AN AIRCRAFT IN PAIN. HIGH ABOVE THE LIVID NIGHTMARE OF THE RUHR VALLEY, P FOR POPSIE SEEMED, TO THE SEVEN MEN WHO SAT INSIDE HER, TO BE THE ONLY SHIP IN THE SKY~ HUGE AND VULNERABLE, AND CRUELLY DEFENCELESS.
SEVEN MEN CLUNG GRIMLY TO THEIR SLIPPING NERVES, SEVEN MEN TASTED FEAR IN THEIR MOUTHS~A FEAR THAT WENT FAR DEEPER THAN THE STEEL-SLIVERED HELL THROUGH WHICH THEY FLEW...

Chapter 1. Flight of Fear

SOME OF THAT FEAR WAS IN FLIGHT-LIEUTENANT BILL WEBB, THE CAPTAIN AND PILOT OF *P FOR POPSIE*. HE BELLOWED HARSHLY ON THE INTERCOM...

WHAT THE HECK ARE YOU PLAYING AT, ABE? WE'VE RUN SMACK INTO A DEFENDED AREA! CHECK YOUR COURSE FIGURES, FOR PETE'S-SAKE!

WEBB'S INCREDULOUS SNARL TORE THROUGH THE INTERCOM. IN THE TAIL-TURRET, YOUNG MIKE SIMPSON HEARD IT AS HE CROUCHED BEHIND HIS BROWNINGS.
WE-WE'VE HAD IT! WE'LL NEVER GET OUT OF THIS ALIVE! HE WAS RIGHT! VIBART WAS RIGHT!

VIBART. THE NAME WAS BURNING IN THE MIND OF EVERY MAN WHO FLEW IN THE GROANING LANCASTER. IT WAS THE NAME OF THE LEAN, BRIGHT-EYED FLIGHT ENGINEER WHO SAT NEXT TO BILL WEBB...
IT LOOKS BAD, SKIPPER! BUT THEN, THE CARDS TOLD US IT WOULD BE, DIDN'T THEY?
CURSE YOU, VIBART! YOU AND YOUR PROPHECY! I DON'T BELIEVE IT! WE'RE GOING TO GET OUT OF THIS, D'YOU HEAR?

THEN, AS WEBB'S EYES FLICKED RIGHT, HE SAW ANOTHER LANCASTER, IMPALED ON A PYRAMID OF SEARCHLIGHTS, CENTRED ROUND THE STEADY, BLUE COLUMN OF A MASTER BEAM.
POOR DEVIL! HE'S CONED!

THE FLAK CLOSED ON THE TRAPPED LANCASTER. SUDDENLY, A DULL RED GLOW SPROUTED ON ITS PORT WING. THE BIG AIRCRAFT SLIPPED DOWN LIKE A SHINING, WOUNDED BIRD. WHEN THE BLAST CAME, IT STRUCK P FOR POPSIE LIKE A WALL OF WATER...
GOOD GRIEF! HE HADN'T JETTISONED HIS COOKIES!

ABRUPTLY, SHOCKINGLY, THE OTHER LANCASTER HAD DISAPPEARED, EXCEPT FOR A SINGLE, BURNING WING-TIP SKIDDING LAZILY DOWN...
THAT COULD HAVE BEEN US, SKIPPER! IT'S BEEN BUILDING UP TO THIS, ALL THE TIME! VIBART WAS RIGHT! YOU'VE GOT TO TURN BACK!

THE FLARING VOICE OF ALBERT SPENCE, THE WIRELESS OPERATOR, STRUCK CLARITY INTO WEBB'S REELING BRAIN...
ARE YOU CRAZY, ALBERT? GET BACK TO YOUR POSITION! WE'RE GOING TO FIND THAT TARGET~AND PLASTER IT! THEN WE'RE GOING HOME, ALL OF US, IN ONE PIECE!

600 MILES TO THE EAST, AT A BOMBER BASE IN LINCOLNSHIRE, THE FIRST WAVES OF LANCASTERS WERE RETURNING FROM THE RAID...
WELL, THAT'S MOST OF 'A' FLIGHT ACCOUNTED FOR! GOT ANYTHING ON P-POPSIE YET?
NO, SIR! SHE RADIOED AN ENGINE FAILURE ABOUT THREE HOURS AGO! BUT THAT'S THE LAST WE'VE HEARD!
BOMBER CONTROL - FLIGH
TAYLOR
BURKE
COCKCROFT
STRATHDEE
HERVEY

THE CODE NAME P-POPSIE WAS ON OTHER LIPS THAT NIGHT. OUTSIDE, IN THE ROARING DARKNESS, THE FITTERS AND MECHANICS WHO SERVICED HER WERE WATCHING OTHER BOMBERS DESCENDING ON THE BRIGHT FUNNEL OF THE FLARE PATH...
BILL WEBB'S BOYS ARE TWENTY MINUTES OVERDUE! D'YOU SUPPOSE ANYTHING'S HAPPENED?
WITH THEIR LUCK? NOT A CHANCE! IF THEY FELL IN THE RHINE, THEY'D COME OUT DRY! AIN'T THAT RIGHT, FLIGHT?
BUT THERE WAS A TINGE OF UNEASINESS IN THE MECHANIC'S COMMENT. IT FOUND AN ECHO IN THE LOW VOICE OF HIS RUGGED FLIGHT-SERGEANT...
I DON'T KNOW, SAMMY! THAT CREW HASN'T BEEN THE SAME SINCE THAT NEW ENGINEER JOINED THEM, JUST OVER A MONTH AGO!

Chapter 2. Card of Death

TWO MONTHS AGO IT COULD HAVE BEEN SAFELY SAID THAT BILL WEBB'S BOYS WOULD HAVE COME BACK... EVEN FROM THE BRUTAL AIR BATTLES OF COLOGNE AND ESSEN. IT WAS IN MAY, 1943, THAT THEY FLEW THEIR 37th. OP. OVER THE FLAME-INFESTED VALLEY OF THE GERMAN RUHR...

FLYING OFFICER EDDIE YATES HAD BEEN THE FLIGHT ENGINEER THEN. HE ADJUSTED BOOSTS AND REVS WITH COOL-FINGERED PRECISION AS WEBB SLAMMED ACROSS THE TARGET AND WEAVED NORTH TO AVOID THE FLAK...
A GOOD PRANG, BILL! AND *POPSIE* ISN'T EVEN SCRATCHED! LOOKS LIKE WE'RE GOING TO MAKE IT AGAIN!
WE'LL MAKE IT ALL RIGHT, EDDIE! WITH A BIT OF LUCK, AS THEY SAY!

LUCK! WHEN CREWS THOUGHT OF LUCK, THEY THOUGHT OF BILL WEBB'S BOYS AND THE LATTER WERE ALWAYS READY TO ADMIT THAT THEY WERE LUCKY. PARTICULARLY MIKE SIMPSON, THE TAIL-GUNNER, AS HE GRINNED AT THE TOY KOALA BEAR MASCOT THAT HE ALWAYS CARRIED...
SURE WE'LL MAKE IT! OLD MONTY'LL SEE TO THAT, WON'T YOU, BOY?

BUT IT WAS MORE THAN LUCK THAT HAD MADE THE CREW OF *P FOR POPSIE* INTO A FIGHTING, CORPORATE TEAM. TAKE ABE NOLAN, THE NAVIGATOR. THEY HAD NEVER KNOWN HIM TO ASK FOR A PINPOINT. HIS NASAL, CANADIAN VOICE WAS CHANTING THE RETURN COURSE LONG BEFORE WEBB NEEDED IT...
ONE MINUTE TO TURNING POINT, SKIPPER! NEW COURSE, ONE-O-EIGHT MAGNETIC!
ONE-O-EIGHT, IT IS!

AND IT WAS NOT LUCK THAT FOCUSED THE SHARP EYES OF BEN STOTT, THE COCKNEY NOSE-GUNNER. IT WAS STOTT WHO SAW THE SLIM SHADOW THAT SUDDENLY BLOTTED OUT THE STARS...
JERRY! A BARBED WIRE JOB! PORT! *DIVE PORT!*

A BARBED-WIRE JOB! AN ME 110, EQUIPPED WITH RADAR ANTENNAE – AND A LETHAL ARMAMENT OF CANNONS THAT THREW DEATH AT THE BUCKING BOMBER...
SIX HUNDRED YARDS! HE'S FIRING CANNON!

WEBB HAD REACTED QUICKLY TO HIS NOSE-GUNNER'S SHOUT – BUT NOT QUICKLY ENOUGH CORDITE FUMES FILLED THE LANCASTER'S COCKPIT AS CANNON SHELLS CRASHED AND RIPPED THROUGH THE CANOPY...
AGH!
EDDIE!

IN THE TAIL-TURRET, THE BROWNINGS WERE SWINGING URGENTLY. BEHIND THEM, MIKE SIMPSON WAS WATCHING THE MESSERSCHMITT AS IT CAME IN AGAIN...
HERE HE COMES, SKIPPER! EIGHT HUNDRED YARDS! PREPARE TO CORKSCREW!
WEBB SUDDENLY HURLED THE LANCASTER INTO A VIOLENT, DIVING TURN...

HELPLESSLY, THE GERMAN OVER-SHOT, AND AS THE WHITE SHAPE FLASHED ACROSS HIS SIGHTS, SIMPSON GAVE IT A DEADLY BURST. A FUEL TANK EXPLODED IN A FIERCE, ORANGE GLARE...
GOOD SHOOTING, MIKE!
GOT HIM!

SLICK TIMING HAD DOWNED THE FIGHTER. P FOR POPSIE TURNED AWAY FROM THE FLAMING INFERNO OF COLOGNE...
LET'S GET OUT OF HERE! HOW'S OUR CASUALTY, ALBERT?
HE CAUGHT A NASTY ONE, SKIPPER! BUT HE'LL MAKE IT BACK TO BASE!

EDDIE YATES *DID* MAKE IT BACK TO BASE. AS HE WAS LIFTED INTO THE AMBULANCE, HE GRINNED AT THE MEN WITH WHOM HE HAD SHARED DANGER AND DEATH FOR TWELVE SAVAGE MONTHS...
SO LONG, BLOKES! HOPE YOU MAKE THAT SECOND TOUR!
WE'LL MAKE IT, EDDIE!
THINK OF US WHILE YOU'RE IN DOCK, EDDIE! YOU'RE DEAD LUCKY, MATE!

THEY WERE SILENT AS THEY WATCHED THE AMBULANCE PULL AWAY. BILL WEBB VOICED THE THOUGHTS OF HIS SOMBRE-FACED MEN...
EDDIE WAS A GOOD NUT! HOPE WE GET ANOTHER ENGINEER AS GOOD AS HE WAS.

BILL WEBB'S CREW DID NOT HAVE TO WAIT LONG FOR THEIR REPLACEMENT. THEY WERE IN THE AIRCREW MESS, TWO DAYS LATER...
JUST LISTEN TO THIS~ 'ONLY ONE MAN IN THREE CAN EXPECT TO COMPLETE HIS SECOND TOUR OF OPERATIONS.'
SOMEONE OUGHT TO TELL THAT NEWSPAPER ABOUT OUR LUCK!

A HARSH VOICE SUDDENLY BROKE ACROSS THEIR BANTER. THEY TURNED QUICKLY TO FACE THE TALL, SALLOW-FACED MAN WHO HAD ENTERED QUIETLY BEHIND THEM.
LUCK, GENTLEMEN? THERE IS NO SUCH THING! WHEN OUR TIME COMES, THEN ALL THE LUCK IN THE WORLD WON'T SAVE US!

THE COLD ASSURANCE OF THE VOICE HAD A DISCOMFORTING EFFECT ON THE GROUP...
THE NAME'S PAUL VIBART~YOUR NEW FLIGHT ENGINEER! I'VE HEARD ALL ABOUT THE LUCKIEST CREW IN BOMBER COMMAND!

EVEN WEBB'S INSTINCTIVE GOOD HUMOUR WAS DISTURBED BY THE NEWCOMER'S STRANGE MANNER...
GLAD TO HAVE YOU WITH US, PAUL! BUT I'M SORRY YOU THINK WE RELY TOO MUCH ON OUR LUCK! WHAT'S YOUR SUGGESTION?

VIBART SEEMED TO SMILE. FROM THE POCKET OF HIS BATTLE-DRESS, HE PULLED A PACK OF PLAYING CARDS...
WHEN MY NUMBER COMES UP, I'LL KNOW! *BECAUSE IT WILL BE ON THE CARDS!*

IT WAS MIKE SIMPSON WHO SPOKE FIRST... MIKE SIMPSON, WHOSE DOGGED RELIANCE ON LUCK WAS ALMOST A SUPERSTITION...
YOU MEAN YOU CAN FORETELL THE FUTURE WITH THOSE CARDS?
THAT'S RIGHT!

CAN THE CARDS TELL ME.. IF I'LL COMPLETE MY SECOND TOUR OF OPS?
TAKE IT EASY, MIKE!
DISTURBED BY THE SUDDEN TENSION IN MIKE SIMPSON'S VOICE, WEBB'S INTERRUPTION WAS SHARP AND INVOLUNTARY...

BUT HE WAS TOO LATE. VIBART HAD MOVED SWIFTLY TO A TABLE. HE BEGAN TO SHUFFLE THE CARDS EXPERTLY.
I'LL NEED A LITTLE INFORMATION FIRST... YOUR AGE, WHETHER YOU'VE ANY BROTHERS OR SISTERS...
I'M TWENTY-ONE, AND I COME FROM A FAMILY OF FOUR! ANYTHING ELSE?

VIBART ASKED A FEW MORE QUESTIONS. THEN HE BEGAN TO LAY OUT THE CARDS. IN THE SUDDEN, HUSHED SILENCE, BILL WEBB FOUGHT DOWN A RISING SENSE OF UNEASINESS...
HE LOOKED HARD AT THIS STRANGER—THE DEEP-SET EYES PROBING THE SLIM PASTEBOARDS FOR SIGNS OF LIFE AND DEATH. HE FELT THAT SOME PROCESS HAD STARTED WHICH NO POWER ON EARTH COULD PREVENT FROM REACHING A CONCLUSION...

SUDDENLY, VIBART STIFFENED... SOMETHING LIKE FEAR FLARED IN HIS DARK EYES. MIKE SIMPSON CROAKED HARSHLY IN THE UNBEARABLE SILENCE...
WHAT DO THE CARDS SAY, VIBART? WILL I FINISH THE TOUR?

THE TIGHTNESS MELTED SUDDENLY FROM VIBART'S FACE. HE GOT UP ABRUPTLY AND HURRIEDLY PICKED UP THE CARDS...
I'M SORRY! THE SIGNS ARE CONFUSED! OR MAYBE I'M JUST NOT IN THE MOOD! SOME OTHER TIME, PERHAPS!

THE TENSION CRUMBLED VISIBLY AS VIBART STRODE AWAY. WEBB THREW OUT A HAND AS MIKE SIMPSON MADE TO FOLLOW HIM...
VIBART! WAIT A MINUTE!
HOLD IT, MIKE! LET HIM GO! WE'VE HAD ENOUGH FAIRGROUND MAGIC FOR ONE NIGHT!

WEBB HAD SPOKEN MORE BRUSQUELY THAN HE HAD MEANT TO HIS WORDS DREW A MILD RUMBLE OF SURPRISE FROM ABE NOLAN...
YOU DON'T TAKE THAT FORTUNE-TELLING STUFF SERIOUSLY, SURELY, SKIPPER?
I DON'T BELIEVE A WORD OF IT, ABE! BUT VIBART DOES! THAT'S WHAT GIVES ME THE CREEPS!

DURING THE NEXT FEW DAYS, ROUTINE GUNNERY AND NIGHT-FLYING PRACTICE HELPED THE CREW OF *P FOR POPSIE* TO FORGET THEIR FIRST, UNEASY ENCOUNTER WITH THEIR NEW FLIGHT ENGINEER...
YOU'VE HIT THREE SMOKE-FLOATS IN A ROW! YOU'RE REALLY ON THE BALL TONIGHT, MIKE!

WEBB SOON REALISED THAT VIBART KNEW HIS JOB, BUT THE ENGINEER'S PAST WAS STILL OBSCURE. WEBB TRIED TO PROBE IT WITH CASUAL CONVERSATION...
I HEAR YOU WERE ON THE MILAN SHOW WITH FIVE GROUP! PRETTY HOT, WASN'T IT?
IT WAS HOT, ALL RIGHT! I SUPPOSE YOUR CREW WOULD SAY THAT I WAS LUCKY...

THE SARCASM WAS HEAVY IN VIBART'S VOICE. WEBB DID NOT SPEAK AS HE TURNED THE LANCASTER INTO LANDING ORBIT ABOVE THE AIRFIELD. IT WAS JOHNNO MARTIN'S SUDDEN WARNING THAT JERKED HIM FROM HIS ANGRY SILENCE...
WATCH IT, SKIPPER! THERE'S A KITE DEAD AHEAD WITHOUT NAVIGATION LIGHTS! MUST BE A SPROG PILOT!

FIERCELY, WEBB'S EYES PROBED THE STARRY BACKDROP OF THE NIGHT. SUDDENLY, HE SAW THE FLOATING BLACK SHAPE ABOVE HIM–JUST AS PAUL VIBART SHOUTED A WARNING...
THAT'S NO TRAINING SHIP! IT'S A JUNKERS EIGHTY-EIGHT–AND IT'S ATTACKING! DIVE!

WEBB DID NOT WAIT FOR CONFIRMATION. HIS REACTION WAS SWIFT AND SAVAGE. TRACER SCYTHED SAVAGELY CLOSE TO THE LANCASTER AS IT HURTLED NOSE-DOWN...

IT WAS A CLOSE THING. P FOR POPSIE SHOT AT FULL THROTTLE ACROSS THE FLARING LIGHTS OF THE RUNWAY...
TELL CONTROL THERE'S A JERRY INTRUDER WAITING TO AMBUSH OUR KITES AS THEY COME IN!
OKAY, SKIPPER!

P FOR POPSIE'S WARNING SOON ALERTED THE AIRFIELD DEFENCES. BUT THE JUNKERS DID NOT STAY LONG TO SEE THEM IN ACTION...

AT LAST, WEBB BROUGHT THE LANCASTER DOWN SAFELY HIS VOICE WAS A LITTLE SHAKY AS HE SPOKE TO PAUL VIBART...
THAT WAS DICEY, PAUL! HOW DID YOU SPOT THAT JUNKERS SO QUICKLY?
I'VE GOT AN INSTINCT FOR DANGER, SKIPPER!

MIKE SIMPSON HAD FORGOTTEN VIBART'S STRANGE REPLY BY THE TIME THEY REACHED THE CREW ROOM. THE TAIL-GUNNER SAW THEIR NARROW ESCAPE IN A DIFFERENT LIGHT...
YOU SAVED US, DIDN'T YOU, MONTY, LAD? THAT JERRY PILOT HADN'T A HOPE OF SHOOTING DOWN THE LUCKIEST CREW IN BOMBER COMMAND!

VIBART MOVED SWIFTLY. MIKE SIMPSON YELLED AS THE TOY BEAR WAS SNATCHED FROM HIS HAND...

HEY! MY MASCOT!
YOUR PITIFUL SYMBOL OF LUCK! GROW UP, SIMPSON! A TOY BEAR WON'T HELP YOU!

THEY STOOD IN FROZEN ASTONISHMENT AS VIBART JERKED THE LID OFF THE STOVE...
SUPPOSE I BURNED YOUR LUCKY CHARM–DO YOU THINK YOU'D DIE, SIMPSON? IS THAT WHAT YOU BELIEVE? IS IT?
VIBART! DON'T!

BILL WEBB DID NOT WAIT TO FIND OUT IF VIBART WOULD CARRY OUT HIS THREAT. HIS HAND CLAMPED LIKE AN ANGRY VICE ON THE ENGINEER'S WRIST...
ALL RIGHT, VIBART! COOL DOWN! HERE, MIKE – TAKE YOUR MASCOT!
GIVE HIM BACK HIS TOY, THEN, WEBB! BUT IT WON'T PROTECT HIM FROM THE FIRST SHELL THAT'S GOT HIS NAME ON IT!

VIBART'S MOCKING VOICE MOVED THE EASY-GOING ABE NOLAN TO A SUDDEN OUTBURST OF ANGER...
LEAVE HIM ALONE, VIBART! THOSE CARDS YOU CARRY ARE JUST ANOTHER SUPERSTITION ANYWAY! MAYBE THEY CAN TELL US IF WE'RE GOING TO GET THE CHOP TOMORROW NIGHT?

NOLAN'S CHALLENGE WAS HALF-HEARTED, BUT VIBART SEIZED ON IT. THE PACK OF CARDS WAS IN HIS HANDS BEFORE BILL WEBB COULD MOVE...
ALL RIGHT! WE'LL PICK TWO CARDS, AND SEE WHAT THEY TELL US! YOU FIRST, SIMPSON!

BILL WEBB WATCHED SIMPSON TAKE A CARD. THE TAIL-GUNNER HISSED SHARPLY AS HE TURNED ITS FACE TO THE LIGHT...
IT... IT'S THE ACE OF SPADES!
IN MOST CARD GAMES THE ACE OF SPADES IS A USEFUL CARD TO HOLD... IN FORTUNE-TELLING- IT IS THE CARD OF DEATH!

NO ONE MOVED AS VIBART SLOWLY SHUFFLED THE PACK. HE OFFERED THE CARDS TO ABE NOLAN...
NOW YOU, NOLAN! YOU STARTED THIS!

A LANCASTER ZOOMED OVERHEAD AS THE NAVIGATOR SLOWLY PICKED A CARD. THE SOUND ALMOST DROWNED HIS MUFFLED WORDS...
IT'S AN EIGHT...
AN EIGHT! GOOD GRIEF! THAT'S THE SERIAL NUMBER OF OUR KITE! FIRST THE ACE, NOW THIS! WE'RE ALL GOING TO BE KILLED!

THE HARSH VOICE OF BILL WEBB CUT ACROSS MIKE SIMPSON'S HYSTERICAL OUTBURST...
I WANT TO BE IN ON THIS, VIBART. LET ME PICK A CARD!
NO, SKIPPER! YOU'LL SPOIL IT...

BUT WEBB TOOK NO NOTICE. HE RIPPED A CARD FROM THE PACK AND FLUNG IT ON THE TABLE...
IT'S THE JOKER! IN FACT, THE WHOLE THING'S NOTHING BUT A GREAT BIG JOKE! THAT'S RIGHT, ISN'T IT, VIBART?
JOKER

VIBART MADE NO REPLY...
IT'S EASY TO LAUGH AT VIBART, SKIPPER! BUT WHAT IF HIS CARDS ARE RIGHT?
CUT IT OUT, MIKE! REMEMBER- WE'RE THE LUCKIEST CREW IN BOMBER COMMAND!

Chapter 3. Figure of Fate

VIBART SAT BEHIND HIS THROTTLES LIKE A TENSE, SILENT SHADOW, UNNERVING A CREW THAT HAD FOUGHT THROUGH SOME OF THE BLOODIEST AIR BATTLES OF THE RUHR...
WHY DOESN'T HE SPEAK? IT'S AS IF HE'S WAITING FOR SOMETHING TO HAPPEN!

AHEAD OF THEM, THEY SAW THE GREEN TARGET-MARKERS GOING DOWN. IN BETWEEN, FLICKERED THE RED, VICIOUS FLASHES THAT THREW A RESTLESS WALL ACROSS THE NIGHT...
BARRAGE FLAK! IT'S GOING TO BE TOUGH GOING!

SURE ENOUGH, IT WAS TOUGH. ATTACKING THE FLANKS OF THE BOMBER STREAM, GERMAN NIGHT-FIGHTERS CLAWED TWO OF THE BIG LANCASTERS OUT OF THE SKY IN THREE MERCILESS MINUTES...
POOR BLIGHTERS... THEY DIDN'T EVEN GET THE CHANCE TO BALE OUT!

POPSIE'S ENTIRE CREW NOW SENSED THE THREAT THAT HUNG OVER THEM. THEY ALMOST JUMPED WHEN BEN STOTT'S VOICE CRACKLED HARSHLY ON THE INTERCOM....
NIGHT-FIGHTER! THREE O'CLOCK! DIVE TO PORT!

THE CREW OF P FOR POPSIE HAD ESCAPED DEATH BY THE SKIN OF THEIR TEETH. THE NEXT LANCASTER WAS NOT SO LUCKY. IT DIVED FRANTICALLY WITH A JUNKERS EIGHTY-EIGHT SITTING ON ITS TAIL...
TRACER FROM THE NIGHTFIGHTER SET FIRE TO ONE OF THE BOMBER'S ENGINES, AND RIPPED INTO HER FUSELAGE...

THE TWO AIRCRAFT VANISHED AS SUDDENLY AS THEY HAD APPEARED. BILL WEBB VOICED THE HELPLESS SHOCK AND FURY THAT ALL OF THEM FELT...
THAT JERRY PILOT WAS JUST WAITING-SHOOTING THEM DOWN LIKE SITTING DUCKS!

THEY SUDDENLY FORGOT ABOUT PAUL VIBART'S CARDS, AND THE OMINOUS FIGURE EIGHT ON *P FOR POPSIE'S* FUSELAGE, AS WEBB BEGAN HIS STRAIGHT, FIFTEEN MILE RUN-UP TO THE TARGET...
OPENING BOMB-DOORS NOW, JOHNNO! LET'S GET EVEN WITH THE JERRIES FOR THE BOYS IN THAT LANCASTER!

THE CREW WORKED WITH THEIR USUAL SMOOTH EFFICIENCY. WEBB JUDGED HEIGHT AND SPEED PERFECTLY. JOHNNO MARTIN DROPPED HIS BOMBS PLUMB ON THE TARGET-MARKERS...
BELOW THEM, THE GERMAN FACTORY DISSOLVED IN A VICIOUS WELTER OF FLAME AND STEEL...

THEY REACHED THE TURNING-POINT WITHOUT SEEING ANY MORE FIGHTERS. AS HE SET COURSE FOR HOME, WEBB SUDDENLY THOUGHT ABOUT PAUL VIBART...
THIS WAS THE NIGHT WE WERE SUPPOSED TO GET THE CHOP, LADS!
WE'LL NEVER GET THE CHOP, SKIPPER! WE'RE JUST DEAD LUCKY, THAT'S ALL!

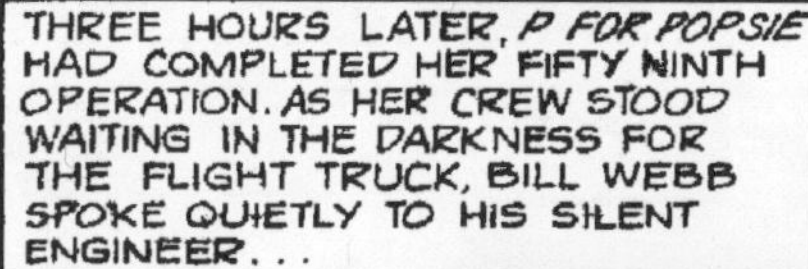
THREE HOURS LATER, *P FOR POPSIE* HAD COMPLETED HER FIFTY NINTH OPERATION. AS HER CREW STOOD WAITING IN THE DARKNESS FOR THE FLIGHT TRUCK, BILL WEBB SPOKE QUIETLY TO HIS SILENT ENGINEER...

WELL, PAUL! WE MADE IT AGAIN! WAS IT LUCK-OR WERE YOUR CARDS WRONG?
VIBART SHRUGGED IMPERCEPTIBLY BUT SAID NOTHING...

THE FOLLOWING MORNING, MOST OF *P FOR POPSIE'S* CREW ATE A LATE BREAKFAST IN THE MESS...
WELL, WE PRANGED THE TARGET LAST NIGHT, DAVE!
SURE, BILL, BUT OUR LOSSES WERE PRETTY HEAVY~ EIGHT KITES SHOT DOWN!

A FORK CLATTERED LOUDLY ON THE TABLE-TOP. IT HAD FALLEN FROM THE TREMBLING HAND OF MIKE SIMPSON...
EIGHT KITES! DON'T YOU SEE? THAT WAS THE NUMBER OF THE CARD WE DREW FROM VIBART'S PACK!

IN THE STUNNED SILENCE THAT FOLLOWED, VIBART'S VOICE SOUNDED QUIET, BUT TRIUMPHANT...
THE CARDS WERE RIGHT, SKIPPER! AND PERHAPS THEY WERE MOCKING US ALL THE TIME! IT WAS YOU WHO PICKED THE JOKER!

VIBART LEFT BEFORE ANYONE COULD SPEAK BUT MIKE SIMPSON HAD BEEN DEEPLY IMPRESSED BY THE NEWS HE HAD HEARD...
..WE PICKED AN ACE OF SPADES... THEN AN EIGHT! AND EIGHT OF OUR KITES GET THE CHOP...
SNAP OUT OF IT, MIKE! THE WHOLE THING'S JUST A COINCIDENCE!

MOST OF THEM WERE READY TO BELIEVE THAT IT *WAS* A COINCIDENCE. BUT MIKE SIMPSON WAS NOT CONVINCED. ALMOST BLINDLY, HE STUMBLED IN PURSUIT OF THE ANSWER...
VIBART'S RIGHT! PERHAPS IT'S OUR TURN TONIGHT! I'VE GOT TO KNOW!
MIKE! *COME BACK!*

BILL WEBB WAS RIGHT ON THE TAIL-GUNNER'S HEELS AS HE BURST INTO PAUL VIBART'S ROOM...
VIBART...THE CARDS! WHAT DO THEY SAY ABOUT TONIGHT? I'VE GOT TO KNOW!
NO, MIKE! DON'T BE A FOOL!

AGAIN, WEBB SAW THE STRANGE, MOCKING TRIUMPH ON VIBART'S FACE AS THE FLIGHT-ENGINEER GATHERED UP HIS CARDS...
WHAT'S THE MATTER, SKIPPER? DON'T SAY THE CARDS HAVE GOT YOU WORRIED?

WEBB WAS WORRIED~NOT BY VIBART'S CARDS, BUT BY THE WAY HIS CREW HAD REACTED TO THEM. HE STRUGGLED HARD TO KEEP THE CONTEMPT FROM HIS VOICE...
ALL RIGHT, VIBART! I RECKON THIS FORTUNE-TELLING LARK IS PHONEY-AND TO PROVE IT, I'LL DRAW TWO CARDS!

QUICKLY, IMPATIENTLY, WEBB DREW THE FIRST CARD. ITS APPEARANCE BROUGHT A SPASM OF FEAR TO SEVERAL FACES IN THE ROOM...
IT'S THE ACE OF SPADES AGAIN!
THE DEATH CARD!

WEBB FOUGHT DOWN THE SHOCK HE FELT. HE WHIRLED TOWARDS HIS CREW, CONTEMPT SEETHING OPENLY IN HIS VOICE...
OKAY, I'LL DRAW AGAIN! IF IT'S AN EIGHT, THEN TONIGHT WE GET THE CHOP, BECAUSE EIGHT'S THE NUMBER OF OUR KITE. BUT IT WON'T BE AN EIGHT!

NO ONE UTTERED A WORD AS WEBB RIFFED ANOTHER CARD FROM THE PACK HE LOOKED AT IT—THEN THREW IT DOWN ON VIBART'S BED IN SAVAGE TRIUMPH...
NOW DO YOU BELIEVE ME? IT'S A SEVEN—AND POPSIE'S NUMBER IS EIGHT. IT CAN'T POSSIBLY MEAN WE'RE GETTING THE CHOP TONIGHT!

DISGUSTEDLY, WEBB MADE FOR THE DOOR. BUT THE FLAT, EMOTIONLESS VOICE OF VIBART HALTED HIM...
YOU'RE WRONG, SKIPPER! THE CARDS DON'T LIE. I'VE JUST SEEN THE FITTERS CHANGING POPSIE'S SERIAL NUMBER—FROM EIGHT... TO SEVEN!

MIKE SIMPSON ALMOST PLUNGED FROM THE ROOM. THE OTHERS FOLLOWED HIM BEFORE WEBB COULD MOVE. HIS FURIOUS ROAR WAS UTTERLY IGNORED...
COME BACK! HE'S LYING!

WEBB KNEW WHERE THEY WERE HEADING LONG BEFORE HE CAUGHT THEM UP. HIS MIND RECOILED FROM THE TERRIFYING MEANING OF PAUL VIBART'S WORDS...
VIBART'S LYING! HE'S GOT TO BE..!

WEBB BURST PAST THE FROZEN FIGURES OF HIS CREW. MIKE SIMPSON'S HUSHED VOICE TOLD HIM ALL HE NEEDED TO KNOW...
VIBART WAS RIGHT, SKIPPER! LOOK!

CLEARLY, THE FITTERS HAD ONLY JUST FINISHED CHANGING THE SERIAL NUMBER...
...ON THE BLACK METAL OF THE AIRCRAFT, THE SEVEN LOOKED STARK AND WHITE AND NEW. IT WAS THE MARK OF DEATH ON P FOR POPSIE!..

TIMELESS SECONDS PASSED BEFORE WEBB FOUND WORDS TO SPEAK. HE ALMOST SNARLED AT THE FLIGHT-SERGEANT FITTER IN CHARGE...
WHAT'S GOING ON, CHIEFY? WHY HAVE YOU CHANGED THE NUMBER?
ORDERS FROM GROUP, SIR! THERE WERE TWO LANCS WITH THE SAME SERIAL NUMBER! WE WERE TOLD TO CHANGE POPSIE THIS MORNING!

IT WAS A MILLION-TO-ONE CHANCE... FOR A YEAR THEY HAD BEEN FLYING AROUND WITH THE WRONG NUMBER DESPERATELY, WEBB WHIRLED ON HIS CREW...
THIS IS JUST A MANUFACTURER'S MISTAKE, BLOKES! IT DOESN'T MEAN A THING!

BUT, FOR MIKE SIMPSON, IT WAS ONE COINCIDENCE TOO MANY FOR HIM, A PACK OF CARDS HAD DEALT A HAND WITHOUT HOPE...
NO, SKIPPER! YOU DREW THE CARDS YOURSELF! FIRST THE ACE OF SPADES, THEN THE SEVEN! IT'S OUR TURN TONIGHT!
STOP IT, MIKE! PULL YOURSELF TOGETHER!

WEBB WALKED AWAY FROM THE WHITE-FACED TAIL-GUNNER. HE FOUND HIS EYES RIVETED ON THE STARK, WHITE SEVEN ON *P FOR POPSIE'S* NOSE...
7
IT'S CRAZY! I WISH I'D NEVER SET EYES ON VIBART AND HIS CARDS! BUT MAYBE WE WON'T BE ON OPS TONIGHT...

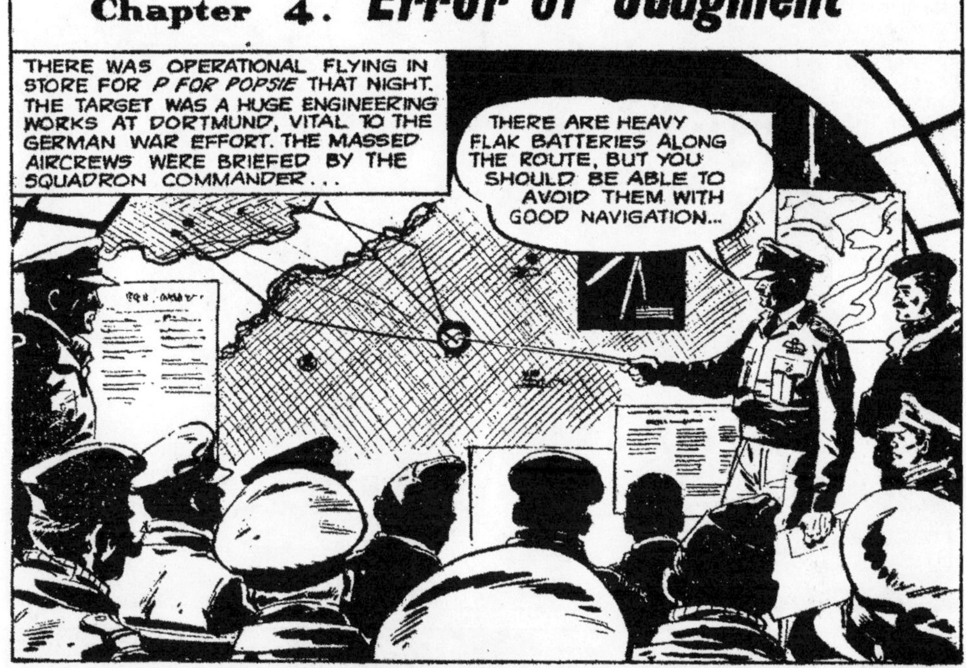
Chapter 4. Error of Judgment
THERE WAS OPERATIONAL FLYING IN STORE FOR P FOR POPSIE THAT NIGHT. THE TARGET WAS A HUGE ENGINEERING WORKS AT DORTMUND, VITAL TO THE GERMAN WAR EFFORT. THE MASSED AIRCREWS WERE BRIEFED BY THE SQUADRON COMMANDER...
THERE ARE HEAVY FLAK BATTERIES ALONG THE ROUTE, BUT YOU SHOULD BE ABLE TO AVOID THEM WITH GOOD NAVIGATION...

THE WAITING BETWEEN BRIEFING AND TAKE-OFF WAS NEVER PLEASANT. FOR BILL WEBB'S CREW THAT NIGHT, IT WAS MORE LIKE TORTURE...
THEY'VE FACED DEATH A HUNDRED TIMES, AND JOKED ABOUT IT! BUT NOW THEY'VE GOT THE JITTERS OVER A PACK OF CARDS!

TWO CARDS, PICKED AT RANDOM, HAD CHANGED A TOUGH, VETERAN CREW INTO A TEAM OF NERVOUS, WORRIED MEN. EVEN THE EYES OF ABE NOLAN HELD A RESTLESS SHADOW OF DOUBT
SURELY THIS HASN'T RATTLED YOU, ABE?
I DON'T KNOW WHAT TO SAY, SKIPPER! IT JUST SEEMS A FANTASTIC COINCIDENCE. MAYBE THERE IS SOMETHING IN IT...

WEBB'S FIRST CHANCE TO SPEAK TO VIBART CAME AS THEY WERE CHANGING IN THE CREW-ROOM...
JUST IN CASE ANYTHING HAPPENS TONIGHT, VIBART, I WANT YOU TO KNOW THAT I DON'T BELIEVE A WORD OF THIS FORTUNE-TELLING TRIPE!
HAVE IT YOUR OWN WAY, SKIPPER, BUT WE'LL KNOW FOR SURE IN SIX HOURS' TIME!

AT 9.P.M., THE AIRCREWS WALKED OUT TO THE WAITING FLIGHT TRUCKS. P FOR POPSIE'S CREW WAS NORMALLY A TALKATIVE, HAPPY BUNCH, BUT THIS NIGHT THEY WALKED IN A KNOT OF TIGHT-LIPPED SILENCE...
IF ONLY SOMETHING WOULD GO WRONG WITH OUR KITE, SO THAT WE'D HAVE TO TAKE THE SPARE! ANYTHING TO GET AWAY FROM THAT CONFOUNDED SEVEN!

BUT THERE WAS NOTHING WRONG WITH P FOR POPSIE WEBB SIGNED FOR A MACHINE IN PERFECT CONDITION. AT LAST, HE SETTLED DOWN BEHIND THE CONTROLS...
ALL RIGHT, VIBART! LET'S GET THIS KITE IN THE AIR!

WEBB PUNCHED THE BUTTONS OF THE BOOSTER COILS. THE ENGINES WHINED AND SPUN EXPLOSIVELY. P FOR POPSIE WADDLED FORWARD AND SWUNG HER NOSE TOWARDS THE NORTH...
FLAPS THIRTY! RADIATORS OPEN! THROTTLES LOCKED! PREPARE FOR TAKE OFF!

THE BLARE OF THE MERLIN ENGINES SLAMMED ACROSS THE FIELD AS P FOR POPSIE ROLLED FORWARD. IT WAS AS THE LANCASTER LEFT THE GROUND THAT A THOUGHT STRUCK WEBB WITH STUNNING FORCE...
GOOD GRIEF! I'VE JUST REALISED! WE'RE THE SEVENTH CREW TO TAKE-OFF!

THE SUN WAS LOW BEHIND THEM AS THEY TURNED SLOWLY ON COURSE-SEVEN MEN WHO SAT IN THE COLD SHADOW OF A PROPHECY... AND ONE WHO STRUGGLED TO REJECT IT WITH EVERY FIBRE OF HIS BODY...
LET'S HOPE NOTHING GOES WRONG BEFORE WE REACH THE TARGET! THE REST OF THE BLOKES WILL RECKON IT'S SOME KIND OF OMEN!

BUT THEY REACHED THE RENDEZVOUS POINT ON TIME. DEAD ON COURSE, THE GREAT BOMBER STREAM RUMBLED ACROSS HOLLAND AND FORGED ON TOWARDS THE RUHR VALLEY...
AHEAD OF THEM, THE PATHFINDERS WERE ALREADY DROPPING THE SKY-MARKERS THAT WOULD PINPOINT THE TARGETS FOR THE HIGH EXPLOSIVE THAT WAS TO FOLLOW...

WEBB WAS STILL THINKING OF *P FOR POPSIE'S* CHANGE OF NUMBER AS THEY CROSSED THE RHINE. *IT WAS THEN THAT A CRAZY, VICIOUS CLATTER CAME FROM THE STARBOARD OUTER ENGINE...*
RUNAWAY AIRSCREW! *FEATHER IT, VIBART! QUICK, MAN!*

HESITATION ON VIBART'S PART COULD HAVE BEEN FATAL BUT THE ENGINEER WAS QUICK TO PRESS THE STOP-BUTTON OF THE STARBOARD-OUTER. THE GREAT, SLASHING BLADES FROZE ABRUPTLY...
P
PHEW! THAT WAS CLOSE!

IN THE TAIL-TURRET, MIKE SIMPSON WAS THINKING ABOUT PAUL VIBART'S CARDS...
WE HAVEN'T A HOPE OF MAKING THE TRIP ON THREE ENGINES! THE SKIPPER'LL *HAVE* TO TURN BACK!

WEBB KNEW WHAT THEY WERE THINKING-THAT THEY WANTED HIM TO TURN BACK. ALMOST MERCILESSLY, HE SHATTERED THE TAUT, EXPECTANT SILENCE OF THE INTERCOM...
CAPTAIN TO CREW! I'M GOING ON TO THE TARGET! IF WE TURN BACK NOW, IT'LL ENDANGER THE OTHER AIRCRAFT IN THE STREAM! CONFIRM MY COURSE, NAVIGATOR!

WEBB COULD ALMOST FEEL THE SILENT RESENTMENT THAT FOLLOWED HIS WORDS. THIRTY SECONDS LATER, HE HEARD THE HARSH, UNSTEADY VOICE OF ABE NOLAN...
NEW COURSE, SKIPPER! ONE-ONE-O MAGNETIC!

THREE MINUTES LATER, THEY LOST CONTACT WITH THE MAIN BOMBER STREAM. WITH ONLY THREE ENGINES RUNNING, WEBB HAD EXPECTED THIS, BUT HE WAS NOT PREPARED FOR THE SUDDEN YELL THAT CAME FROM JOHNNO MARTIN...
HEAVY FLAK, SKIPPER! IT-IT'S ALL AROUND US!

THE LANCASTER ROCKED SAVAGELY AS A HUNDRED UNSEEN GUNS BELCHED STEEL FROM THE LIVID WELL OF THE NIGHT. WEBB BELLOWED HARSHLY ON THE INTERCOM...
WHAT THE HECK ARE YOU PLAYING AT, ABE? THIS FLAK WASN'T PREDICTED ON OUR ROUTE! YOUR COURSE FIGURES MUST BE WRONG!

ABE NOLAN WAS ONE OF THE FINEST NAVIGATORS IN BOMBER COMMAND... BUT TONIGHT HE WAS THINKING OF THE FIGURE SEVEN - AND THE BLACK ACE OF SPADES...
I..I CAN'T UNDERSTAND IT, SKIPPER! I MISREAD MY OWN FIGURES! WE'VE RUN STRAIGHT OVER THE FLAK BATTERIES OF DUISBERG!

Chapter 5. *Unlucky for Some*

THE MASTER BEAM PROBED NEARER. IN ITS DIFFUSED LIGHT, THE FIGURE 7 ON P-POPSIE'S FUSELAGE WAS CLEAR AND STARK. BESIDE WEBB, THE THIN FIGURE OF PAUL VIBART SAT AS STILL AS DEATH...
VIBART SEEMS ALMOST PLEASED THAT HIS PROPHECY IS COMING TRUE! DOESN'T HE REALISE THAT HE'LL GET THE HAMMER, ALONG WITH THE REST OF US?

DAZEDLY, WEBB SHOOK HIS HEAD. NO, THE CARDS COULD NOT BE RIGHT. THE WHOLE THING WAS FANTASTIC. IT WAS THE GHASTLY, BLUISH GLARE THAT SUDDENLY FLOODED THE WHOLE COCKPIT THAT WRENCHED HIM BACK TO REALITY...
THE MASTER BEAM! IT'S GOT US! DIVE, SKIPPER, DIVE!

WEBB KNEW WHAT HE HAD TO DO HE WAS PUSHING HARD ON THE STICK WHEN A STREAM OF YELLOW TRACER PUNCHED UP INTO THE LANCASTER'S PORT-INNER ENGINE...
A HIT! WE'RE HIT!

THEY SAT THERE, STARING AT THE STILL PROPELLER, WAITING FOR THE FATAL EXPLOSION OF IGNITED FUEL. THEY WERE STILL WAITING WHEN ALBERT SPENCE GASPED HOARSELY...
THE FUEL-TANK! IT-IT DIDN'T CATCH FIRE!

IT TOOK WEBB THREE SECONDS TO REALISE WHAT HAD HAPPENED. THE RELIEF MADE HIM NEARLY HYSTERICAL . . .
OF COURSE THE TANK DIDN'T GO UP! IT WAS EMPTY! *VIBART MUST HAVE FORGOTTEN TO SWITCH TO THE RESERVE!*

WEBB WENT ON QUICKLY, HIS VOICE RINGING WITH TRIUMPH . . .
DID YOU GET THAT, BOYS? WE WERE LUCKY! EVEN VIBART'S CARDS CAN'T KNOCK US DOWN! FIRST WE'RE GOING TO FIX ONE OF THESE SEARCHLIGHTS!

WEBB PUSHED ON THE CONTROL COLUMN WITH ALL HIS STRENGTH. *P FOR POPSIE* HURTLED DOWN THROUGH THE BLINDING GLARE AND FLAK, TO ONE THOUSAND FEET...
NOW, BEN! GIVE THAT SEARCHLIGHT A SQUIRT!
FAIR ENOUGH, SKIPPER!

IN TEN SECONDS, BEN STOTT'S BROWNING GUNS POURED A DEVASTATING BURST AT THE ROOT OF THE BEAM AND SMASHED THE SEARCHLIGHT INTO SCRAP...

WEBB LEVELLED OUT IN THE MERCIFUL WELL OF DARKNESS AS THE PLANE STRAINED FOR HEIGHT ON ITS TWO REMAINING ENGINES. ABE NOLAN'S VOICE CRACKLED THROUGH THE RADIO...
I THINK I'VE GOT MY BEARINGS NOW, SKIPPER!
GOOD SHOW, ABE! LET'S HAVE THE NEW COURSE.

TEN MINUTES LATER, THEY FOUND THE TARGET. PAUL VISART WAS FORGOTTEN AS THEY BEGAN THE RUN-UP. ONCE AGAIN, THEY WERE THE LUCKIEST CREW IN BOMBER COMMAND...
LEFT... STEADY, STEADY! BOMBS GONE!

THEY SAW THE SLOW, RED ERUPTIONS AS THE BOMBS WENT HOME. THEN THE FIRE AND THE TUMULT WERE BEHIND THEM, AND WEBB COULD HEAR THE JUBILANT VOICES OF HIS CREW...
NICE WORK JOHNNO!
TAKE US HOME, SKIPPER!
DEAD ON TARGET!

DARKNESS MASKED THE WHITE SEVEN ON P-POPSIE'S FUSELAGE AS WEBB STEERED A DOG-LEG COURSE FOR HOME. AS THE DUTCH COAST CAME UP, HE SPOKE QUIETLY TO PAUL VIBART...
LOOKS AS IF WE'RE GOING TO MAKE IT, PAUL! PERHAPS THE CARDS WERE WRONG!

VIBART HAD NO TIME TO ANSWER. THEY WERE OVER THE NORTH SEA WHEN THE PORT-OUTER ENGINE COUGHED, FALTERED, THEN DIED...
PORT-OUTER ENGINE'S PACKED UP! FLAK MUST HAVE HOLED THE FUEL TANKS!

WEBB KNEW THERE WAS NO CHANCE OF REACHING THE ENGLISH COAST ON ONE ENGINE. THE LANCASTER COULD STILL FLY FOR SOME TIME, BUT WITH A GRADUAL LOSS OF HEIGHT...
WE'LL HAVE TO DITCH! CALL UP AIR-SEA RESCUE-GIVE THEM OUR POSITION!
RIGHT, SKIPPER!

WEBB TOOK THE LANCASTER DOWN TO ONE THOUSAND FEET. BESIDE HIM, PAUL VIBART WAS SILENT...
WE'RE IN LUCK, SKIPPER! A COUPLE OF RESCUE SHIPS ARE PATROLLING TEN MILES DEAD AHEAD!
GOOD! KEEP TRANSMITTING OUR POSITION AS LONG AS YOU CAN!

WITH HER SINGLE, BOOMING ENGINE, P-POPSIE BATTLED ON TOWARDS THE DAWN. FIFTEEN MINUTES LATER, WEBB KNEW THAT SHE COULD NOT GO MUCH FARTHER...
DINGHY! DINGHY! PREPARE FOR DITCHING!

THE CREW TOOK UP THEIR CRASH POSITIONS, AND PUT THEIR FAITH IN THEIR SKIPPER...
THEY THOUGHT OF THE WHITE FIGURE SEVEN ON P-POPSIE'S NOSE - AND WONDERED IF, AT LAST, THEIR LUCK HAD RUN OUT...

SLOWLY, WEBB LET THE LANCASTER DOWN AT TWO HUNDRED FEET, HE SAW THE SEA....
IT'S ROUGH! JUST OUR LUCK!

THE WAVES LOOKED AS TALL AS HOUSES, AS WEBB TURNED GENTLY INTO THE WIND AND TRACKED ALONG THE SWELL AT 110 MILES PER HOUR, THE LANCASTER'S NOSE DUG INTO A WAVE-CREST...
THEN THE WHOLE AIRCRAFT SMACKED DOWN, BOUNCING FROM WAVE-TOP TO WAVE-TOP TO A VIOLENT HALT. P POPSIE WAS DOWN!

THE CREW RUSHED OUT OF THE HATCHES AND STRUGGLED TO THE STARBOARD MAINPLANE. ABE NOLAN HAD THE DINGHY READY, STRUGGLING TO INFLATE IT IN THE TOWERING SEA...
TAKE YOUR TIME, ABE! *POPSIE* WON'T GO DOWN YET! SHE'S RIDING THE SEA PRETTY WELL!
IT WAS A GOOD LANDING, SKIPPER!
GOH4117D

NOLAN SOON GOT THE DINGHY INFLATED SOMEHOW. IT BROKE FROM HIS GRASP. IN THREE SWIFT SECONDS, THE WAVES HAD SNATCHED IT BEYOND THEIR REACH...
THE DINGHY! I'VE GOT TO GET IT!
NO, ABE! YOU WOULDN'T HAVE A CHANCE! WITH LUCK, THE RESCUE SHIPS SHOULD BE HERE SOON...

IT WAS THEN THAT VIBART SPOKE IN COLD, CONTEMPTUOUS FURY...
YOUR PRECIOUS LUCK WON'T GET YOU OUT OF THIS, WEBB! I'M GOING AFTER THAT DINGHY!
VIBART! DON'T BE A FOOL!

VIBART DIVED BEFORE ANYONE COULD STOP HIM. HE STRUCK AWAY FROM THE WALLOWING HULK OF *P-POPSIE*, AWAY FROM THE SIX MEN CLINGING DESPERATELY TO THEIR LUCK...
PERHAPS IT WAS FEAR THAT GAVE HIM STRENGTH...PERHAPS IT WAS A FANATICAL REFUSAL TO BELIEVE HIS CARDS COULD BE WRONG...

WHEN THEY LAST SAW VIBART, HE WAS STILL STRIKING OUT STRONGLY IN THE DIRECTION OF THE DINGHY...AND THE LANCASTER WAS SETTLING FAST INTO THE WATER...
MAYBE VIBART DID THE RIGHT THING! ANYTHING'S BETTER THAN JUST SITTING HERE, WAITING TO SINK!
CUT IT OUT, MIKE!

THE PORT MAINPLANE WAS AWASH WHEN THEY FINALLY HEARD THE THROB OF A LAUNCH'S ENGINE...
YAHOO! WHAT A BEAUTIFUL SIGHT!
WE MADE IT, SKIPPER!
OF COURSE WE DID, MIKE! WE'RE THE LUCKIEST CREW IN BOMBER COMMAND, REMEMBER?

THE LAUNCH CLOSED ALONGSIDE, AND THE GRINNING CREW PULLED THEM ABOARD...
ONE OF MY CREW IS STILL IN THE WATER, SKIPPER! HE WENT AFTER OUR DINGHY WHEN IT BROKE AWAY!

THEY FOUND THE DINGHY, BUT THERE WAS NO SIGN OF VIBART. AFTER TWENTY MINUTES, THEY WERE FORCED TO GIVE UP THE SEARCH...
POOR BLOKE! THE CARDS WERE RIGHT~FOR VIBART, AT LEAST!
OR MAYBE HE WAS JUST UNLUCKY!

PERHAPS, AS BILL WEBB SAID, PAUL VIBART WAS JUST UNLUCKY. PERHAPS THE CARDS MEANT NOTHING AT ALL. IT DID NOT OCCUR TO THEM THEN, THAT VIBART'S NAME HAD BEEN THE SEVENTH ON P-POPSIE'S CREW LIST...

AIR COMMANDO
N-5162
THE FIRST GLIDER-BORNE CHINDIT INVASION OF JAP-HELD BURMA ROSE UP ONE MOONLIT NIGHT IN MARCH, 1944 AND SWEPT OVER ENEMY-HELD JUNGLE TO DESCEND UPON A CHOSEN CLEARING WHICH WAS DESTINED TO EARN UNDYING FAME. THEY NAMED IT BROADWAY. BUT SKILFUL THOUGH THE AIRMEN OF THE AMERICAN AIR TASK FORCE WERE, UNEXPECTED SNAGS EXACTED A GRIM TOLL OF VALUABLE LIVES.

Chapter 1. JUNGLE AIRLIFT

JUNGLE BROADWAY, FORTIFIED AND FED FROM THE AIR BY AMERICAN DAKOTAS, SOON PROVED ITS TACTICAL WORTH. BUT THE EARLY CASUALTIES AND HAZARDS WERE STILL IN THE MINDS OF MEN AT THE BRIGADE H.Q. AT GHATALAT WHEN A PARTY OF FRESHLY-TRAINED CHINDITS ARRIVED, EAGER FOR THEIR FIRST TASTE OF JUNGLE FIGHTING.

THESE JUNGLE TRAINEES MAY HAVE LOOKED YOUNG, BUT THEY WERE ALL SEASONED CAMPAIGNERS FROM OTHER BATTLE ZONES. THERE WAS CORPORAL 'DOGGER' BANKS, TOUGH EX-DESERT RAT, FOR EXAMPLE...

THE LEADER OF THIS CONTINGENT, MAJOR MALCOLM McDUFF, D.S.O., HAD SO FAR SHARED HIS MEN'S HIGH HUMOUR, BUT AS HIS EYES NOW SWEPT THE SCENE AROUND, THE SMILE LEFT HIS LEAN FACE.
THE OLD PLACE HAS CHANGED, DRIVER... AMERICANS EVERYWHERE!
YOU'RE RIGHT, SIR. GHATALAT'S GONE ALL YANKEE SINCE YOU'VE BEEN AWAY.
KGD-285

VETERAN OF TWO JUNGLE CAMPAIGNS, THE RANGY SCOT HAD BEEN SENT BACK-COUNTRY TO TRAIN FRESH JUNGLE FORCES IN THE RIGOROUS CHINDIT TRADITION OF WHICH HE WAS JEALOUSLY PROUD. NOW HE RETURNED TO ONE DISTURBING DISCOVERY AFTER ANOTHER.
YE GODS! GLIDERS IN BURMA! IS EVERYBODY OFF THEIR ROCKERS?

THE RUDE REMARKS OF TWO AMERICAN GROUND CREW ONLY INCREASED MALCOLM'S TROUBLED THOUGHTS AS HE HASTENED TO REPORT TO HIS COMMANDING OFFICER, BRIGADIER KNOX.
HIYA, SCOTTIE!
LOST YOUR KILT BUD?

HE FOUND THAT CHEERFUL BUT TOUGH LITTLE BRIGADIER SURROUNDED BY MAPS, PAPERS AND SUPPORTING STAFF. HE GREETED MALCOLM WARMLY...
MY WORD, YOU'RE ONLY JUST IN TIME, MALCOLM! THE AIRLIFT INVASION ON HARRINGAY—THE NEW JUNGLE BASE—HAS BEEN ADVANCED FOUR DAYS.
AIRLIFT?

MALCOLM'S SHARP QUERY BROUGHT A SUDDEN SILENCE. THEN KNOX ANSWERED QUIETLY...
OF COURSE, AIRLIFT! YOU'VE BEEN OUT OF TOUCH TOO LONG, MY SON... CHINDITS GO TO WAR IN GLIDERS NOW!

PLEADING PRESSURE OF WORK, KNOX HANDED THE SET-FACED MALCOLM OVER TO A YOUNG CAPTAIN, WHO DESCRIBED THE BEGINNINGS ALREADY MADE IN THE NEW BURMA OFFENSIVE...
BLACKPOOL
BURMA
BROADWAY
HARRINGAY
THE TROOPS WERE FLOWN IN BY TOWED GLIDERS AND LANDED WITH PRETTY MIXED LUCK ON BROADWAY—FIRST MEN, THEN ARMS, EQUIPMENT, EVEN A BULLDOZER. AND NOW WE'RE GOING FOR HARRINGAY, HERE, SIXTY MILES SOUTH OF BROADWAY.

YOU TALK OF GLIDERS LANDING WITH MIXED LUCK. HOW MIXED ?
THERE WERE SOME SMASH-UPS ON LANDING—OTHERS DID NOT FIND THE LANDING STRIP AND DROPPED IN THE JUNGLE. WE LOST QUITE A FEW MEN...

THAT EVENING THE BRIGADIER SOON SENSED THAT HE HAD SOMETHING OF A REBEL ON HIS HANDS.
ALL WE ASKED, SIR, WAS FOR LIGHT PLANES TO FLY IN SUPPLIES AND TO EVACUATE THE WOUNDED. INSTEAD WE HAVE AN AMERICAN AIR FORCE WHICH DOESN'T KNOW THE FIRST THING ABOUT JUNGLE FIGHTING TELLING US HOW TO RUN A JOB WHICH WE CHINDITS HAVE FOUGHT AND DIED TO LEARN!

TIMES HAVE CHANGED, MALCOLM. THE OLD PUNISHING MARCHES THROUGH JUNGLE HAVE BEEN SUCCEEDED BY FLIGHT. WE'VE PROVED THAT AT BROADWAY.
YES, BUT AT WHAT COST IN CHINDIT LIVES? LOOK, SIR, I'VE GOT FRESH TROOPS UNUSED TO GLIDERS. GIVE ME MULES, AND I'LL GRAB ANY BASE YOU WANT... IN THE TRUE CHINDIT MANNER.

AT THIS MOMENT A SHORT THICK-SET FIGURE STROLLED AMIABLY INTO THE ROOM. KNOX ROSE TO HIS FEET...
THIS IS SAM BOLEY, ONE OF OUR BEST GLIDER PILOTS.

SAM BOLEY SUFFERED MALCOLM'S SHARP LOOK IMPERTURBABLY AND A GRIN SPLIT HIS GOOD-NATURED FACE.
MULES DID I HEAR YOU SAY? THERE'S JUST NO TIME FOR MULES NOW, MAJOR. US AIR COMMANDOS HAVE CHANGED ALL THAT – AND I'LL TELL YOU HOW . . .

MALCOLM LISTENED TO THE AMERICAN'S COLOURFUL CLAIMS IN GRUDGING SILENCE.
WE'VE GOT EVERYTHING, MAJOR – GLIDERS TO TAKE YOUR MEN IN, DAKOTAS TO KEEP YOU SUPPLIED, MITCHELL BOMBERS TO SUPPORT YOUR ATTACKS AND PURSUIT PLANES TO KEEP AIR SUPERIORITY. WHAT MORE CAN YOU WANT?

IT WAS A FORMIDABLE ARGUMENT AS MALCOLM HAD TO ADMIT. BUT HE WAS NOT YET CONVINCED...
HOW ABOUT EVACUATING THE WOUNDED? WE CHINDITS HAVE SWORN NEVER AGAIN TO LEAVE OUR WOUNDED TO THE MERCY OF THE JUNGLE AS WE HAD TO BEFORE.
THAT'S EASY—WE'LL PUT 'EM IN GLIDERS, AND SNATCH 'EM OUT BY DAKOTA!

SNATCH THEM OUT IN GLIDERS! IN THE JUNGLE! ...DO YOU KNOW WHAT YOU'RE TALKING ABOUT?
SOUNDS CRAZY I KNOW, MALCOLM, BUT WE BELIEVE IT WILL WORK.

BUT MALCOLM HAD HEARD ENOUGH. TO HIS REALISTIC MIND THE WHOLE IDEA OF GLIDERS SOUNDED JUST TOO FANTASTIC...
GLIDER SNATCHING IN THE JUNGLE! WHAT NEXT?
GOSH, I'D LIKE TO SHOW THAT FELLER!
MAYBE YOU WILL, SAM—MAYBE YOU WILL!

NEXT MORNING, THE STAND-BY SIGNAL FOR "OPERATION HARRINGAY" CAME THROUGH. BY MIDDAY THE TAKE-OFF WAS CONFIRMED FOR 1840 HOURS—JUST AFTER SUNDOWN. ALREADY THE GLIDERS WERE MARSHALLED, THEIR TOW ROPES LAID IN ORDERLY LINES BEFORE THEM. DAKOTA TUG-PLANES WERE WARMING UP.

THE ROLE OF MALCOLM AND HIS MEN WAS SIMPLE BUT HAZARDOUS.
MAJOR McDUFF—YOU AND YOUR MEN ARE TO EMBARK IN THE FIRST BATCH OF GLIDERS. ON LANDING AT HARRINGAY YOU WILL SEIZE THE STRIP AND DEFEND IT AGAINST POSSIBLE ATTACK UNTIL THE BASE IS ESTABLISHED.
I UNDERSTAND, SIR.
THE DIE WAS CAST. NONE OF MALCOLM'S MISGIVINGS ABOUT GLIDERS MATTERED NOW.

COMING AWAY FROM THE BRIEFING, THE SCOT PASSED THE INFORMATION ON TO HIS MEN. HE WAS NOT ANXIOUS ABOUT THEIR ROLE ON THE GROUND, ONLY OF THE METHOD OF GETTING THEM THERE.
ONCE THE STRONGHOLD IS ESTABLISHED, OUR MAIN JOB WILL BE TO STRIKE OFF INTO THE JUNGLE TO ATTACK AND CUT JAP SUPPLY LINES *AND KEEP THEM CUT!* ANY QUESTIONS?

IT SEEMED THERE WERE DOUBTS IN THE MINDS OF THE MEN, TOO. EX-DESERT RAT, DOGGER' BANKS, ROSE UP TO EXPRESS IN A NUTSHELL MALCOLM'S OWN MISGIVINGS.
BUT, SIR ... TWO GLIDERS IN TANDEM! IT'LL BE MURDER!
WE MUST HAVE CONFIDENCE IN THE AMERICAN PILOTS, BANKS— THEY KNOW THEIR JOB, I'M SURE.

THEN LEADERS AND MEN WERE SECTIONED OFF, TWENTY-FOUR MEN AND EQUIPMENT TO A GLIDER . . .
HERE THEY COME, BOY!
THIS IS IT!

AS MALCOLM AND HIS PARTY DREW NEAR TO THE LEADING GLIDER, A FAMILIAR FIGURE ROSE FROM ITS HAUNCHES AND GAVE MALCOLM A LAZY SALUTE. IT WAS GLIDER-PILOT SAM BOLEY.
I'M FLYING YOUR CRATE, MAJOR. COINCIDENCE, AIN'T IT?
THAT'S FINE!
BUT MALCOLM WAS NOT SO EASILY DECEIVED. HE GUESSED WITH AN INWARD SMILE THAT SAD. BOLEY MUST HAVE ARRANGED THIS.

GET ABOARD, LADS, AND MOVE CAREFULLY!
WHAT'S THE BETTING THE BOTTOM FALLS OUT!
SOON I'LL BE SHOWING THIS McDUFF FELLER JUST WHAT WE CAN DO WITH GLIDERS.

IT WAS ALMOST DARK WHEN THE FIRST TUG-PLANE, DRAWING ITS TWO GLIDERS, TOOK OFF. THEY WERE THE PATHFINDER TEAM. THEY CLIMBED IN SLOW SPIRALS TO EIGHT THOUSAND FEET AND THEN SET COURSE.

AFTER TEN MINUTES THE MAIN WAVE FOLLOWED. ENGINES ROARING AT FULL BOOST, THE TUG-PLANES LUMBERED DOWN THE DARK FIELD, PRESENTLY TO LIFT PONDEROUSLY INTO THE JUNGLE SKY. NO LIGHTS WERE PERMITTED. RADIO SILENCE WAS IMPERATIVE. *OPERATION HARRINGAY HAD BEGUN!*
21852

SAM, PILOTING THE LEADING GLIDER OF HIS PAIR, WATCHED THE TOW ROPE WITH PRACTISED EYE AS HIS TUG-PLANE BEGAN ITS LABORIOUS CIRCLING CLIMB.
EASY DOES IT, BOY!

WITH NOTHING TO HEAR BUT THE WHISPERING FLIGHT OF THE GLIDER, THE SILENCE IN MALCOLM'S MACHINE WAS TENSE UNTIL THE IRREPRESSIBLE 'DOGGER' BANKS BROKE THE SPELL.
WILL I BE ON A CHARGE IF I COUGH, SIR?
AS THE CHUCKLES WENT ROUND, MALCOLM FOUND HIMSELF LIKING THIS TOUGH LITTLE CORPORAL. HIS COCKNEY HIGH SPIRITS COULD BE INVALUABLE IN THE TESTING TIME AHEAD.

IN THE GLIDER COUPLED TO SAM BOLEY'S, A COMPANY OF SEPOYS, UNDER THE VETERAN SUBADAR AMRI SINGH, WATCHED THEIR OWN TAKE-OFF WITH AWE AND DELIGHT.
IN TRUTH, A HEAVENLY WAY TO GO TO BATTLE!
OUR ANCESTORS WOULD BE PROUD OF THEIR CHILDREN!

NEW YORK BORN PETE SKAUFER, PILOTING THIS SECOND GLIDER, GRINNED AT THE CHATTER OF THESE SIMPLE YET FEARLESS SOLDIERS.
IN A TOUGH SPOT, I'D PICK YOUR BOYS EVERY TIME, SUBADAR!
YOUR GRACIOUS OPINION IS BELIEVED, SAHIB!

Chapter 2. CRASH LANDING
BY 1950 HOURS, ALL GLIDERS WERE AIRBORNE AND ON COURSE. THE BURMA MOON ROSE AND SHED ITS LIGHT UPON THIS VAST AIR FLEET WINGING OVER THE BLACK JUNGLE CARPET.
18

THE SLOW MINUTES PASSED, AND AHEAD LOOMED THE PEAKS OF THE SOMRA HILLS. GENTLY, THE TUG-PLANES CLIMBED FOR THE ADDED HEIGHT.

SAFELY OVER THIS RANGE, THE GLIDER FORCE PRESSED ON. THE RIVER CHINDWIN WAS CROSSED AND THEY WERE OVER ENEMY COUNTRY.

BUT AS THE ONCE FRIENDLY MOONLIGHT GATHERED STRENGTH IT REVEALED THE GLIDER FORCE TO A JAP ZERO RETURNING FROM A LONG-RANGE PATROL...
AIRCRAFT! MANY ENEMY AIRCRAFT! I MUST LOOK CLOSER!

AS THE JAP PILOT CLOSED IN HE SAW THAT THE ENEMY AIRCRAFT BORE NO GUN TURRETS... AND RECOGNISED THEM AS DEFENCELESS GLIDERS.
A JAP! DOGGONE THIS MOONLIGHT!
SO...! THE ENEMY ARE NOT ARMED! THIS WILL BE EASY!

THEN, TEETH BARED IN A WOLFISH GRIN, THE ZERO PILOT HURTLED TOWARDS ONE OF THE GLIDERS, HIS THUMB JAMMING DOWN THE FIRING BUTTON!
BANZAI!

IT WAS SAM'S GLIDER THAT THE JAP SINGLED OUT FOR HIS ATTACK. THE AMERICAN INSTINCTIVELY DUCKED AS HOLES WERE PUNCHED ACROSS THE WINDOWS OF HIS CABIN...
SUFFERIN' CATS! THAT NIP'S GOT US COLD!

AGAIN, THE ZERO ATTACKED—GUN-FLAME LANCING AT SAM BOLEY'S GLIDER...

BUT THIS TIME THE JAP'S AIM WAS LESS SURE. HIS HEAVY CALIBRE CANNON SHELLS RIPPED INCHES PAST THE NOSE OF THE GLIDER... AND CUT CLEAN THROUGH THE TAUT TOW-LINE!
THE YELLOW SKUNK'S CUT THE TOW-LINE! WE'RE ADRIFT!

THE ZERO PILOT SCREAMED WITH FEAR AS HE SAW THE SEVERED TOW-LINE WHIP UP TOWARDS HIM. DESPERATELY, HE SIDE-SLIPPED...BUT THE ROPE SMASHED WITH TREMENDOUS FORCE ACROSS HIS TAIL...

SUDDENLY FREED FROM ITS TUG-PLANE, THE GLIDER REARED AND LUNGED, CAUSING SAM TO FIGHT THE CONTROLS WITH ALL HIS STRENGTH.
DON'T PANIC BACK THERE! WE'RE IN TROUBLE ... BUT NOTHING WE CAN'T GET OUT OF!

TO THE CHINDITS INSIDE THE GLIDER IT SEEMED AN ETERNITY BEFORE THE AMERICAN SUCCEEDED IN RIGHTING HIS MACHINE...
OKAY, NOW SHE'S BEHAVING HERSELF AGAIN!
PHEW! I'D RATHER TACKLE A HUNDRED-MILE JUNGLE MARCH THAN GO THROUGH THAT AGAIN!
ME, TOO! GIVE ME FOOT-SLOGGING ANY DAY!

WHILE SAM USED ALL HIS SKILL TO KEEP THE GLIDER IN THE AIR, MALCOLM COOLLY UNFOLDED HIS MAP.

I RECKON THERE'S ANOTHER FIFTY MILES TO THE TARGET... DO YOU THINK YOU CAN MAKE IT?

NOT A HOPE, MAJOR!

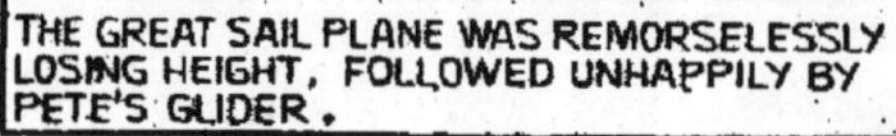

SLEWING WILDLY, THE GLIDER SKIMMED INTO THE TREES. A WING WAS RIPPED OFF, THE FUSELAGE BUCKLED...

MIRACULOUSLY UNINJURED, SAM SCRAMBLED OUT OF HIS SEAT AND PEERED ANXIOUSLY INTO THE DARKNESS OF THE FUSELAGE...
YOU FELLERS OKAY? HOW IS IT, MAJOR?
WE'RE OKAY, I THINK.
AND FOR THE FIRST TIME MALCOLM'S MATTER-OF-FACT TONES BROUGHT SAM RELIEF RATHER THAN THE USUAL EXASPERATION.

NOBODY WAS SERIOUSLY HURT. THEN, SUDDENLY, SAM REMEMBERED THE OTHER GLIDER. HE RACED TOWARDS THE CLEARING TO WAVE A WARNING . . .
MIND THE CROSS WIND, PETE!

BUT PETE MISTOOK SAM'S SIGNAL FOR ENCOURAGEMENT . . .
LOOK, THERE'S MY BUDDY WAVING US IN. HERE WE GO!

THE SECOND GLIDER HIT HARD, CANNONING FROM TREE TO TREE AS IT SKIDDED INTO THE UNDERGROWTH. ONCE AGAIN, HOWEVER, THE PILOT ESCAPED WHAT SEEMED CERTAIN DEATH . . .
IS IT BAD IN THERE, SOLDIER?
WE REJOICE THAT OUR INFERIOR LIVES HAVE BEEN SPARED! WE ARE ALL IN ONE PIECE!

AS SAM PUT A STEADYING HAND ON PETE'S SHOULDER, MALCOLM AND SOME OF HIS MEN DASHED UP TO THE WRECKAGE...
TEAR THIS COVERING OFF! LET'S GET THEM OUT OF THERE!
A TRICKY LANDING, PETE! HOW D'YOU FEEL?
I'LL BE BETTER WHEN THIS GROUND STOPS SPINNING!

SAM BOLEY'S EYES WERE BLEAK AS HE LOOKED AT THE TOTAL RUIN OF HIS PROUD CLAIMS...
WE WASHED THAT UP, PETE! BUT McDUFF'S *GOT* TO KNOW WE'RE STILL RIGHT ABOUT GLIDERS!

SAM MADE TO LURCH TOWARDS THE TALL SCOT BUT CHECKED THE IMPULSE. McDUFF SEEMED TO HAVE HIS HANDS FULL. IT WAS NOT THE TIME FOR EXCUSES.
HOLD THAT MAN, SUBADAR, THE POOR FELLOW'S HALF CRAZY.
IT IS THE SHOCK, MAJOR SAHIB, HE SOON BE BETTER!

UNEASY IN THE AIR, MALCOLM WAS INSTANTLY IN HIS ELEMENT ON THE JUNGLE FLOOR. THIS WAS WHAT HE HAD TRAINED FOR—TO STAY ALIVE IN THE JUNGLE NO MATTER WHAT THE ODDS.
... AND THE REST OF YOU FAN OUT IN A CIRCLE IN CASE THERE ARE ANY JAPS AROUND.

AFTER THE INJURED HAD BEEN CARED FOR, MALCOLM CALLED A COUNCIL...
WE'LL MOUNT THE INJURED ON BAMBOO STRETCHERS AND MARCH FOR HARRINGAY. IT'S ABOUT A FIVE DAYS' TREK, I RECKON.
FIVE DAYS IS JUST A STROLL TO THE MAJOR.
SURE, WE'LL BE OKAY WITH HIM!

NOT A WORD HAD BEEN SPOKEN TO THE AMERICAN GLIDER PILOTS AND THEY WATCHED DISPIRITEDLY AS MALCOLM ISSUED FIRM, CONFIDENT ORDERS . . .
I GUESS THEY THINK WE TALKED TOO BIG ABOUT GLIDERS, HUH ?
WE KNOW IT CAN BE DONE THOUGH, PETE. IT WAS JUST GOSHDARN BAD LUCK MEETING UP WITH THAT JAP.

ANXIOUS TO PUT SOME MILES BETWEEN THEMSELVES AND THE TELL-TALE GLIDERS BEFORE DAYBREAK, MALCOLM LED THEM ON A NORTHERLY COURSE FOR DISTANT HARRINGAY.
REMEMBER YOUR TRAINING, CHINDITS, AND THE JUNGLE WILL BE YOUR FRIEND.
YOU'RE RIGHT, SIR . . . THESE LEECHES JUST LOVE ME!

Chapter 3. CHINDIT AMBUSH

THE JAPANESE-HELD RAILWAY WAS A PERFECT OBJECTIVE FOR JUNGLE RAIDERS, AND WHEN THE MEN GATHERED BEFORE HIM, MALCOLM'S PLANS WERE ALREADY HALF-FORMED . . .
I RECKON THIS JAP RAILWAY IS FEEDING THE THIRTY-FIRST JAPANESE DIVISION UP NORTH OPPOSING GENERAL STILWELL'S ARMY. MY INTENTION IS TO CUT THIS LINE AND HELP STARVE THOSE JAPS OF ARMS, FOOD AND REINFORCEMENTS.

MALCOLM WARMED TO HIS MEN'S ENTHUSIASM . . .
CUTTING THE LINE WILL BE SIMPLE. CAN WE KEEP IT CUT LONG ENOUGH TO MAKE ITS EFFECT FELT?
WE'LL NEED FOOD . . . AMMUNITION.
NO REASON WHY WE SHOULDN'T TAKE ALL WE WANT FROM THE JAPS!

THE NEXT DAY WAS SPENT SECURING A BASE ON THE HEIGHTS OF 'CHUKKERDUCK HILL' AND WHEN NIGHT CAME MALCOLM LED HIS MEN DOWN TO THE RAILWAY TRACK AND SUPERVISED THE PLACING OF EXPLOSIVE CHARGES. SAM AND PETE LOOKED ON WITH INTEREST.
I'M BEGINNING TO THINK THIS McDUFF IS NO SLOUCH.
YEAH, HE SURE SEEMS TO KNOW WHAT HE'S ABOUT.

RIGHT, EVERYBODY! BACK INTO THE JUNGLE — AT THE DOUBLE!

AS MALCOLM WAITED FOR THE FUSES TO RUN THEIR DREAD COURSE, HE FOUND THE TWO AMERICANS GRINNING BESIDE HIM. INSTANTLY, HE SENSED THEIR CHANGED ATTITUDE . . .
THE JAPS WILL SURE BE MAD AT YOU, MAJOR!
THEY'LL BE HERE LIKE A BUNCH OF SCALDED CATS!
LET'S HOPE THEY WILL—WE'LL BE WAITING FOR THEM!

NEXT MOMENT, THE NIGHT WAS RENT BY A SERIES OF EXPLOSIONS THAT ECHOED FROM ONE SIDE OF THE VALLEY TO THE OTHER...

DARKNESS FELL AGAIN AND THE CHINDITS STUDIED THEIR HANDIWORK WITH GRINS OF SATISFACTION...
WHAT NOW MAJOR?
WE'LL WAIT FOR A SUPPLY TRAIN. IF THERE AREN'T TOO MANY JAPS FOR US, WE'LL ATTACK IT.
MM! SOUNDS INTERESTING—WELL, ME AND SAM DON'T AIM TO BE LEFT OUT!

IT WAS NOT UNTIL DAWN THAT THEIR LONG VIGIL WAS REWARDED BY THE SOUND OF A TRAIN. AS ONE MAN, THE CHINDITS SLIPPED OFF THE SAFETY CATCHES ON THEIR WEAPONS...

THE TRAIN, BOUND, AS MALCOLM HAD SURMISED, FOR THE JAP NORTH-WESTERN FRONT, WAS MAKING GOOD SPEED THROUGH THE OPEN COUNTRY...

BUT THE FIRST RAYS OF THE RISING SUN, GLINTING ALONG THE SINGLE LINE, MADE THE BROKEN GAP APPARENT TO THE SHARP-EYED ENGINEER.
BRAKE! EMERGENCY BRAKE! THE LINE IS BROKEN!

INSTANTLY, THE SCREAM OF TORTURED BRAKES REACHED THE EARS OF THE AMBUSHERS.
STAND BY! SHE'S GOING TO PULL UP!
THIS IS IT, PETE!
HONOURABLE JAP HAS DISCOVERED OUR PERFIDY, SAHIB MAJOR!

THE TRAIN SHUDDERED TO A HALT AMIDST A CLOUD OF STEAM WITHIN YARDS OF THE BREAK. WAS IT A TROOP TRAIN OR WAS IT MERELY CARRYING SUPPLIES?
WAIT!

OUT OF THE CORNER OF HIS EYE, MALCOLM NOTICED HIS MEN POISED EAGERLY FOR THE ATTACK. THAT DECIDED THE CHINDIT OFFICER — HE THRUST THE VEREY PISTOL INTO THE AIR AND PRESSED THE TRIGGER . . .
HERE WE GO!
THE SOARING SIGNAL HAD HARDLY REACHED ITS ZENITH WHEN THE CHINDITS LET FLY WITH A HAIL OF LEAD THAT BEAT A DEADLY TATTOO ON THE SIDES OF THE TRUCKS.
JUST A POLITE KNOCK BEFORE WE GO IN!
WITH THE EARLY CUPPA TEA, EH?

INSIDE THE WAGONS, TWO COMPANIES OF SLEEPY JAP INFANTRY WERE INTERRUPTED IN THEIR CURSING OF THE SUDDEN HALT WHEN THE SIDES OF THEIR TRUCKS WERE SUDDENLY PIERCED BY FLYING LEAD.
AAGH!

THEY FOUGHT BACK WITH THE FEROCIOUS SAVAGERY OF CORNERED ANIMALS. DOOR AFTER DOOR SLID OPEN AND THE FIGHT MOUNTED... UNTIL THE VALLEY WAS FILLED WITH THE DEAFENING CHORUS OF GUNS.
BY JUPITER, IT IS A TROOP TRAIN!

IN A SERIES OF SHORT, ALMOST SUICIDAL RUSHES, DOGGER BANKS AND A FEW OTHERS CLOSED WITH THE HALTED WAGONS...
SHARE THAT AMONGST YOU, 'EATHENS!
GET READY TO RUSH 'EM, LADS!

THE GRENADE EXPLODED DEAFENINGLY IN THE CONFINED SPACE AND THEN DOGGER'S PARTY STORMED ABOARD THE TRUCK...
HOLD THAT ONE, MATE!
HEY! LOOK..! AMMUNITION!

SUBADAR SINGH, TOO, WAS BRINGING HIS OWN SUBTLE ARTS TO BEAR ON THE SAME PROBLEM...
UGH!
A CUNNING HAND NEEDS NO STRENGTH!

SEEING NO PROFIT IN FURTHER FIGHTING, MALCOLM DECIDED TO BREAK OFF THE ACTION. HE FOUND THE TWO AMERICANS HIGHLY PLEASED WITH THEMSELVES.
WE'LL KNOCK OFF NOW AND GET BACK UP THE HILL.
OKAY, MAJOR!
JUST ONE MORE BURST FROM UNCLE SAM!

AT A BLAST FROM MALCOLM'S WHISTLE, THE CHINDITS VANISHED AS IF SPIRITED AWAY, TO RE-UNITE AGAIN, HIGH ON CHUKKERDUCK HILL.
AMMUNITION! WELL DONE CORPORAL!
WE'VE GOT HALF A TON MORE DOWN THERE, SIR... STACKED AWAY!

THEIR STRONGHOLD WAS WELL CHOSEN. FROM THAT LOFTY POINT A CLOSE WATCH COULD BE KEPT ON THE RAILWAY. YET IT WAS A DIFFICULT POSITION FOR THE ENEMY TO ASSAIL.
LOOK, THOSE JAPS ARE SPREADING OUT THIS WAY!
AYE! THEY'RE BOUND TO COME LOOKING FOR US.

THOUGHTFULLY, THE CHINDIT LEADER SUMMED UP THE SITUATION...
THIS RAILWAY MUST BE VITAL TO THE JAPS. IF WE HAD MORE MEN WE COULD KEEP IT CUT INDEFINITELY. AS IT IS, WE CAN ONLY MAKE OURSELVES A NUISANCE AND HOPE A MIRACLE WILL BRING US REINFORCEMENTS.

AS SAM PONDERED THESE WORDS, AN IDEA BEGAN TO FORM IN HIS MIND. EAGERLY, THE AMERICAN DREW HIS BUDDY, PETE, TO ONE SIDE...
PETE, WHAT A CHANCE FOR THE GLIDER BOYS! THE AIR COMMANDOS COULD FLY IN MORE CHINDITS, MORE ARMS, FOOD... THE LOT!
YEAH, BUT HOW ARE YA GOIN' TO GET WORD BACK WITHOUT A RADIO? WE'RE CUT OFF, PAL!
ONCE ALIGHT WITH HIS IDEA, SAM'S ENTHUSIASM COULD NOT BE QUENCHED. THERE MUST BE A WAY, HE DECIDED.

Chapter 4: THE PHANTOM RAIDERS
FOR TWO DAYS MALCOLM AND HIS CHINDITS WATCHED THE JAPS VAINLY COMB THE JUNGLE HILLS FOR SIGNS OF THEIR VANISHED ENEMY. MEANWHILE A REPAIR GANG HAD ARRIVED TO LAY FRESH TRACKS FOR THE WAITING TRAIN. IT WAS PLAIN THAT THE LINE WOULD SOON BE REOPENED.
THIS TRAIN WILL LEAVE—BUT I BET THOSE JAPS WON'T UNTIL THEY'VE GOT US CORNERED. SOMEHOW WE'VE GOT TO KEEP THAT LINE CUT.

ONCE AGAIN MALCOLM FOUND SAM AT HIS ELBOW... A SUPPRESSED EXCITEMENT SEEMED TO GRIP THE AMERICAN.
LOOK, MAJOR, YOU DON'T STAND A MONKEY'S CHANCE AGAINST ALL THESE NIPS.. YOU WANT REINFORCEMENTS AND US AIR COMMANDOS COULD BRING THEM UP BY GLIDER!
FINE! AND HOW ARE YOU GOING TO WHISTLE THEM UP?

I'LL FETCH 'EM MYSELF! I'LL FIND MY WAY TO HARRINGAY AND ORGANISE EVERYTHING!
HARRINGAY— A THREE-DAY TREK THROUGH THICK JUNGLE? YOU'D NEVER MAKE IT!

SAM'S IMPATIENT RETORT DID NOT DISTURB MALCOLM'S CALM REASONING.
HECK! I AIN'T SCARED OF THE JUNGLE, BUT IF YOU WANT, YOU COULD SEND SOMEBODY WITH ME!
YOU'D NEED A PARTY. I COULDN'T SPARE THE MEN THE WAY THINGS ARE!

THE BURNING AMBITION TO SHOW WHAT GLIDERS COULD DO, DROVE SAM TO FURTHER ARGUMENT BUT HE COULD NOT MOVE THE STUBBORN SCOT.
SORRY, SAM. BUT DON'T WORRY—IF THINGS GET BAD WE'LL CLEAR OUT!
GOSHDARN IT! WE COULD DO IT—I'LL BET MY BOTTOM DOLLAR WE COULD DO IT!

THE NEXT NIGHT MALCOLM ACTED. WITH A HANDFUL OF PICKED MEN HE SLIPPED PAST THE JAP CAMPS DOTTED ABOUT THE HILLSIDES AND REACHED THE RAILWAY UNSEEN.
FIRST DESPATCH THE SENTRIES TO THEIR ANCESTORS!
WE SHOULD HAVE SCUPPERED THAT LOCO LAST TIME, BUT WE'LL MAKE SURE OF IT NOW!

LIKE SINISTER PHANTOMS, THE JUNGLE RAIDERS CREPT CLOSE TO THE ARGUING SENTRIES.
NEI! NEI! YOKOHAMA NUMBER ONE, KOBE NUMBER TEN!
YOU LIE!

THE SHRILL CHATTER OF THE JAPANESE WAS ABRUPTLY STILLED AS THE CHINDITS SPRANG UPON THEM . . .
UGH!

ROCK-HARD FISTS AND STEEL-TIPPED GUN-BUTTS STIFLED ANY CRIES THE SENTRIES MIGHT HAVE MADE . . .
KAAGH!

BUT, EVEN SO, THE SHORT, FIERCE STRUGGLE WAS HEARD BY OTHER JAPS . . .
BREAK OFF! GET AWAY!
JUST A TICK, MAJOR!

HEEDLESS OF THE PERIL FROM ENEMY REINFORCEMENTS, DOGGER BANKS LEAPED INTO THE LOCOMOTIVE CAB AND TOSSED A COUPLE OF GRENADES INTO THE FIREBOX.
THIS OUGHTA WRECK THINGS A BIT!

THE DEAFENING ESCAPE OF STEAM FROM THE ENGINE'S MANGLED BOILER TUBES COULD NOT DROWN THE VENGEFUL CRIES OF THE JAPANESE AS THEY SURGED AFTER THE RETREATING CHINDITS.
KILL THE DOGS! AFTER THEM...

BUT THE DEADLY FIRE FROM THE RAIDERS' GUNS KEPT THE ENEMY AT ARM'S LENGTH AND THEY WERE ABLE TO MELT INTO THE JUNGLE UNHARMED.

WILD, ERRATIC GUNFIRE FOLLOWED THEM AND THE SOUNDS OF BATTLE REACHED THE SHARP EARS OF THOSE LEFT AT THE CAMP.
THE JAPS ARE CHASING THE MAJOR HOME! COME ON!
EVERY SEPOY HIS KNIFE! FOLLOW MY BLADE!

THE SHOUTS AND BLUNDERING MOVEMENTS OF THE JAPS DREW THE SWIFT-MOVING CHINDITS LIKE TIGERS AFTER THEIR PREY...
GET 'EM! BEFORE THEY CAN GET AWAY!

MEANWHILE, THE SUBADAR'S SEPOYS WERE ALSO BUSY—STRIKING SILENTLY OUT OF THE GREEN JUNGLE.

THE JAPS WERE ROUTED AND THE JUBILANT CHINDITS ESCORTED THEIR LEADER BACK TO CAMP.
THAT WAS A NEAR GO! BUT WE DID WHAT WE SET OUT TO DO!
AYE! WE SHOWED THE LITTLE PERISHERS!

THE NIGHT PASSED WITHOUT ALARM, BUT ONE MAN AT LEAST, SAM BOLEY, HAD SCARCELY SLEPT. IN THE CHILL LIGHT OF DAWN HE ROUGHLY ROUSED HIS FELLOW AMERICAN.
LISTEN, WE'RE GETTING OUTA HERE—JUST YOU AND ME! THESE JAPS WILL KEEP ON COMING TILL THEY WIPE US OUT. WE GOTTA GET HELP—WE'RE LEAVING FOR HARRINGAY.
HARRINGAY!

NOTHING LESS THAN LOYALTY TO HIS PAL COULD HAVE MADE PETE AGREE TO WHAT HE CONSIDERED A CRAZY IDEA. AS THEY SLIPPED AWAY IN THE DAWN-LIGHT, CARRYING A SMALL SUPPLY OF FOOD, HE PROTESTED PLAINTIVELY...
HOW DO WE GET TO HARRINGAY? BY SUBWAY?
I'VE GOT A MAP AND A COMPASS. WE'RE SUPPOSED TO BE AIRMEN, AREN'T WE? WE'LL NAVIGATE!
WITH PETE'S MUTTERING IN HIS EARS, SAM LED THE WAY INTO THE THICKLY MATTED JUNGLE...

Chapter 5. BATTLE OF CHUKKERDUCK HILL

BACK AT THE CAMP THE CHINDITS WERE FACING THE FIRST OF MANY ATTACKS FROM THE JAPANESE—FANATICAL IN THEIR SCREAMING WRATH AND SUICIDAL IN THEIR RUSHES.

INEVITABLY COMBING OVER THE SCENE OF THE PREVIOUS NIGHT'S AMBUSH, THE ENEMY HAD TRACKED THE SIGNS LEADING TO MALCOLM'S STRONGHOLD. *THE FIGHT WAS ON!*

THE MORNING WAS STRANGELY SILENT AND SCANNING THE SCENE BELOW, MALCOLM SOON SAW THE REASON...
LOOK, THE LITTLE BEGGARS HAVE BROUGHT UP GUNS!

MALCOLM WAS RIGHT. THE ENEMY HAD BEEN FORCED TO CALL UP ARTILLERY SUPPORT AND FRENZIED EFFORTS WERE BEING MADE TO UNLOAD THE GUNS FROM A TRAIN...
SPEEDO! HURRY!

IT WAS DURING THE MORNING THAT SUBADAR SINGH REPORTED THAT SAM AND PETE WERE MISSING FROM CAMP.
I FOUND THEIR TRACKS, MANY HOURS OLD – VERY FIRM, VERY PURPOSEFUL, SAHIB!
YOU MEAN THEY JUST WALKED OFF INTENTIONALLY!

MALCOLM RECEIVED THE NEWS WITH MINGLED CONCERN AND ANNOYANCE.
THE AMERICANS ARE IGNORANT OF THE JUNGLE. THEY MUST BE BROUGHT BACK OR THEY WILL PERISH.
I WILL GO, SAHIB!
NO – I WILL, SUBADAR! YOU STAY IN COMMAND HERE.

MALCOLM QUICKLY PICKED UP THE AMERICANS' TRAIL, FOLLOWING FAINT SIGNS INVISIBLE TO ANY BUT THE EYE OF A JUNGLE-TRAINED MAN.
IT'LL BE A MIRACLE IF THEY AREN'T DEAD BY NOW, THE CRAZY CHUMPS!

MEANWHILE, PETE HAD BADLY STRAINED A MUSCLE AND HAD AGREED WITH SAM TO RETURN TO CAMP. AFTER A DAY AND NIGHT ALONE IN THE JUNGLE, HE KNEW WITH A COLD PRICKLE OF SWEAT THAT HE WAS LOST.
MUSTN'T PANIC! GOTTA KEEP CALM! MUST FIND MY WAY BACK!

SAM HAD BEEN TORN BETWEEN HIS CONCERN FOR PETE AND HIS SENSE OF DUTY. DOGGEDLY, HE BLUNDERED ON WITH THE STRAIN AND TORMENT OF THE EERIE JUNGLE BEGINNING TO SAP HIS STRENGTH.
HE HAD LOST ALL IDEA OF DISTANCE, BUT HE WAS SURE OF HIS COURSE.

SOMEWHERE IN THAT DENSE TANGLE OF UNDERGROWTH, MALCOLM HAD LOST THE AMERICANS' TRAIL, DESPITE HIS CHINDIT SKILL. BUT SUDDENLY, A MOVEMENT CAUGHT HIS EYE...
WHO'S THERE?

WITH A CRY, MALCOLM RAN TO CATCH A FAMILIAR FIGURE THAT SWAYED EXHAUSTEDLY.
PETE! FOR HEAVENS' SAKE, WHERE'S SAM?
SAM'S GONE. MILES AWAY. GOTTA GET HELP!

SAM FOUGHT HIS WAY ONWARDS, ACHING IN EVERY LIMB, SCARCELY ABLE TO PUT ONE FOOT BEFORE THE OTHER—ALL UNAWARE THAT HE WAS WALKING STRAIGHT INTO THE ENEMY.

HIS FIRST WARNING WAS THE HARSH CLATT AND ORANGE MUZZLE FLASH OF A JAPANESE MACHINE-GUN . . .

THE UNWARY GLIDER PILOT'S BODY PLUNGED DOWN INTO A JUNGLE-CHOKED GULLY.

THE OVERHANGING CREEPERS AND FOLIAGE PREVENTED THE JAP PATROL FROM SEEING ANY SIGNS OF THEIR VICTIM AND THEY MOVED ON, CONFIDENT THAT THE FIGURE HAD BEEN RIDDLED WITH BULLETS.

IT TOOK A FULL DAY FOR THE JAPS TO BRING THEIR GUNS INTO ACTION AND THE FOLLOWING DAWN THE BATTERY FIRED A FEW SITING SHOTS ON THE CHINDIT POSITION. IT WAS AN IDEAL GUNNERS' TARGET AND THEY SAVOURED THEIR TASK WITH SLOW RELISH.
FIRE!
NEI, NEI! TOO WIDE!

THE CHINDITS WERE BRACING THEMSELVES FOR THE BARRAGE THAT MUST FOLLOW WHEN TWO FIGURES APPEARED AT THE EDGE OF THE JUNGLE.
IT'S THE MAJOR – AND ONE OF THE YANKS!
COMING, SIR!
BY SHEER GRIT AND INDOMITABLE STRENGTH, MALCOLM HAD FOUGHT HIS WAY BACK TO THE BASE WITH THE HALF-CONSCIOUS PETE.

AND IT WAS AT ALMOST THE SAME TIME THAT SAM BOLEY WAS FOUND BY A PATROL OF CHINDITS FROM HARRINGAY. HE HAD BEEN UNTOUCHED BY THE JAPS' BULLETS AND HAD STAGGERED ON TOWARDS HIS OBJECTIVE WITH GALLANT OBSTINACY. THE CHINDITS LISTENED EAGERLY TO HIS STORY...
COME ON, MATE, WE'LL TAKE YOU TO THE BRIGADIER!
SURE – HE'LL LAY ON HELL FOR THOSE JAPS OF YOURS!
HE'LL HAVE TO BE QUICK – OR THE OTHER'S WILL BE OVER-RUN!

AS THE BURMA SUN CLIMBED HIGH INTO THE BRASSY SKY, THE JAP SHELLING BEGAN IN EARNEST—FIRST IN SINGLE ROUNDS, AS IF TASTING THE PLEASURE OF PRECISION, AND THEN IN STEADY SUCCESSION. THE CHINDITS COULD DO NOTHING BUT LIE LOW AND TAKE IT.
COR — NOW I KNOW WHAT A CLAY PIGEON FEELS LIKE, SIR!

FOR TWO GRUELLING HOURS, THE JAP GUNNERS KEPT UP THE BARRAGE, HURLING SALVO AFTER SALVO AT THAT TINY HILL-TOP.
THERE WILL BE NOTHING FOR OUR INFANTRY TO FIND. ONLY MANGLED BODIES OF ACCURSED CHINDITS!
BUT THE THUNDER OF THEIR OWN GUNS HAD HIDDEN FROM THEIR EARS THE FAST APPROACHING ROAR OF AMERICAN MITCHELL BOMBERS, LAID ON FROM HEADQUARTERS IN ANSWER TO HARRINGAY'S SIGNAL.

WITH THE TIDAL FORCE OF A TYPHOON, VENGEFUL DESTRUCTION SWEPT UPON THE JAPANESE GUNNERS. PANIC-STRICKEN AT THE TOTALLY UNEXPECTED ATTACK, THEY DESERTED THEIR GUNS AND FLED FROM THE HOLOCAUST THAT THREATENED TO ENGULF THEM.

THE JAP INFANTRY HESITATED—A PAUSE THAT WAS TO COST THEM DEARLY—FOR ACROSS THE JUNGLE TOPS THERE SWEPT AN ARMADA OF DAKOTA-TOWED GLIDERS. EACH WAS PACKED WITH CHINDITS, FIERCELY RESOLVED TO RESCUE THEIR GALLANT COMRADES FROM THE DEATH-TRAP THAT WAS CHUKKERDUCK HILL.
NC 25705
IF EVERY MAN HAS HIS SUPREME MOMENT, THIS SURELY MUST HAVE BEEN SAM BOLEY'S. SITTING BESIDE THE PILOT OF THE LEADING GLIDER, THE AMERICAN'S FACE SHONE WITH EXCITEMENT AND PRIDE AS THE AIR COMMANDO GLIDERS BEGAN TO FLOAT OVER BESIEGED CHUKKERDUCK.
THERE THEY ARE! BY GLORY, NOW I'LL SHOW THAT STUBBORN STREAK OF A McDUFF JUST WHAT GLIDERS CAN DO!

THE GLIDERS CUT FREE FROM THEIR TUG-PLANES AND SWEPT DOWN TO THE BASE OF THE HILL, TO DISGORGE THEIR LOADS.
DUMP YOUR HEAVY KIT BY THE TREES—AND THEN CARRY STRAIGHT ON UP THE HILL. YOU'LL FIND COMMAND H.Q. HALF-WAY UP...

FROM THE HILL-TOP STRONGPOINT, MALCOLM WATCHED THE DRAMATIC ARRIVAL OF THE GLIDER REINFORCEMENTS WITH WONDERING DISBELIEF IN HIS EYES...
GREAT HEAVENS..! SAM MUST HAVE GOT THROUGH...
WHAT DID WE ALWAYS TELL YOU, MAJOR?
A WARNING CRY FROM CORPORAL DOGGER BANKS BROKE THE SPELL...
HERE COME THE JAPS, SIR!

SENSING THE SUDDEN TURN OF FORTUNE, THE JAP INFANTRY LAUNCHED ITSELF IN A CHARGE MORE FEROCIOUSLY SUICIDAL THAN ANY SO FAR, ONLY TO MEET WITH THE SAME WITHERING RECEPTION FROM THE STUBBORN DEFENDERS, NOW BUOYED BY NEW HOPE.
BANZAI!
BANZAI!

ONCE MORE THE DESPERATE CHARGE WAS FLUNG BACK, ONLY TO RENEW ITSELF AGAIN AND YET AGAIN WITH SICKENING DISREGARD FOR LOSSES.

THE DIN OF THAT BITTER STRUGGLE REACHED THE EARS OF THE REINFORCEMENTS FRANTICALLY STRUGGLING UP THE JUNGLE-CLAD MOUNTAINSIDE, SPURRING THEM ON TO ALMOST SUPERHUMAN EFFORTS. AT LAST THEY BROKE OUT OF THE UNDERGROWTH INTO THE HILL-TOP CLEARING WHERE JAPS AND CHINDITS WERE LOCKED IN A LAST HAND TO HAND FIGHT TO THE DEATH.
THERE ARE THE YELLER VERMIN!
INTO 'EM, LADS!
UP THE CHINDITS!

WITH BLACK DESPAIR IN THEIR EYES, THE JAPS TURNED TO FACE THE CHINDIT REINFORCEMENTS, KNOWING FULL WELL THAT THEIR DOOM WAS SEALED. MALCOLM AND PETE HAD A MOMENT TO GRASP THE HAND OF THE JUBILANT SAM . . .
YOU OLD SON OF A McDUFF! GLAD TO SEE YOU!
I DON'T CARE WHOSE SON HE IS, SAM— THE MAJOR GOT ME OUT OF THE JUNGLE!
WELL DONE SAM!

GRATEFULLY, PETE TOLD HOW MALCOLM HAD TRACKED THEM AND HAD BROUGHT HIM BACK TO BASE. THEN SAM RELATED HIS EPIC MARCH TO HARRINGAY AND THE BATTLED-SCARRED CHINDIT LEADER GREETED THE AMERICAN'S FINAL WORDS WITH A WIDE GRIN . . .
. . . AND BRIGADIER KNOX SAYS, 'ANY COMPLAINTS ABOUT AMERICAN AIR COMMANDOS?'
YOU'VE GOT ME COMPLETELY SOLD ON GLIDERS—I'LL TELL THE BRIGADIER MYSELF! AND AS FOR YOU, SAM, ANY TIME YOU WANT TO JOIN THE CHINDITS, THERE'LL BE A PLACE FOR YOU!

THE FRESH CHINDIT TROOPS TOOK OVER THE CHUKKERDUCK HILL STRONGPOINT TO CONTINUE THE THROTTLING GRIP ON THE ENEMY SUPPLY ROUTE. A WHILE LATER, AT HARRINGAY, BRIGADIER KNOX WAS DELIGHTED WITH MALCOLM'S FRANK ADMISSION ...
YOU WIN, SIR—IN FUTURE I GO BY GLIDER!
THE AIR COMMANDOS ARE PROVING EVERY WORD THEY SAID, MALCOLM. THEY'RE DOING MAGNIFICENTLY.
THAT'S ALL I WANTED THE MAJOR TO HEAR!

FIRE POWER

FIVE RUTHLESS YEARS OF AIR FIGHTING HAD HAMMERED SQUADRON LEADER JOHNNIE JARVIS INTO A FLINT-HARD LEADER. BUT THE SUMMER OF 1944 WAS TO BRING HIM HIS GREATEST TEST.

A SPECIALIST IN LOW-FLYING ATTACKS, HE HAD BEEN ASSIGNED THE TOUGH JOB OF COMMANDING A ROCKET TYPHOON SQUADRON OF HARD-FIGHTING, HARD-TO-PLEASE CANADIANS.

Chapter 1. ROCKETS AWAY

FOR JOHNNIE JARVIS, THE PEACE OF THAT SUMMER MORNING WAS WHOLLY BELIED BY THE GATHERING STORM HE HAD LATELY DETECTED IN THE MANNER OF HIS PILOTS.

HURRY IT UP THERE, YOU CHAPS!

FLIGHT LIEUTENANT GRANT SCULLY, A HARD-BITTEN TORONTO MAN WAS THE LOUDEST IN VOICING THEIR COMPLAINTS...
IT'S CRAZY THE WAY JARVIS MAKES US FLY LOW OVER THE WATER.
YEAH! TOO DICEY BY HALF!

BUT NOT EVERY MAN SHARED GRANT SCULLY'S TRUCULENT OUTLOOK. THERE WAS "B" FLIGHT'S COMMANDER, THE GOOD-NATURED FLIGHT LIEUTENANT WESLEY GOODMAN.
AW! CAN IT, YOU GUYS! JARVIS HAS BEEN SENT TO DO A JOB—AND HE'S DOING IT!

IGNORING FLIGHT LIEUTENANT SCULLY'S BLACK LOOKS, JOHNNIE LED THE SQUADRON INTO THE AIR WITH A THUNDEROUS ROAR THAT GAVE VENT TO HIS OWN SORELY-TRIED FEELINGS.
I DON'T BELIEVE IN FORCE, BUT IF THESE CANUCKS DON'T PULL WITH ME, I'LL HAVE TO USE THE BIG STICK.
US O K
US O L

THEIR TARGET WAS AN ELECTRICAL SUB-STATION NEAR ORLY IN FRANCE. ANY PILOT WOULD HAVE EXPECTED TO FLY LOW ACROSS THE CHANNEL TO ESCAPE RADAR DETECTION... BUT HARDLY AS LOW AS JOHNNIE JARVIS NOW TOOK THEM.

GOOD FLYER THOUGH HE WAS, THE STRAIN OF FLYING AT ZERO FEET FOR LONG PERIODS ALWAYS INCENSED THE QUICK-TEMPERED GRANT SCULLY...
BLAZES TAKE THAT JARVIS! YOU NEED SOME MARGIN FOR ERROR WITH THESE KITES...

BUT JOHNNIE'S THOUGHTS WERE RANGING AHEAD EVEN OF THEIR IMMEDIATE TARGET AT ORLY. SOON, THEY WOULD FLY ON ANOTHER MISSION--TO A TARGET WHICH HAD NOT BEEN DIVULGED EVEN TO HIM...
WHATEVER IT IS, IT'S GOING TO BE PRETTY DODGY... ACCORDING TO GROUP. MAKE THIS SORT OF OP. A PICNIC!

THEY CROSSED THE FRENCH COAST AT 350 MPH PLUS AND WERE STREAKING INLAND BEFORE THE GERMAN DEFENCES COULD RECOVER FROM THEIR SURPRISE...

SKIMMING THE TALL POPLARS OF THE ROLLING FRENCH LANDSCAPE, JOHNNIE JARVIS BANKED ON TO A COURSE FOR THE TARGET. HE BROKE WIRELESS SILENCE
TARGET-DEAD AHEAD! SEE THE TRANSFORMERS? LINE AHEAD-FOLLOW ME IN!

THE TEARAWAY HBS OF JOHNNIE'S FIFST ROCKETS WAS LOST IN A SUDDEN CRESCENDO OF FLAK WHICH SAILED UP TO MEET THE TYPHOONS
ACH– ROCKETS!
FLAK

THEY PRESSED HOME THE ATTACK THROUGH A SLEETING CURTAIN OF STEEL. BUT THERE WAS NO STOPPING THE EXPLOSIVE DESTRUCTION OF THE ROCKET PROJECTILES.
FITTED WITH A 60 LB WARHEAD, EACH POCKET PACKED A PUNCH THE EQUAL OF A SIX-INCH GUN. MULTIPLIED EIGHT TIMES, THE TOTAL EFFECTIVENESS OF A SINGLE TYPHOON WAS DEVASTATING.

HAVING EMPTIED ALL HIS OWN ROCKETS INTO THE ILL-STARRED TARGET, JOHNNIE WATCHED THE OTHERS COMPLETE THE DESTRUCTION OF THE ELECTRICAL SUB-STATION...
THESE CANADIANS MAY BE A SURLY BUNCH - BUT THEY CAN CERTAINLY FLY!

THE TYPHOONS TURNED EXULTANTLY FOR HOME, BUT THE CANADIANS' JOY WAS SHORT-LIVED. ONCE MORE JOHNNIE'S INSISTENT DEMANDS GRATED IN THEIR EARPHONES...
LOWER! GET LOWER, EVERYBODY!
HEY, CAN'T THAT GUY LET UP FOR ONCE!

THE SLOW DRAWL OF THE MORE AMIABLE WESLEY GOODMAN BROKE IN TO GIVE JOHNNIE MUCH NEEDED SUPPORT...
DON'T YOU FELLAS EVER LEARN SENSE? THIS IS GOOD PRACTICE...SO GET LOW!

THEN TRAGEDY STRUCK! FIED TWO'S PORT WING CLIPPED A WAVE TOP...
GUS! HE'S GOING IN!

IN SECONDS, THE SAVAGE FORCE OF THE IMPACT HAD SMASHED THE SLEEM FIGHTER TO A WHIRLING MASS OF WRECKAGE...

THE HORRIFIED PILOTS COULD DO NOTHING BUT CIRCLE HELPLESSLY. THEIR MINDS WERE FILLED WITH A DREAD VISION OF THEIR FRIENDS TERRIFYING END IN THOSE COLD GREEN DEPTHS.
GOOD GRIEF! HE WAS GONE IN A SECOND!
DIDN'T HAVE A CHANCE!

WHEN THEY REACHED BASE, JOHNNIE FOUND HIMSELF THE STORM-CENTRE OF BITTER ACCUSATIONS...
YOU AS GOOD AS KILLED GUS BAKER, JARVIS! THE OP. WAS OVER-- WHY RISK OUR NECKS ON DARN FOOL UNNECESSARY LOW FLYING! IT WAS PLAIN MURDER!

DESPITE THE SHOCK OF THE LOSS, JOHNNIE FELT HIS OWN ANGER MOUNTING WITHIN HIM. BUT ONCE AGAIN, THE SOOTHING DRAWL OF WESLEY GOODMAN CUT IN...
THAT'S STUPID TALK, GRANT! LOW FLYING'S OUR BUSINESS -- IT SAVES OUR NECKS! ALL THE MORE REASON THAT WE SHOULD PRACTISE ALL WE CAN.
YOU'LL BE GLAD OF EVERY BIT OF LOW FLYING PRACTICE YOU CAN GET BEFORE LONG. I CAN'T SAY MORE...

WITH TEMPERS BARELY COOLING, THE CANADIANS MADE OFF TO THE MESS. AS JOHNNIE FOLLOWED, HE FOUND WESLEY GOODMAN STILL BESIDE HIM...
TAKE NO NOTICE OF THEM, JOHNNIE. GUS HAD BEEN WITH US A LONG TIME. THEY DON'T LIKE SEEING HIM GO THAT WAY. IT SEEMS A PITY THE BOYS CAN'T BE TOLD THIS SPECIAL TARGET YOU HINTED AT. MIGHT MAKE THINGS KINDA EASIER.
NOT A CHANCE, WES... A LEAK MIGHT WARN THE ENEMY JUST HOW NEAR THE INVASION IS.

LOW-LEVEL ATTACK WORK WAS ONE OF THE MOST DANGEROUS JOBS OF THE FLYING WAR. JOHNNIE COULD UNDERSTAND WHY THESE MEN RESENTED ANY SEEMINGLY UNNECESSARY RISKS...
THEY'RE A TOUGH MOB... BUT IT'S A TOUGH JOB. WHATEVER THIS MISSION IS, IF IT CAN BE DONE, THESE BOYS WILL DO IT!
R.A.F.

Chapter 2. TENSION MOUNTS

AFTER THAT TRAGIC INCIDENT, THERE FOLLOWED DAYS OF BARELY-CONCEALED RANCOUR. THEN CAME A CHANGE IN ROUTINE...

WE'RE COMING OFF OFS. FOR A SPELL–BUT I HAVE BEEN INSTRUCTED TO STEP UP OUR LOW LEVEL FLYING PRACTICE. IN FACT, A DUMMY TARGET HAS BEEN COOKED UP FOR US.

WITHIN THE HOUR, THE TYPHOONS WERE RACING TOWARDS THE PRACTICE RANGE—AND AS ALWAYS, JOHNNIE'S SHARP DEMANDS HAD THE MEN CURSING PROTESTINGLY...
NOT LOW ENOUGH, RED FOUR! GET LOWER!
AW, HECK! QUIT BAWLING!

AS THE MORNING WORE ON, THEIR LEADER INSISTENT VOICE BEGAN TO FRAY THE PILOTS' NERVES. IN SHEER REVOLT, GRANT SCULLY PULLED HIS STICK BACK...
HEY! WHAT ARE YOU GOING FOR, SCULLY—THE ALTITUDE RECORD?
SARCASTIC CUSS!

SCULLY SNARLED INTO HIS MICROPHONE IN A FIT OF SUDDEN ANGER...
WHY DON'T YOU COME DOWN AND SHOW US INSTEAD OF STICKING UP THERE, NICE AND SAFE!

JOHNNIE'S REACTION WAS INSTANTANEOUS.
RIGHT, BY GLORY... I'LL SHOW THE LOT OF YOU!

FURIOUSLY INTENT ON ANSWERING SCULLY'S CHALLENGE, JOHNNIE HAD NO EYES FOR A DESTROYER WHICH HAD ARRIVED ON THE SCENE, BRINGING A PARTY OF INTERESTED SERVICE SPECTATORS.
IS THAT BLACK SQUARE THE TARGET?
YES, SIR... AND HERE COMES ANOTHER TYPHOON.

UNNOTICED, THE DESTROYER'S BOWS HAD SET UP A RIPPLING WAVE WHICH CREPT ACROSS JOHNNIE'S WATER-FLAT APPROACH TO THE TARGET...
I'LL SHOW SCULLY AND CO JUST WHAT ZERO FLYING REALLY IS!

TOO LATE, JOHNNIE SAW THE MOVING WALL OF WATER IN HIS PATH...
GOOD GRIEF!

JOHNNIE WAS FLUNG VIOLENTLY FORWARD IN HIS HARNESS AS THE TYPHOON'S HEAVY NOSE PLOUGHED INTO THE SEA...

NEXT MOMENT, THE ROARING WATERS CLOSED OVER THE COCKPIT AS THE PLANE PLUNGED BENEATH THE SURFACE. FRANTICALLY, JOHNNIE STRUGGLED TO FREE HIMSELF...

WITH THE BRUTE FORCE OF PANIC, HE FORCED THE COCKPIT COVER OPEN, THEN FOUND HIMSELF CAUGHT BY HIS PARACHUTE HARNESS. HE THUMPED DESPERATELY AT THE CENTRAL CATCH AND THE STRAPS FLEW APART...

HIS HEAD REELING FROM LACK OF AIR, JOHNNIE FOUGHT HIS WAY UPWARDS...

AFTER WHAT SEEMED AN ETERNITY, HE BROKE SURFACE, HIS LUNGS GASPING AGONISINGLY FOR LIFE-GIVING AIR...
I...I MADE IT!

THE DESTROYER'S COMMANDER HAD ACTED SWIFTLY. ALREADY, THE SHIP'S WHA!.ER WAS RACING TO THE SCENE, AND JOHNNIE WAS HAULED FROM THE SEA BY WILLING HANDS.
RIGHT, LIE HIM FLAT AND GET THE WATER OUT OF HIS LUNGS!
AYE, AYE, SIR.

JOHNNIE WAS CARRIED BACK TO STATION SICK-QUARTERS, BUT NO ADVICE OF THE MEDICAL OFFICER COULD KEEP HIM THERE. IT WAS TYPICAL OF WESLEY GOODMAN TO BE THE FIRST TO GREET THE SQUADRON LEADER'S REAPPEARANCE...
HOW ARE YOU, SKIPPER? BY GOLLY, YOU MUST BE THE IRON MAN HIMSELF!
I FEEL OKAY, WES. LET'S GET BACK TO WORK!

IF THE REST OF THE SQUADRON FELT ANY SYMPATHY, THEIR FACES DID NOT SHOW IT. WESLEY GOODMAN HAD A QUICK WORD WITH HIS LEADER...
DON'T MIND THE BOYS TOO MUCH, SKIPPER. THEY RECKON YOUR ACCIDENT IS JUST ANOTHER REASON WHY THEY SHOULD QUIT THIS LOW-LEVEL FLYING.
I'LL SPEAK TO THEM.

JOHNNIE LET GRANT SCULLY HAVE HIS SAY FIRST...
SO WE GO LOW... BUT NOT SO TARNATION LOW AS TO LEAVE A MAN NO CHANCE IF HE SLIPS... LIKE WHAT HAPPENED TO YOU.
YEAH, THAT'S RIGHT, SKIP!
MAKES SENSE TO US!

LOOKING INTO THOSE HARD-BONED CANADIAN FACES, FLUSHED WITH INDIGNATION, JOHNNIE JARVIS KNEW THAT HE DARE NOT YIELD AN INCH TO HIS PILOTS...
I WISH I COULD AGREE WITH YOU. BUT I'M TOLD THAT OUR ROCKETS WILL NEVER HIT THIS SPECIAL TARGET UNLESS WE *DO* FLY AT WATER LEVEL.

BRANT SCULLY CAME CLOSE, HIS EYES BLACK PINPOINTS OF ANGER...
YOU MEAN YOU'LL RISK SOMEBODY ELSE BUYING IT?
I MEAN JUST THAT, SCULLY!

GIVING JOHNNIE A LONG HOSTILE STARE, GRANT SCULLY SAID NO MORE BUT LED THE OTHERS AWAY. THE SQUADRON LEADER WATCHED THEM GO, FILLED WITH MISGIVINGS...
IF SOMEBODY ELSE DOES BUY IT, THERE'LL BE THE DEVIL TO PAY FROM THESE CANUCKS.

THAT NIGHT, SLEEP CAME HARD TO JOHNNIE JARVIS AS HE RE-LIVED THOSE HORRIFYING MOMENTS OF HIS PLUNGE BENEATH THE WAVES...
SCULLY'S RIGHT...ONE SLIP AND YOU'VE HAD IT!
IT HAD HAPPENED SO SUDDENLY, SO EASILY. HOW COULD HE DRIVE THESE MEN IN SUICIDALLY LOW-LEVEL FLYING WITH THE MEMORY OF THAT EXPERIENCE FRESH IN HIS MIND?

Chapter 3. THIRD VICTIM
THE NEXT DAY, RED-EYED FROM LOSS OF SLEEP, JOHNNIE JARVIS WAS CALLED TO THE BRIEFING ROOM. THE INTELLIGENCE OFFICER GREETED HIM WITH AN OFERATIONAL ORDER...
IT SEEMS COMMAND ARE SWITCHING YOU BACK TO LIVE TARGETS, JOHNNIE. HERE'S A PICTURE OF IT.
GOOD HEAVENS, IT LOOKS LIKE A SEASIDE PIER!

JOHNNIE WENT OVER THE DETAILS WITH THE OTHER AND THEN CALLED A BRIEFING. FACING THOSE UNFRIENDLY FACES, THE SQUADRON LEADER FOUND THAT NOT EVEN THE STRANGE NATURE OF THEIR TARGET COULD RAISE A SMILE...
IT'S AN ORDINARY SEASIDE PIER BUT STRENGTHENED AND ARMED WITH A BATTERY OF TWENTY-MILLIMETRE FLAK. HERE IS A PICTURE OF IT WHICH YOU CAN ALL STUDY. THE OBJECT OF THE ATTACK IS TO PUNCH THE PIER'S LEGS FROM UNDER IT.

GRIMLY, HE PRESSED ON...
AS YOU CAN GUESS, THE ONLY WAY YOU'LL DO IT WILL BE TO GO IN ABSOLUTELY FLAT ON THE WATER.

NOTHING MORE WAS SAID AND JOHNNIE FOLLOWED THE TIGHT-LIPPED PLOTS OUT ON TO THE TARMAC. WATCHING THEM MOUNT INTO THEIR WAITING AIRCRAFT, HIS OWN NEW-FOUND DREAD CAME CROWDING BACK...
IT'S UP TO ME TO GO IN REALLY LOW AND SHOW THESE BEGGARS. BUT IF THE SEA'S CHOPPY...IF I JUST CLIP AN UNLUCKY WAVE-TOP...

THANKFUL THAT THERE WAS NO PROLONGED WAITING IN WHICH HIS FEARS MIGHT GROW SQUADRON LEADER JARVIS LED HIS TYPHOON SQUADRON SCREAMING OFF THE RUNWAY.

IT DEMANDED IRON SELF-CONTROL TO KEEP HIS OWN PLANE SKIMMING THE HUNGRY-LOOKING WAVES. BUT HE KNEW EVERY PILOT'S EYE WAS ON HIS LEADING AIRCRAFT, WATCHING, JUDGING...
IF I LET UP NOW, I'LL NEVER HOLD THESE CANUCKS ANOTHER MINUTE!

RIGID WITH CONCENTRATION, JOHNNIE MANAGED TO KEEP THEM ALL AT THE LOW LEVEL HE DEMANDED OF HIMSELF, HIS MIND SEARCHING FOR THE REASON OF AN ATTACK ON SUCH AN UNUSUAL TARGET.
I GUESS SOMEBODY WANTS TO FIND OUT IF WE REALLY CAN FIRE ROCKETS AT WATER LEVEL.

HIS NAVIGATION WAS, AS USUAL, DEAD ACCURATE...
I CAN SEE THE PROMENADE.. THE PIER..
IN THAT MOMENT OF THE ATTACK, HIS FEAR OF THE JOSTLING WAVES BENEATH WAS FORGOTTEN...

AT ABSOLUTE WATER-LEVEL, HE AIMED HIS TYPHOON AT THE TARGET— AND LET FLY HIS ROCKETS...
CAUGHT BASKING IN THE SUMMER SUN, THE GERMAN GUNNERS WERE MAKING A DESPAIRING SCRAMBLE FOR THEIR GUNS.
JOHNNIE'S FIRST PAIR OF ROCKETS WERE DEFLECTED BY THE WATER, BUT THE REST OF HIS SALVO ~360 LBS. OF EXPLOSIVE WARHEAD~ SMASHED HOME...

HARD BEHIND THEIR LEADER CAME MORE TYPHOONS, MORE FLARING ROCKETS TO SPLINTER THE PIER'S TIMBERS LIKE MATCH-STICKS.
THE PIER'S COLLAPSING!

JOHNNIE LOST ALL ANXIETY IN THE HEARTENING SUCCESS OF THIS ATTACK. HE CAUGHT SIGHT OF WESLEY GOODMAN'S TYPHOON, HUGGING THE WATER AND ABOUT TO DELIVER THE KNOCK-OUT...
GOOD BOY, WES!

NEXT SECOND, JOHNNIE'S HEART TURNED OVER AS HE SAW GOODMAN'S WING-TIP CLIP THE WATER...
NO! UP, WES-UP!

WITH ANGUISHED EYES, JOHNNIE SAW THE SWIFT DEATH PLUNGE...
AND AGAIN HE WAS FEELING THE TERROR OF HIS OWN ENTOMBMENT IN A COCKPIT...

GRANT SCULLY'S HORROR TURNED SWIFTLY TO RAGE—RAGE AGAINST THE MAN HE FELT RESPONSIBLE...
FIRST GUS BAKER... AND NOW, WES GOODMAN.. AND ALL THROUGH THIS JARVIS GUY AND HIS SUICIDAL LOW-FLYING IDEAS!

JOHNNIE'S FIRST IMPULSE WAS TO CIRCLE IN THE HOPE THAT WESLEY GOODMAN MIGHT SURFACE. BUT SWIFT-MOVING SPECKS AGAINST WHITE CLOUD CAUGHT HIS EYE...
BANDITS! BANDITS UP-SUN! BREAK! BREAK!

THE GERMAN FIGHTERS WERE MOVING IN FAST. DESPERATELY, THE TYPHOON PILOTS PULLED BACK ON THEIR CONTROL COLUMNS.
CLIMB! GET HEIGHT!

THE SLOWER-MOVING TYPHOONS WERE NO MATCH FOR THE FAST AND DEADLY ROCKET WULF 190'S. THE MOST EFFICENT FIGHTER THE GERMANS EVER PRODUCED. ONE TYPHOON CAUGHT THE RAKING BLAST OF THEIR CANNON FIRE...

A SECOND TYPHOON, CAUGHT IN ITS LABOURED CLIMB, PRESENTED AN EASY TARGET FOR A FOCKE-WULF DIVING AT TOP SPEED...

IT WAS ONLY JOHNNIE'S VETERAN EXPERIENCE THAT BNUNS HIM HIGH AND CLEAR OF THE ENEVIYTS FIRST WHIRLWIND ATTACK. THEN, WITH HEIGHT TO SPARE, HE SHAPED FOR A SAVASE REPLY...
NOW IT'S *OUR* TURN, FRITZ !

HIS THUMB JASBED THE GUN BUTTON AND THE SCREAM OF HIS ENGINE WAS DROWNED IN A ROAR OF 20-MILLIMETRE CANNONS.

A VICIOUS SEVEN-SECOND BURST SENT THE FOCKE-WULF INTO A SPIRALLING DIVE, ITS PILOT SLUMPED OVER THE CONTROLS

SUDDENLY, THE SKY WAS CLEAR OF ENEMY PLANES CALLING THE TYPHOONS INTO FORMATION JOHNNIE JARVIS LED HIS BATTERED MEN HOME HIS OWN HEART WAS HEAVY...
WES GOODMAN – THE ONLY ONE I COULD CALL A FRIEND – AND NOW HE'S GONE

THE MOMENT JOHNNIE CLIMBED OUT OF HIS COCKPIT, HE SENSED TROUBLE...
HEY, JARVIS!
GRANT SCULLY'S CALL HAD A HOSTILE RING ABOUT IT...

THE TOUGH TORONTO MAN CAME STRIDING OVER JOHNNIE BRACED HIMSELF
GUS BAKER AND NOW WES GOODMAN! I SAID YOU'D KILL US ALL!
TAKE THAT BACK, SCULLY!

IT WAS BAD ENOUGH LOSING THE ONLY FRIEND HE HAD, BUT TO BE BLAMED FOR HIS TRAGIC DEATH WAS TOO MUCH. JOHNNIE'S TEMPER FLARED...
YOU KEEP YOUR MOUTH SHUT, BEFORE I...
...SHUT IT FOR ME? WHY DON'T YOU TRY IT? MURDERER!

SOMETHING SEEMED TO SNAP INSIDE JARVIS, AND STUNG BEYOND ENDURANCE, HE LASHED OUT...
UGH!

WHITE AND SHAKEN, JOHNNIE JARVIS STARED DOWN AT THE CRUMPLED FORM OF HIS TORMENTOR. THEN HE SWUNG ON HIS HEEL AND STRODE AWAY...
I MUST BE CRAZY! I'LL BE GLAD WHEN THIS SPECIAL TARGET BUSINESS IS OVER. THEN I'LL ASK FOR A TRANSFER.

STILL SHAKEN FROM HIS BRUSH WITH SCULLY, JOHNNIE JARVIS WAS JUST ABOUT TO DRIVE OFF IN HIS ANCIENT SPORTS CAR WHEN THE CHEERY VOICE OF THE INTELLIGENCE OFFICER HAILED HIM...
IT'S COME, SIR!
WHAT'S COME?
THE SPECIAL TARGET..AT LEAST, YOUR INSTRUCTIONS FOR IT.

JOHNNIE CUT HIS ENGINE AND JUMPED OUT TO QUESTION THE I.O. FURTHER...
THE SQUADRON IS TO FIT LONG RANGE TANKS AND FLY TO TREPANNORTH IN CORNWALL.
WHEN?
TONIGHT, SIR!

Chapter 4. LONG HAUL

THAT AFTERNOON SAW FEVERISH PREPARATION. BY EVENING, JOHNNIE JARVIS WAS LEADING HIS SQUADRON OVER THE WILD CORNISH LANDSCAPE. THE QUESTION THAT NAGGED AT THEIR MINDS PARTICULARLY WORRIED JOHNNIE.

WHY SO FAR WEST? WHAT THE DICKENS CAN THIS SPECIAL TARGET BE?

AFTER A TERSE GREETING, THE BIG MAN WENT AHEAD TO THE BRIEFING ROOM WHERE PRESENTLY HE ANNOUNCED HIMSELF READY...
THE A.O.C. WILL BRIEF YOU HIMSELF.

THE MEN'S STARTLED EYES FOCUSSED ON A DETAILED PLASTER MODEL OF A SHIPPING HARBOUR-BUT WITH AN OMINOUS DIFFERENCE.
THE U-BOAT PEN BASED ON THE ILE DE NEZ, OFF THE WEST COAST OF FRANCE-YOUR TARGET FOR TOMORROW, GENTLEMEN!

IN SOMBRE TONES THE AIR VICE-MARSHAL WENT ON TO EXPLAIN THAT NO AMOUNT OF BOMBS, EVEN OF THE BLOCK-BUSTER TYPE, HAD MADE ANY IMPRESSION ON THIS IMMENSELY STRONG SUBMARINE BASE...

BUT WE ARE OF THE OPINION THAT A ROCKET ATTACK MIGHT DO THE TRICK.

SIR BARTLETT HAD THE ROOM DARKENED AND CALLED FOR A PROJECTED PICTURE OF A U-BOAT FITTED WITH THE NEWEST GERMAN INVENTION—THE SCHNORKEL BREATHING DEVICE...
WITH THIS SPECIAL DEVICE, THESE U-BOATS AT ILE DE NEZ CAN SLIP THROUGH INTO THE CHANNEL AND BECOME A SERIOUS MENACE TO OUR INVASION SHIPPING. THEY MUST BE DESTROYED!

THE PICTURE GAVE PLACE TO ANOTHER—THE CAVERN-LIKE ENTRANCE TO THE U-BOAT PEN AT ILE DE NEZ. SIR BARTLETT'S DRY TONES WENT ON...
THANKS TO THOSE LOCK-GATES YOU SAW IN THE MODEL, THE GERMANS CAN MAINTAIN A WATER-LEVEL WHICH KEEPS THEIR U-BOATS ALMOST OUT OF SIGHT. SO FIRST, YOU'LL HAVE TO BREACH THE LOCK-GATES! ANY QUESTIONS?

THE BRIEFING CONCLUDED, JOHNNIE JARVIS BRACED HIMSELF TO GIVE HIS INSTRUCTIONS IN THE METHOD OF ATTACK...
WE'LL SPLIT INTO TWO FLIGHTS - THE FIRST WILL BREACH THE LOCK-GATES, THE SECOND WILL FOLLOW UP AND BLITZ THE U-BOATS!

IT WAS PLAIN HIS MEN THOUGHT THE WHOLE THING A SUICIDE MISSION, BUT NOBODY QUESTIONED JOHNNIE'S PLAN OF ATTACK.
IF YOU HAVE TO BALE OUT, THERE'LL BE A LINE OF BRITISH SUBMARINES ON THE ROUTE BACK TO PICK YOU UP.

AFTER JOHNNIE HAD OUTLINED HIS PLAN, IT WAS SCULLY WHO POSED THE BIG QUESTION...
BUSTING THE LOCK-GATES WILL BE A PIECE OF CAKE COMPARED TO THE SUB PEN ITSELF. WHO'S DOING WHICH?
YOUR FLIGHT CAN TAKE THE GATES, SCULLY...YOU CAN LEAVE THE U-BOATS TO MY FLIGHT. SATISFIED?
CANADA
JOHNNIE KNEW THE SECOND ATTACK WAVE WOULD BE THE MORE DANGEROUS. HIS FEAR OF DROWNING SURGED UP ANEW AND HE KNEW HE MUST DESTROY IT FOR ALL TIME...

AT FIRST LIGHT THE NEXT MORNING, 198 ROCKET TYPHOON SQUADRON BROKE EVERYONE'S SLEEP WITH A ROARING TAKE-OFF...

TO SAVE FUEL, JOHNNIE PLOTTED THEIR COURSE ACROSS THE BRETON PENINSULA AT ZERO FEET. THEY WHIPPED THE TREE-TOPS WITH THEIR SLIPSTREAM...
MA FOI!
US K

BUT THIS LOW-LEVEL STRATEGY WAS ONLY PARTIALLY SUCCESSFUL IN ITS AIM TO AVOID DETECTION...
ACHTUNG! TAIFUN!

FAST THOUGH THE TYPHOONS WERE, THE ALARM SPED FASTER. A BARRAGE-BALLOON UNIT WAS ALERTED IN THE RAIDERS' EXPECTED PATH...
FASTER, YOU DOLTS - FASTER!

JOHNNIE SPOTTED THE LURKING TRAP IN THE NICK OF TIME AND PULLED EVERYONE AFTER HIM IN A ZOOMING CLIMB – ONLY TO MEET A VICIOUS GUN BARRAGE THAT WAS WAITING FOR THEM...
BREAK!
HOLY MACKEREL!

BUCK CALDWELL, THE EX-POLICEMAN FROM EDMONTON, WAS MORTALLY HIT...

TAKING SWIFT EVASIVE ACTION, JOHNNIE ALTERED COURSE TOWARDS THE SAFETY OF THE OPEN SEA. PRESENTLY, JUDGING THEIR TARGET TO BE DUE SOUTH, HE TURNED THROUGH 90 DEGREES.

SOON, AN ALDIS LAMP FLASHING BELOW THEM CAUGHT JOHNNIE'S EYE...IT WAS GOOD TO KNOW THAT FRIENDLY SUBMARINES WERE ALERT TO THEIR ARRIVAL.

FOR TWELVE, NERVE-RACKING MINUTES, THE SQUADRON LEAP-FROGGED THE ROLLERS OF THE BAY OF BISCAY. SUDDENLY, JOHNNIE STRAINED FORWARD.
THE TARGET! I CAN SEE THE HARBOUR ENTRANCE!

NOW HE COULD BREAK RADIO SILENCE . .
OKAY, IN YOU GO, SCULLY... GOOD LUCK!
WE'RE ON OUR WAY!

Chapter 5. FINEST HOUR

BUT THE GATES GIANT-TIMSERED AND IRON-BOUND, WERE A TOUGHER PROPOSITION THAN EXPECTED. THEY DID NOT YIELD TO THE FIRST ATTACK. SCULLY'S SALVO ONLY PUNCHED GREAT HOLES IN THEM

SCULLY HAD RUN THE GAUNTLET UNSCATHED, BUT THE NEXT IN LINE WAS CAUGHT IN A STINGING CROSSFIRE...

THE STRICKEN TYPHOON SUDDENLY BLEW UP, FORCING THE OTHERS BEHIND TO BREAK FORMATION...
WATCH OUT!
BREAK!
GOOD GRIEF!

SEEING THE LEADING ATTACK FALTER IN ITS VITAL ROLE, JOHNNIE WENT DIVING IN LIKE AN AVENGING FURY, YELLING AT THE SCATTERED TYPHOONS...
THOSE LOCK GATES MUST BE SMASHED! COME ON, TRY AGAIN!
EVERY SECOND LOST MEANT A REDOUBLING OF THE ENEMY'S DEFENCES.

WITH THE COURAGE OF DESPAIR, THE THREE FALTERING PILOTS FASTENED ON TO JOHNNIE'S TAIL AS HE SPED TOWARDS THE TARGET...
GET LOW!
NO ONE GUESSED THAT JOHNNIE'S SHARP COMMAND WAS MEANT AS MUCH FOR HIS OWN DREAD-FILLED MIND AS FOR THEM. NEVER DID THE EVIL-LOOKING WAVES LICK SO HUNGRILY CLOSE...

TIGHT-LIPPED, JOHNNIE STORMED THE HARBOUR GAP AND BORE DOWN ON THE LOCK-GATES. SIX OF HIS EIGHT ROCKETS SPED LIKE FIERY ARROWS...
GOT THEM!

HE WRENCHED THE TYPHOON INTO A TEARING CLIME AND TWISTED TO SEE THE LOCK GATES CRUMBLING, AS SALVO AFTER SALVO SLAMMED HOME.

WITHIN THE U-BOAT PEN ITSELF, THE SUDDEN OUTPOURING OF PENT-UP WATER SPREAD INSTANT ALARM...
ROCKETS! TYPHOONS! THEY SMASH THE GATES!
THE WATER-LEVEL IS DROPPING FAST!
EVERYONE OUT—QUICKLY!

JOHNNIE JARVIS SWUNG BACK TO HIS OWN FLIGHT CIRCLING ABOVE THE COAST CLOSE BY...
RIGHT, THIS IS IT! FOLLOW ME... AND KEEP LOW!
ROGER!

ONCE AGAIN, THE SQUADRON LEADER LED HIS FLIGHT CLOSE TO THE WAVE-TOPS THROUGH THE VICIOUS BARRAGE OF FLAK.
STRAIGHT THROUGH THAT GAP!
RIGHT BEHIND YOU, SKIP!

EYES NARROWED, JOHNNIE JUDGED THE GAP AHEAD AND ARROWED THROUGH. . .
I'M GOING IN!
..BUT BEHIND HIM, PILOT OFFICER CRANE WAS ANOTHER WHO PAID THE SUPREME PRICE IN THE DESPERATE ATTACK . . .

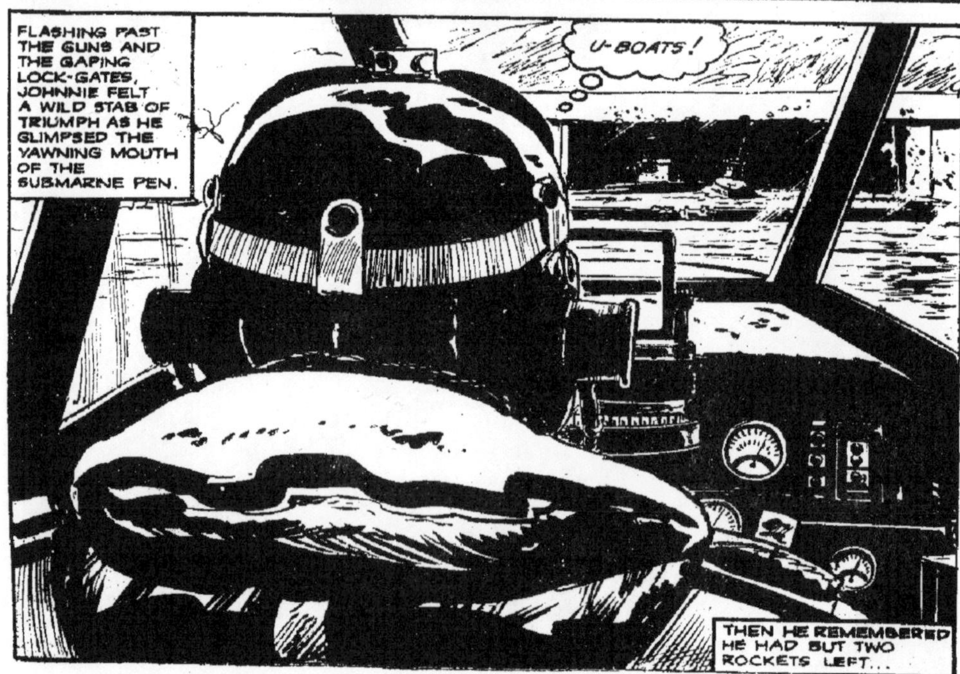
FLASHING PAST THE GUNS AND THE GAPING LOCK-GATES, JOHNNIE FELT A WILD STAB OF TRIUMPH AS HE GLIMPSED THE YAWNING MOUTH OF THE SUBMARNE PEN.
U-BOATS!
THEN HE REMEMBERED HE HAD BUT TWO ROCKETS LEFT...

THERE WAS NO TIME FOR CAREFUL AIM. HE THUMPED THE ROCKET RELEASE...
US O Y

BUT THE FLARING PROJECTILES MISSED THEIR TARGET BY INCHES, SMASHING HARMLESSLY AGAINST THAT IMPREGNABLE MASS OF CONCRETE...

ANGRY WITH HIMSELF, JOHNNIE SWUNG CLEAR ONLY TO SEE THE FOLLOWING SALVO STRIKE SHORT INTO THE WATER...

BUT WORSE WAS TO FOLLOW. THE THIRD TYPHOON LIMPED OFF WITH A SHATTERED WING AND THE FOURTH HIT THE LOCK-GATES IN A BLINDING EXPLOSION...

THE LAST TWO PILOTS WERE FLUNG OFF THEIR MARK AND THEIR ROCKETS SOARED OFF INTO EMPTY AIR...
LOOK OUT!

JOHNNIE GROANED IN DESPAIR, FOR THE AGONISING FACT HIT HIM LIKE AN ICE-COLD SHOCK OF WATER...
EVERY ROCKET GONE... AND THE U-BOATS AREN'T TOUCHED! WE'VE FAILED!
SOMETHING HAD TO BE DONE.. SOMETHING DESPERATE...

HIGH OUT OF HARM'S WAY, THE REST OF THE SQUADRON STARED IN HORROR AS JOHNNIE'S TYPHOON PLUNGED DOWN AGAIN INTO THE CAULDRON OF THE TARGET...
WHAT'S THAT CRAZY JARVIS UP TO NOW?
HE CAN'T DO A THING WITHOUT ROCKETS!

JOHNNIE JARVIS KNEW THAT HE WOULD HAVE TO FACE THAT NIGHTMARE RUN ALL OVER AGAIN, OVER THE BLUSTERING WAVE-TOPS, THROUGH THAT KILLING LOOPHOLE OF MURDEROUS FIRE...

SPRAY SMEARED JOHNNIE'S VISION, BULLETS THUDDED AND TORE AT THE TYPHOON'S FRAME AND THE THUNDEROUS BELLOW OF THE POWERFUL MOTOR CRASHED AT HIS EARDRUMS...

NEXT INSTANT, THE MOTOR CHECKED, COUGHED, AND PICKED UP ONCE MORE. BUT IN THAT SPLIT SECOND, THE TYPHOON HAD SCOOPED SEA WATER WITH ITS WING-TIP...

IT TOOK ALL THE PILOT'S STRENGTH TO WRENCH THE SHUDDERING PLANE INTO LEVEL FLIGHT AGAIN. THEN, MIRACULOUSLY, HE WAS THROUGH THE FEARSOME GAP.
THE FOUR CANNONS BEGAN TO HAMMER DEFIANTLY...

THE DARK, GAPING MAW OF THE PEN WAS LARGE IN THE TYPHOON'S SIGHTS ~ AND JOHNNIE SAW HIS SHOTS SLAMMING INTO IT...
THIS IS IT ~ NOW OR NEVER!

NEXT MOMENT, A REFUELLING PONTOON FLARED INTO A SHEET OF FLAME. JOHNNIE HAD HIT ITS FUEL TANK...
AGH!
LOOK OUT!

A SEARING ORANGE FLASH LIT THE DARKNESS OF THE CONCRETE CAVERN AS THE PONTOON BLEW UP, TOUCHING OFF A REFUELLING HOSE. A TORRENT OF LIQUID FIRE GUSHED INTO THE WATER...
HIMMEL!
RUN FOR YOUR LIVES!

THEN A LARGER FUEL BOWSER BLEW UP, AND WHAT WAS FIRST A SCRAMBLE NOW BECAME A PANIC-STRICKEN STAMPEDE...

JOHNNIE HAD FLUNG HIS PLANE SKYWARDS ONLY FEET FROM THE PEN AND BANKING ROUND, HE CAST A QUICK GLANCE BELOW...
EXPLOSIVES ! MUST BE TORPEDOES GOING UP !
IT WAS SUCCESS FAR BEYOND HIS WILDEST HOPES...

THE BRIEF GLARE INSIDE THE SUBMARINE PEN SUDDENLY ERUPTED INTO A MIGHTY EXPLOSION AS THE MASSIVELY THICK ROOF SPLIT APART...

IN SOBER, THANKFUL RELIEF, JOHNNIE CLIMBED TO REJOIN HIS SQUADRON. THEN CAME AN OMINOUS CLATTER FROM BENEATH HIS ENGINE COWLING AND A STREAM OF SMOKE TRAILED FROM THE STUBBY EXHAUSTS.
SOMETHING'S WRONG!
SEA WATER, SCOOPED UP IN THAT PERILOUS RUN-UP, WAS WREAKING HAVOC WITH THE TYPHOON'S ENGINE.

THE CIRCLING SQUADRON HAD WATCHED JOHNNIE'S DARINGLY SUCCESSFUL ATTACK IN AWE AND IT WAS GRANT SCULLY WHO SENSED THAT SOMETHING WAS AMISS . . .
HEY, JARVIS IS IN TROUBLE!

THE HARD-HEADED CANADIANS GATHERED PROTECTIVELY ABOUT THEIR LEADER . . .
KEEP GOING, JOHNNIE!
WE'RE KEEPING OUR FINGERS CROSSED, SKIP!
THANKS, BOYS — BUT I SHALL HAVE TO DITCH HER SOON!

FOR SEVERAL MILES THEY CROWDED AROUND THE FAILING TYPHOON WHILE IT SANK LOWER AND LOWER TOWARDS THE HUNGRY WAVES.
THE SUBS WILL PICK ME UP. YOU CHAPS GET HOME . . . FUEL MUST BE GETTING SHORT.
NIX, JOHNNIE . . . WE'RE GONNER SEE YOU ON A SUB FIRST!

FIVE MORE MINUTES OF LIMPING FLIGHT AND JOHNNIE'S MOTOR COUGHED INTO A LAST AN
FINAL SILENCE. HE CLAWED HIS WAY OUT OF THE COCKPIT AS THE FIGHTER BEGAN TO SPIN.

THOUGH THEY COULD ILL-SPARE THE FUEL, GRANT SCULLY AND THE REST WOULD NOT LEAVE UNTIL THEY HAD CONTACTED ONE OF THE SUBMARINES MARKING THE ROUTE BACK TO BASE.
SIGNAL, 'MESSAGE UNDERSTOOD. WILL PROCEED IMMEDIATELY.'
AYE, AYE, SIR.

SATISFIED, THE SQUADRON RACED BACK TO REASSURE THEIR WAVE-SOAKED LEADER, HIS YELLOW LIFE-JACKET SHOWING CLEARLY AGAINST THE DARK SEA. THEN, IN FINAL SALUTE, THEY DIPPED THEIR WINGS AND TURNED FOR BASE.
YOU KNOW, HE'S QUITE A GUY! MAYBE WE WERE A BUNCH OF DUMB SOUR-PUSSES, FELLERS!
I RECKON YOU'VE GOT SOMETHING THERE, GRANT!

IT WAS LONELY FOR JOHNNIE IN THE WATER WHEN THEY HAD GONE BUT BEFORE LONG, HE HEARD THE DEEP THROB OF THE SUBMARINE'S ENGINES...
AHOY, THERE!
AH! MY PASSAGE HOME... THANKS, SCULLY!
WATCHING THE SLEEK LINES OF THE SUBMARINE PUSH TOWARDS HIM, JOHNNIE JARVIS AT LAST FELT THAT PEACE WHICH COMES WITH DIFFICULTIES FACED AND CONQUERED.

A WEEK LATER, ON THAT EPIC 6TH. JUNE, 1944, SQUADRON LEADER JOHNNIE JARVIS WAS ABLE TO LOOK DOWN WITH AN EASY MIND ON THE GREATEST SEABORNE ASSAULT IN ALL HISTORY.
HIS SUPREMELY TOUGH TASK HAD PROVED TO BE THREE-FOLD — THE OVERCOMING OF HIS OWN FEARS, THE VANQUISHING OF PERSONAL ENMITY AND THE UTTER DESTRUCTION OF A LURKING MENACE TO THE INVASION SHIPS BELOW.
JOHNNIE JARVIS COULD NEVER MAKE UP HIS MIND WHICH OF THE THREE GAVE HIM THE BIGGEST KICK.

The RED DEVILS

OUT OF THE BATTLE-FILLED HISTORY OF THE SECOND WORLD WAR BLAZES THE STIRRING SAGA OF A GREAT REGIMENT. IN THOSE YEARS OF BITTER COMBAT IT WON PRIDE AND HONOUR SECOND TO NONE... *YET IT WAS THE YOUNGEST FIGHTING REGIMENT IN THE BRITISH ARMY!*
HATED AND FEARED BY THE GERMANS, ITS MEN JUMPED INTO BATTLE FROM THE SKIES...FOR THEY WERE THE PARACHUTISTS WHO HAD EARNED FOR THEMSELVES THE NAME OF....

Chapter 1. TO THE LAST MAN
SUMMER, 1942. ALLIED FORCES WERE LOCKED IN RELENTLESS WAR WITH THE JACK-BOOTED HORDES OF NAZI GERMANY... AND IN THE STEAMING JUNGLES OF BURMA, MEN OF A FORGOTTEN ARMY FOUGHT A BITTER BATTLE AGAINST THE JAPANESE...
MESSAGE FROM H.Q., SIR. STRONG ENEMY UNITS REPORTED ADVANCING TOWARDS US. PREPARE FOR HEAVY ATTACK!

IN THE SILENCE, LIEUTENANT DICK NORTON'S GAZE SEARCHED THE GRIM-SET FACES ABOUT HIM. THE MEN OF HIS PLATOON HAD HEARD THAT MESSAGE... AND KNEW WHAT IT MEANT...
WE'RE THE FORWARD TROOPS AND THE JAPS OUTNUMBER US BY FIVE TO ONE! WE'VE GOT TO HOLD THEM BACK UNTIL OUR MAIN POSITIONS ARE READY BEHIND US.

LONG MINUTES TIGHTENED NERVES ALREADY WORN WITH FATIGUE AND MONTHS OF FIGHTING ON THE WITHDRAWAL. THEN A LOW VOICE GRATED HARSHLY...
HERE HE COMES... THE LEADING SCOUT OF THE JAPS, THE REST OF 'EM SHOULD BE RIGHT BEHIND HIM, SIR!
AND HE'S GOING TO LEAD 'EM RIGHT UP TO US BEFORE WE OPEN FIRE! KEEP DEAD QUIET!

THEN THE TREES BECAME ALIVE WITH MOVEMENT AND A WIDESPREAD WAVE OF JAPANESE TROOPS FLOODED SLOWLY UP THE RIDGE SLOPE. THEY WERE BARELY A HUNDRED YARDS FROM THE TOP, WHEN SUDDENLY...
RAPID FIRE!

IN THOSE FIRST DEVASTATING SECONDS, AN INVISIBLE SCYTHE OF FLYING LEAD CUT THE LEADING JAPANESE DOWN LIKE CORN. THEN THE REST WERE SCUTTLING DESPERATELY FOR COVER...
THAT HIT 'EM WHERE IT HURT, SIR!
WE PLAYED THE ONLY ACE WE HAD... SURPRISE! NOW IT'S OUR TURN TO TAKE IT!

THE BRITISH TROOPS DID NOT HAVE LONG TO WAIT. OVER THE CRACKLING RIFLE FIRE A HIGH-PITCHED WHINE SUDDENLY GREW IN THE AIR...
HEADS DOWN! MORTAR FIRE!

A PATTERN OF SEARING ORANGE FLASHES MUSHROOMED AROUND THE BRITISH POSITION WITH VICIOUS CRUMPS...AND SCREAMING STEEL SPLINTERS SLICED MENACINGLY OVER THE RIDGE TOP...

AGAIN THE EARTH SHUDDERED AS IT WAS TORN APARY BY A NEW CLUSTER OF MORTAR BOMBS.
THEY'RE GOING TO CHARGE! GET READY FOR 'EM!

IN A RAGGED LINE THE JAPS SWEPT TOWARDS THE RIDGE TOP... AND CRUMPLED AS THEY MET A WALL OF FLAMING GUN MUZZLES.
RUNNER... URGENT MESSAGE TO THE MORTARS TO PUT HEAVY BARRAGE ON THE ACCURSED ENGLISH!

BUT THE BRITISH POSITION SOMEHOW SURVIVED THE FURY OF THAT MORTAR BOMBARDMENT... AND THE NEXT... THEN ANOTHER. AGAIN AND AGAIN THE JAPANESE CHARGED...ONLY TO BE HURLED BACK. BUT THE PRICE WAS HEAVY...
WE'RE PRACTICALLY SURROUNDED, SIR! NOW THEY'VE GOT A SNIPER UP IN THOSE TREES. AND FIVE OF US LEFT AGAINST THE WHOLE FLIPPING JAP ARMY!
OPERATOR...GET H.Q. TELL THEM WE'RE ALMOST OUT OF AMMUNITION AND REQUEST PERMISSION TO WITHDRAW!

THE WIRELESS OPERATOR SPOKE INTO THE MICROPHONE...TURNED HIS HEAD TO LISTEN ...AND BY A *HAIRSBREADTH* A SNIPER'S BULLET FANNED HIS FACE... **AND SMASHED INTO THE RADIO SET!**
SORRY, SIR... ALL I GOT FROM H.Q. WAS "*DO NOT...*" AND THEN *WHAM!*
ALMOST CERTAIN TO HAVE MEANT NOT TO WITHDRAW! SO WE'VE GOT TO STAY ... UNTIL THE END!

IN THE MANNER SO TYPICAL OF BRAVE MEN, NO MORE WORDS WERE NEEDED. SILENTLY THEY WAITED FOR WHAT HAD TO COME ... THE NEXT ATTACK ... AND THE LAST!
COME AND GET ME, YOU APES... AND PAY FOR THE CHANCE!
AAAGH!

THE DEADLY CHATTER OF THE TOMMY GUN STUTTERED TO A FINAL END AS THE MAGAZINE EMPTIED. BUT STILL DICK NORTON FOUGHT ON... ALONE... MAGNIFICENT IN HIS UNDYING COURAGE; SURROUNDED BY HIS FALLEN FOES...

THEN, TWENTY YARDS FROM THAT GLORIOUSLY BATTLING FIGURE, A JAPANESE LIFTED HIS RIFLE AND FIRED. PAIN EXPLODED IN DICK NORTON'S HEAD, FLOODING THROUGH HIM... AND HE PITCHED FORWARD INTO A YAWNING CAVERN OF BLACKNESS...
DIE, ENGLISHMAN... AS WILL ALL WHO DEFY THE MIGHT OF THE EMPIRE OF NIPPON!

HEEDLESS OF THEIR HEAVY LOSSES, THE JAPANESE SPEARHEAD SWEPT ON. HOURS LATER... INCREDIBLY... A FAINT WHISPERING SIGH ROSE FROM THAT SHATTERED RIDGE TOP.
WOULDN'T... BELIEVE... I'M... STILL... ALIVE... IF... I... DIDN'T... HAVE... THIS... HAMMER... IN... MY... HEAD!

WITH THE WORLD SPINNING ABOUT HIM, AND HIS HEART BEATS THUNDERING IN HIS EARS, DICK STAGGERED TO HIS FEET...
BULLET MUST HAVE CREASED ME... WONDER IS, THE JAPS DIDN'T MAKE SURE I'D HAD IT!

AND SO, STUMBLING AND FALLING, FEEBLY DRAGGING HIMSELF UP AGAIN, DICK NORTON REACHED THE JUNGLE'S EDGE. IN A MOMENT HE WAS LOST IN THE STEAMING MURK OF ITS DEPTHS... AND FROM THE SIGHT OF ANY LIVING MAN.
NOW OUR STORY MUST MOVE IN DISTANCE AND TIME...TO THB BORDERS OF INDIA A HUNDRED MILES WEST... AND A HUNDRED DAYS LATER...

SERGEANT BILL REED'S EYES RAKED THE JUNGLE'S EDGE FOR THE THOUSANDTH TIME THAT DAY... SUDDENLY THEY WIDENED...
GREAT GUNS... A WHITE MAN! AND THAT'S THE REMAINS OF A BRITISH UNIFORM HE'S WEARING!

AS THE STAGGERING FIGURE LURCHED FORWARD UNSTEADILY, A DRAGGING FOOT TRIPPED...
YOU'RE ALL RIGHT NOW, CHUM... I'VE GOT YOU.
MUST... TELL... COLONEL ... ENEMY... BROKE... THROUGH...

THE FAINT VOICE WITHERED AS BILL LOWERED THE FRAIL FORM TO THE GROUND. THEN, BESIDE HIM THE OFFICER GASPED IN DISBELIEF...
IT'S... IT'S LIKE SEEING A GHOST! SERGEANT... THIS MAN IS LIEUTENANT NORTON... YOU REMEMBER HE WAS REPORTED AS BEING WIPED OUT WITH HIS PLATOON THREE MONTHS AGO!

A NERVE FLICKERED AND JUMPED IN THE SERGEANT'S HARD JAW AS HE STARED DOWN AT THE PITIABLE FACE OF DICK NORTON ...
I'LL NEVER FORGET THAT MASSACRE... OR THAT MY BROTHER WAS THE PLATOON CORPORAL!
STRETCHER PARTY... AT THE DOUBLE!

A FEW MINUTES LATER, TWO FIRST AID MEN CAREFULLY CARRIED THE LADEN STRETCHER TO THE UNIT MEDICAL OFFICER'S POST...
IT'S A MIRACLE HOW HE SURVIVED THREE MONTHS IN THE HEART OF THAT BLACK JUNGLE!
YES... AND HOW WAS IT HE WASN'T KILLED WITH MY BROTHER? SOMEHOW HE GOT BACK HIMSELF ...WHY COULDN'T HE HAVE SAVED THE OTHERS, TOO?

FOR THREE DAYS DICK LAY IN A COMA, WATCHED UNCEASINGLY BY A MEDICAL ORDERLY. WHEN FINALLY HIS EYES OPENED, THE BURNING FIRE OF FEVER HAD LEFT HIM...
HOW ARE YOU FEELING, OLD MAN?
I JUST WANT TO SLEEP FOR A MONTH, DOC.
YOU TRY AND DO JUST THAT. I'LL BE BACK LATER!

OUTSIDE THE TENT, THE M.O. SHOOK HIS HEAD AS IF IN DESPAIR... AND THEN WENT OFF TO FIND THE UNIT'S ADJUTANT.
AFTER WHAT THAT YOUNGSTER WENT THROUGH, IT BEATS ME HOW HE'S STILL ALIVE. AND I'LL BET MY BEST STETHOSCOPE HE'LL NEVER BE FIT FOR ACTIVE DUTY AGAIN!
RIGHT, DOC... WE'LL HAVE HIM EVACUATED TO DELHI HOSPITAL BY THE NEXT CONVOY GOING BACK!

STRANGELY ENOUGH HE DOESN'T REMEMBER HIS BATTLE WITH THE JAPS. IT'S A SORT OF WOUND OF THE MIND THAT IS STILL TO HEAL!
DOC... IF NORTON HADN'T HELD THOSE JAPS OFF, THE WHOLE BATTALION WOULD HAVE CAUGHT IT! BUT WHY DIDN'T HE OBEY OUR ORDER ...DO NOT HOLD POSITION ANY LONGER! NOW IT SEEMS WE'LL NEVER KNOW!

Chapter 2. PARACHUTE SCHOOL
DICK NORTON REMEMBERED LITTLE OF THE DAYS WHICH FOLLOWED... ONLY THAT THERE WERE LONG HOURS OF TRAVEL IN AN AMBULANCE FINALLY ENDING AT A MILITARY HOSPITAL IN DELHI...
NOW IS THERE ANYTHING YOU NEED, LIEUTENANT?
ONE THING I DON'T NEED, NURSE, IS THIS FACE FUNGUS! BUT I THINK I'D LOSE MORE SKIN THAN BEARD IF I TRIED TO SHAVE IT OFF!
THAT'S ONE OPERATION THE HOSPITAL BARBER CAN PERFORM!

IT TOOK WEEKS OF PATIENT CARE AND NURSING FOR DICK TO REGAIN HIS STRENGTH. AT LAST HE WAS CALLED BEFORE A MEDICAL BOARD FOR EXAMINATION...
LIEUTENANT NORTON...IT IS THE OPINION OF THIS BOARD THAT YOU CAN NO LONGER BE CONSIDERED FIT FOR ACTIVE SERVICE!

DICK STARED UNBELIEVINGLY AT THE SENIOR MEDICAL OFFICER...
YOU MEAN... I'M FINISHED WITH THE ARMY?
NO... IT'S NOT QUITE LIKE THAT! PHYSICALLY YOU WILL RECOVER COMPLETELY... BUT WE ARE SURE THAT AFTER YOUR ORDEAL, YOUR NERVES WILL NEVER STAND UP TO BATTLE AGAIN! YOU ARE MEDICALLY DOWN GRADED TO NON-COMBATANT!

STRICKEN BY THAT FATEFUL DECISION, DICK STUMBLED FROM THE OFFICE AND IN THE DEPTHS OF DESPAIR REPORTED TO THE HOSPITAL ORDERLY ROOM...
WE'VE BEEN ON TO G.H.Q. FAR EAST, AND FIXED YOUR POSTING. IT'S TO THE PARACHUTE SCHOOL NEAR MANCHESTER AS THE OFFICER IN CHARGE OF TRAINING STORES.

SO WHILE EVERYONE ELSE THERE IS AIRBORNE... I'LL BE CHAIRBORNE!
YOU DON'T KNOW YOUR LUCK, LADDIE... BACK TO DEAR OLD ENGLAND... AND YOUR THIRD PIP GOES WITH THE JOB, CAPTAIN NORTON!

ON THE TROOPSHIP BOUND FOR BELEAGUERED BRITAIN, O HER OFFICERS TRIED TO BE FRIENDLY WITH DICK BUT HIS BLEAK MISERY WAS AN IMPENETRABLE BARRIER...
ONLY TEN DAYS AND WE'LL BE HOME ...WONDERFUL, EH, NORTON?
I SUPPOSE. SO... IF THAT'S WHERE YOU WANT TO BE!

AFTER THAT THEY LEFT HIM ALONE...AND FOUND THEIR OWN REASONS FOR HIS COLDNESS...
SURLY BRUTE THAT NORTON... IS HE BEING SENT HOME IN DISGRACE?
NOTHING LIKE THAT, OLD BOY! HE TOOK A REAL BEATING IN THE JUNGLE ...LOST HIS NERVE... ABSOLUTELY USELESS AS A FIGHTING TYPE NOW!

UNNOTICED, DICK HEARD EVERY WORD...AND EACH ONE WAS A HAMMER BLOW DRIVING HIM DEEPER INTO THE GLOOM OF DEJECTION...
MAYBE THEY'RE RIGHT! EVERY TIME I TRY TO REMEMBER THOSE DAYS IN THE JUNGLE, MY MIND JUST WON'T LET ME...AND THE THOUGHT OF PAIN AND DANGER TURNS ME WEAK AND FAINT!

SO THE DAYS WHICH FOLLOWED BECAME A KIND OF PRIVATE NIGHTMARE FOR DICK. AT LIVERPOOL HE LEFT THE SHIP AND TRAVELLED BY TRAIN TO MANCHESTER ...
CAPTAIN NORTON? I'M FROM THE SCHOOL, SENT TO MEET YOU. I'VE GOT A JEEP...AS I UNDERSTOOD YOU WERE BRINGING SOME SORT OF STORES!
GOOD MORNING, SERGEANT. STORES? ALL I'VE GOT IS MY OWN LUGGAGE ...THIS SUITCASE!

THE SERGEANT CHEERFULLY GRINNED AT DICK... AND THE YOUNG OFFICER STOOD STATUE STILL, FROZEN WITH AMAZEMENT!
WE ONLY GOT NEWS OF YOUR POSTING TO US FOR TRAINING YESTERDAY, SIR.. LUCKILY FOR YOU, BECAUSE WE'RE JUST STARTING A NEW PARACHUTING COURSE TOMORROW!
EXIT
STORES... TRAINING... PARACHUTING... WHAT'S GONE WRONG HERE?

PUZZLED, DICK CLIMBED INTO THE JEEP... AND THEN UNDERSTANDING FLARED LIKE A BRIGHT NEW FLAME IN HIS HEAVY HEART...
BY GLORY... THE SIGNALS FROM INDIA MUST HAVE BECOME MESSED UP! OFFICIALLY I'M HERE FOR PARACHUTE TRAINING... AND NOT TO LOOK AFTER TRAINING STORES! AND IF I BACK OUT OF THIS, IT MEANS I AM FINISHED. BUT I'M GOING TO DO IT... TO PROVE TO MYSELF I'VE STILL GOT SOME NERVE LEFT. I'VE GOT TO CONQUER MY FEAR!

HALF AN HOUR LATER, THE JEEP PASSED THROUGH THE GATES OF AN AIRFIELD OUTSIDE THE CITY...
THREE WEEKS TOUGHENING UP TRAINING, SIR... AND YOU'LL HAVE YOUR FIRST DATE WITH OLD BESSIE UP THERE!
I'D RATHER DO IT NOW THAN LET THE TENSION BUILD UP FOR THREE WEEKS!
MP

BUT DICK FOUND HE HAD LITTLE TIME TO THINK ABOUT THE SUPREME TEST OF COURAGE WHICH WAS TO COME. EVERY HOUR OF THE DAY WAS FILLED WITH MUSCLE WRACKING WORK.
GET THOSE LOGS MOVING! FASTER... FASTER! BY THE TIME I'VE FINISHED WITH YOU, YOU'LL BE THROWING THEM TO EACH OTHER!

...PARACHUTE LANDING DRILL...
GET OUT OF YOUR HARNESS, SIR, BEFORE YOUR HANDS AND FACE ARE SKINNED RAW!

THEY WERE TWENTY ONE DAYS OF GRINDING PHYSICAL EFFORT... BUILDING THE RECRUITS INTO SUPERBLY FIT AND DISCIPLINED FIGHTERS. EVERY ORDER HAD TO BE OBEYED INSTANTLY.
GREEN ON, GO!

THEN AT LAST THE ORDER CAME TO DRAW 'LIVE' PARACHUTES... "BESSIE" WAS WAITING!
YOU'RE NUMBER ONE, CAPTAIN NORTON! LAST IN... FIRST OUT!
WIND SPEED FOURTEEN M.P.H., SIR... JUST UNDER THE SAFETY LIMIT. THEY'LL PROBABLY LAND ALL OVER THE DROPPING ZONE!

SLOWLY THE MOTOR WINCH LET THE MASSIVE BALLOON RISE, CARRYING ITS SWAYING CAGE FULL OF DRY-LIPPED, SILENT MEN.
EIGHT HUNDRED FEET, CHAPS! WHAT COMES UP MUST GO DOWN... AND THAT MEANS YOU! NUMBER ONE, STAND IN THE DOOR!

DICK FELT AS IF IT WERE SOMEONE ELSE WHO STOOD THERE IN THE OPEN DOORWAY, FORCING HIS EYES TO GAZE DOWN THROUGH HUNDREDS OF FEET OF NOTHING...
NICE CLEAN EXIT NOW, SIR... NO HURRY! GREEN ON... GO!

INSTINCTIVE REACTION TO THE
COMMAND SENT DICK HURTLING
FORWARD... AND DOWN!

PLUMMETING EARTHWARD THROUGH A TEARING RUSH OF AIR, DICK DROPPED A HUNDRED FEET BEFORE A GIANT HAND GRABBED HIS SHOULDERS AND HELD HIM SUSPENDED...
THAT'S IT, NUMBER ONE! GOOD POSITION...FEET AND KNEES TOGETHER... REACH UP AND GRASP YOUR LIFT WEBS! YOU'RE ONLY A LITTLE PINK IMP NOW... BUT WE'LL MAKE A RED DEVIL OUT OF YOU YET!

THE CALM MEASURED VOICE FROM THE LOUDSPEAKER GUIDED DICK DOWN TO EARTH... WHICH AT FIRST SEEMED SO FAR AWAY... THEN SUDDENLY... THUMP!
BUT DICK DID NOT FEEL THE BONE JARRING FALL...HIS WHOLE BEING WAS DROWNED IN A SEA OF EXULTATION! HE HAD DONE IT! HE HAD WON THE BATTLE AGAINST FEAR!

AFTER THAT CAME ONE MORE JUMP FROM A BALLOON...AND THEN SIX FROM A DAKOTA AIRCRAFT. IN THE ONE HUNDRED MILES PER HOUR SLIPSTREAM MEN WERE THROWN THROUGH THE AIR LIKE DOLLS...

THEN CAME THE PROUDEST DAY IN DICK'S LIFE... THE PRESENTATION OF HIS PARACHUTE WINGS...
FIRST-CLASS EFFORT, CAPTAIN NORTON. YOU'LL GET YOUR INSTRUCTIONS TO JOIN A PARACHUTE UNIT FROM THE SCHOOL ADJUTANT!
THANK YOU, SIR!
IT SEEMED THAT GOOD FORTUNE NOW FOLLOWED DICK...FOR HE FOUND THAT HE WAS POSTED TO A NEW SPECIAL AIRBORNE ASSAULT SECTION FORMING IN THE SOUTH OF ENGLAND ...AND THAT HE WAS TO COMMAND IT!
TWO DAYS LATER HE REACHED THE UNIT CAMP...AND FOUND THAT FATE HAD YET ANOTHER SURPRISE FOR HIM....

GOOD HEAVENS... SERGEANT REED! ARE YOU IN THIS NEW UNIT, TOO?
YES, SIR...MY TRANSFER TO THE AIRBORNE CAME WHILE YOU WERE STILL IN HOSPITAL IN DELHI!
N.1 AIRBORNE SPECIAL ASSAULT SECTION
BA 3045

DICK MISSED THE BITTERNESS WHICH SHADED THE SERGEANT'S RUGGED FEATURES...
THERE ARE TWENTY FIVE OF US IN THE OUTFIT, SIR... SO FAR I'VE BEEN IN CHARGE BUT I'LL HAND OVER TO YOU NOW. MOST URGENT THING IS THE CONFERENCE CALLED AT PARACHUTE BRIGADE HEADQUARTERS FOR THREE O'CLOCK THIS AFTERNOON! SOMETHING BIG IS IN THE WIND, SIR!
IT'S ONE THIRTY ALREADY... I'D BETTER MAKE TRACKS FOR IT NOW!
WHEN DICK'S JEEP RACED AWAY, SERGEANT BILL REED'S QUESTIONING GAZE FOLLOWED IT THROUGH THE GATES...
SO THAT WAS THE NEW O.C., EH, SARGE... AND YOU KNEW HIM OUT IN BURMA, DIDN'T YOU? WHAT'S HE LIKE IN ACTION?
I KNEW HIM... BUT I NEVER FOUGHT BESIDE HIM SO I CAN'T SAY!
BUT HE LOST MY BROTHER AND ALL HIS MEN IN BATTLE... AND CAME BACK ALONE AND MAYBE WE'LL GET THE SAME TREATMENT!

WHEN DICK RETURNED TO THE CAMP SOME HOURS AFTERWARDS, HE SOON CONFIRMED THE RUMOURS OF "SOMETHING BIG" COMING OFF ...
SO FAR I'M A STRANGER TO YOU ALL... BUT IT WON'T BE FOR LONG! COMRADESHIP IS FORGED IN THE HEAT OF BATTLE... AND WE'LL BE IN IT UP TO OUR NECKS SOON!

TENSION GREW AS DICK'S CALM UNHURRIED VOICE WENT ON....
LET'S GET DOWN TO IT. THE SECOND BRITISH ARMY ARE ON THE RIVER MEUSE AND THE ESCAUT CANAL. TO SPEED UP ITS ADVANCE INTO THE HEART OF GERMANY THE ALLIED FIRST AIRBORNE CORPS ARE GOING TO CLEAR THE WAY FOR THEM!

ON SECOND ARMY'S ASSAULT ROUTE ARE FOUR BRIDGES WHICH HAVE TO BE CAPTURED. THE AMERICAN AIRBORNE DIVISIONS ARE TACKLING NUMBER ONE, TWO AND THREE... AND OUR FIRST AIRBORNE DIVISION IS GOING FOR NUMBER FOUR *THE BRIDGE AT ARNHEM!*
Arnhem
4
RHINE
3
WAAL
2
Nijmegen
MAAS
CANAL
Grave
1
SIEGFRIED

OUR TASK IS TO CAPTURE THE MAIN CROSS ROADS LEADING INTO ARNHEM... AND BEAT OFF JERRY RE-INFORCEMENTS TRYING TO GET AT OUR MAIN FORCE ATTACKING THE BRIDGE! *WE MUST NOT FAIL!*

THE DAYS THAT FOLLOWED WERE FULL OF VITAL PREPARATION FOR THE GREAT AIRBORNE OPERATION. THE CAMP WAS SEALED, WITH NO ENTRY OR EXIT, FOR SECURITY REASONS...
COR, THEY CALL THIS SLUDGE TEA! WHAT I WOULDN'T GIVE FOR A NICE HOT CUPPA REAL CHAR DOWN AT THAT CAFE IN THE VILLAGE!
CAMP C
YOU JUST TRY AND GET OUT FOR IT, SMUDGER... YOU'LL BE IN THE CELLS SO FAST YOUR FEET WON'T TOUCH THE GROUND!

BUT "SMUDGER" SMITH, THE CHEERFUL COCKNEY SOLDIER, DID NOT HAVE LONG TO WAIT TO LEAVE THE CAMP... FOR WITH THE NEXT DAY'S PERFECT DAWN THE UNIT WAS ORDERED TO THE AIRFIELD...
WE TAKE OFF IN TWENTY MINUTES, EH, YANK... THAT IS, OF COURSE, IF YOU CAN GET THIS FLYING SCRAPHEAP OFF THE GROUND!
LISTEN, LIMEY... IF I CAN'T, YOU GUYS WILL JUST HAVE TO GET OUT AND PUSH!
LUCKY DUCK

Chapter 3. AIR ARMADA
AND SO IT WAS THAT ON THAT SUPERB SUMMER MORNING, SUNDAY THE 17TH. SEPTEMBER, 1944, A VAST ARMADA OF ALLIED AIRCRAFT TOOK TO THE AIR FROM MANY AIRFIELDS IN THE SOUTH AND EAST OF ENGLAND. ONE MASSIVE STREAM FORMED UP OVER NORFOLK...
THE CASTL
ARMS

...ANOTHER DARKENED THE SKY NORTH OF THE BOMB-RAVAGED CITY OF LONDON...

IN THE TIGHTLY-PACKED PLANE OF THE SPECIAL ASSAULT SECTION SPIRITS RAN HIGH...AND IN EVERY MAN'S EYES FLICKERED THE BRIGHT FLAME OF EAGERNESS FOR THE TASK AHEAD...
WATCH YOUR SHOVING, TOSH...ANOTHER GOOD PUSH FROM YOU AND I'LL BE DOING A SOLO JUMP... RIGHT INTO THE FLIPPIN' CHANNEL!
OKAY... BUT DON'T ASK ME FOR A PUSH LATER ON... WHEN YOU'RE TREMBLING IN THE DOOR!

THEY MIGHT HAVE BEEN ON A TRAINING FLIGHT SO UNEVENTFUL WAS THE JOURNEY OVER THE RESTLESS GREY SEA. THEN THEY CROSSED THE DUTCH COAST AND THE GERMAN ANTI-AIRCRAFT FIRE CAME UP TO MEET THEM.
GUESS THOSE KRAUT BRICK THROWERS DOWN THERE ARE SURE GOING TO GET A HEADACHE WHEN THOSE SPITFIRE BEAUTIES START SHOOTING AROUND THEIR EARS!

IN A RELENTLESS FLOOD THE HUGE CONVOYS OF PLANES DRONED ON TOWARDS THEIR OBJECTIVE...THE BRIDGES! SOON, FAR AHEAD OF DICK NORTON'S PLANE, THE LEADERS COULD BE SEEN CIRCLING OVER ARNHEM...
THEN SUDDENLY... WHOOMP!
LUCKY DUCK
...DISASTER STRUCK!

THE STURDY DAKOTA SHUDDERED FROM TIP TO TAIL AS THE EXPLOSIVE BLAST HAMMERED AT HER... STEEL SPLINTERS SLICED SAVAGELY INTO THE WING...
STARBOARD ENGINE'S PACKED UP AND THAT WING LOOKS LIKE A SIEVE! BROTHER, WHAT A MESS!
ONE ENGINE WON'T KEEP THIS CRATE FLYING WITH THOSE BOYS ABOARD. EITHER THEY HIT THE SILK NOW...OR WE TAKE A NOSE DIVE... STRAIGHT DOWN!

THERE WAS NO OTHER CHOICE... AND THE RED DEVILS KNEW IT. IN SECONDS THEY WERE LINED UP AT THE DOOR... AND DICK NORTON LED THEM THROUGH INTO SPACE....

LIKE THE WIDENING RIPPLES ON A POND, THE CLUSTERED WHITE CANOPIES DRIFTED APART... AND DICK WATCHED THE DAMAGED DAKOTA TURN AND STAGGER BACK TOWARDS ENGLAND...
WITH A LOT OF LUCK AND NO MORE TROUBLE; HE'LL MAKE IT... BUT HE'S LEFT US A HECK OF A LONG WALK TO ARNHEM!

QUICKLY HE COUNTED THE PARACHUTES AROUND HIM... TWENTY FOUR, TWENTY FIVE... ALL THERE. THEN A HUNDRED FEET OFF THE GROUND, A VICIOUS WHINE SANG HOTLY PAST HIS CHEEK...
WE'RE SITTING DUCKS FOR TARGET PRACTICE NOW... BUT IN JUST TEN SECONDS YOU JERRIES ARE GOING TO GET ALL THE TROUBLE YOU'RE ASKING FOR!

DICK HIT THE GROUND HARD; ROLLED TO TAKE THE SHOCK; AND WRENCHED OUT OF HIS HARNESS...
IMPATIENCE WILL GET YOU NOWHERE, SQUAREHEADS!

A PARACHUTIST IS AT HIS MOST VULNERABLE WHILE IN THE AIR AND IN THE FIRST MOMENTS OF LANDING. THE GREY CLAD GERMANS RACED TO REAP THAT ADVANTAGE; BUT THEY HAD RECKONED WITHOUT DICK NORTON'S LIGHTNING SPEED...
ENGLISH LEAD... DELIVERED FREE AND FAST!

THE FIGHT WAS SHORT AND SAVAGE...AND DISASTROUS TO THE GERMANS...
SERGEANT REED...GET THAT SECOND TRUCK! I'LL GRAB THE FIRST ONE... IT'S OUR BUS FOR ARNHEM!
THEY WON'T KNOW WHAT HIT 'EM, SIR! COME ON, CORPORAL!

THE APPROACHING LORRY'S BRAKES SCREAMED AS IT CAME UP...AND TWO GRENADIES HURTLED THROUGH THE AIR TO MEET IT!

AND THIS LITTLE LOT IS SMUDGER SMITH'S PARTY PIECE!

ITS FRONT WHEELS SHATTERED, THE CRAZILY CAREERING LORRY CHARGED OFF THE ROAD, SLAMMED INTO A DITCH AND TURNED OVER . . .
ROOM FOR ONE MORE ON TOP ? EARLY MORNING SINGLE TICKET. . TO 'AMMERSMITH BROADWAY VIA ARNHEM!
NICE WORK, SERGEANT! GET THE MAP OUT AND NAVIGATE TO OUR OBJECTIVE. I'LL PILOT... AND THIS IS A NON-STOP TRIP!

WITH THE ACCELERATCR PLAT ON THE FLOOR BOARDS. THE LORRY ROARED UP THE ROAD ...TYRES SCREAMING ON THE BENDS TAKEN AT TOP SPEED...MILES FLASHED UNDER THE HUMMING WHEELS...THEN...
A ROAD BLOCK! THAT'S WHERE THE LORRIES CAME FROM... AND WE WON'T BUST THROUGH THAT SET UP, SIR!
THAT'S WHAT THOSE ERRIES THINK, TOO...AND THEY'RE IN IN FOR A SURPRISE! TELL THE MEN TO HANG ON FOR THEIR LIVES!

ONLY AT THE LAST MOMENT DID THE GERMANS REALISE THAT THE LORRY WAS NOT SLOWING DOWN...BUT INCREASING SPEED! THUNDERSTRUCK, THEY COULD ONLY STARE SLACK JAWED AS DICK DRAGGED THE WHEEL ROUND...
COR...WHY DID I LEAVE MY 'CHUTE BEHIND? SOMEBODY TELL ME WHEN TO OPEN ME PEEPERS!
WH-86186

AS THE LORRY LURCHED BACK ON TO THE ROAD, THE GERMANS CAME TO LIFE... BUT, TOO LATE!
SHOOT THE ACCURSED ENGLISH PIGS DOWN... AAAGH!
LEAVE 'EM SOMETHING TO REMEMBER THE RED DEVILS! RAPID FIRE!
WH-

THEN THE LORRY WAS GONE... AND DICK DISMISSED THE HAVOC STRUCK ROAD BLOCK FROM HIS MIND...
LET ME KNOW WHEN WE'RE HALF A MILE FROM THE CROSS-ROADS, SERGEANT. ACCORDING TO THE AIR PHOTOS I STUDIED, THERE'S A DARNED HEFTY JERRY BLOCKHOUSE OVERLOOKING IT FROM THE EAST... AND I DON'T WANT TO RUN SMACK INTO ITS FIELD OF FIRE!
RIGHT, SIR, ABOUT TWENTY MILES TO GO!
WH-85186

TOUGH AS THEY WERE, THE PARACHUTISTS GRINNED WITH RELIEF TWENTY NIGHTMARE MINUTES LATER...AS, FOR THE FIRST TIME, THE HURTLING LORRY SLOWED ITS BREAKNECK SPEED...
I'D RATHER DO A DOZEN JUMPS THAN FIVE SECONDS MORE OF THAT GRAND PRIX STUFF!
CROSS-ROADS THREE HUNDRED YARDS BEYOND THIS BEND, SIR!
GOOD...WE'LL DITCH THIS MOBILE JUNK YARD HERE AND THEN WE'LL MOVE ON FOOT WIDE AROUND THE FLANK OF THE BLOCKHOUSE AND COME UP BEHIND IT! SURPRISE IS THE ONE ADVANTAGE WE'VE GOT!

THE GERMAN BLOCKHOUSE WAS BADLY NAMED...FOR IT WAS MORE LIKE A FORTRESS, BUILT ON THE ONLY HILL IN THE AREA. ITS GARRISON WAS SURE AND CONFIDENT BEHIND ITS STEEL AND CONCRETE STRENGTH...
MORE ENEMY PLANES THAN I HAVE EVER SEEN...AND GLIDERS, TOO! THEY MUST BE CARRYING TEN THOUSAND MEN!
ALREADY OUR WIRELESS REPORTS PARACHUTISTS LANDING NEAR ARNHEM! THAT WILL BE A BATTLE WE ARE WELL OUT OF, FRITZ! SOON THE CROSS-ROADS WILL BE FLOODED WITH OUR RE-INFORCEMENTS RUSHING TO ATTACK THOSE FIGHTING FIENDS!

SURE OF THEIR OWN SAFETY, THE SENTRIES STILL WATCHED THE FLEET OF PLANES PASSING . . . THEN SUDDENLY, IT HAPPENED . . .
GRAAAH!
UUUUH!

GRINNING FEROCIOUSLY, SMUDGER SMITH WAS FIRST THROUGH THE DOOR . . .
FREEZE! THE FIRST DOZEY CLOWN WHO GETS UNFRIENDLY IDEAS COLLECTS A MAGAZINE FULL OF LEAD!
ACHTUNG! WE ARE ATTACKED!

THE BLACK MENACING MUZZLE OF SMUDGER'S BREN GUN SWEPT THE ROOM...AND THE GERMANS FROZE...ALL EXCEPT THE BULL-NECKED SERGEANT.
TRY THAT AGAIN, TOSH, AND YOU'LL GET TIRED OF BREATHING!

DICK'S PLAN HAD WORKED BRILLIANTLY...HE HAD CAPTURED THE FORTIFIED POST WITHOUT A CASUALTY!
CORPORAL SMITH... TAKE THE PRISONERS BACK DOWN THE HILL THE WAY WE CAME. THEN TURN 'EM LOOSE... WITHOUT THEIR BELTS AND BOOTS!
GET THOSE MACHINE GUNS READY FOR ACTION. SIGHTS ON THE CROSS-ROADS AND STAND BY... WE WON'T HAVE LONG TO WAIT!

EVERY MAN WAS TENSE AND SILENT BEHIND A WEAPON WHEN SMUDGER RETURNED . . .
YOU SHOULD'VE SEEN THOSE JERRIES... HOLDING THEIR TROUSERS UP AND TRYING TO RUN IN BARE FEET!
CUT THE CACKLE, CORPORAL, AND GET THAT DOOR SHUT...AT THE DOUBLE!
HERE COMES THE FIRST JERRY COLUMN TRYING TO GET TO ARNHEM!

AND THERE, RACING ALONG THE ROAD FROM THE WEST, WAS A BIG CONVOY OF GERMAN TROOP CARRIERS... LED BY A POWERFUL ARMOURED CAR...
STRAIGHT ON, HERR HAUPTMAN. TO LEFT OR RIGHT WOULD PUT ANOTHER THREE HOURS ON OUR ROUTE TO ARNHEM.
GOOT! EVERY MOMENT IS PRECIOUS IF WE ARE TO DESTROY THOSE PIG DOG PARACHUTISTS BEFORE THEY CAN GAIN A FOOTING!

SILENTLY THE GRIM, GREY BLOCKHOUSE SEEMED TO FROWN DOWN ON THE SPEEDING LORRIES AS THEY NEARED THE CROSS-ROADS. SUDDENLY THE SILENCE WAS GONE... IN ITS PLACE CAME ROARING VIOLENCE...

TONGUES OF FLAME SPAT SAVAGELY FROM THE BLOCKHOUSE SLITS AS THE MACHINE GUNS CHATTERED. IN TEN TERRIBLE SECONDS, STREAMS OF SEARING LEAD TURNED THE CONVOY INTO A SHAMBLES OF WRECKED VEHICLES AND PANIC-STRICKEN MEN...
SCHNELL! SCHNELL! FASTER, IDIOTS... WE HAVE GOT TO STOP THOSE MACHINE GUNS!
BUT...BUT THEY ARE OUR OWN MEN... OR HAVE THOSE RED DEVIL FIGHTERS REACHED THIS AREA ALREADY?

CRUMP! A SIX-POUNDER SHELL SPLATTERED HARMLESSLY AGAINST THE CONCRETE CASING WHICH SHIELDED THE JUBILANT AIRBORNE TROOPS...
THEY WON'T EVEN DENT THE PLACE WITH THAT PEA-SHOOTER, SIR... BUT SHALL I GIVE 'EM A TASTE OF THIS?
NOT WORTH THE AMMUNITION, SERGEANT... AND WE'LL BE NEEDING ALL WE'VE GOT WHEN THEY BRING UP THEIR TANKS... THEN WE'LL FIND OUT JUST HOW TOUGH THIS FORTRESS IS!

A WRY SMILE TWISTED DICK'S FIRM LIPS...
WE'VE GOT STACKS OF FOOD AND AMMO... AND PLENTY OF TIME TO USE THEM BOTH! THE ALLIED ARMY SPEARHEAD SHOULD LINK UP WITH THE AIRBORNE DIVISION AT ARNHEM IN THREE DAYS... AND WE'RE STAYING HERE UNTIL IT DOES! AND THE MORE JERRIES WE TIE UP HERE, THE LESS CAN CRACK DOWN ON THE LADS AT ARNHEM!

DOWN ON THE ROAD THE GERMANS WERS STRAGGLING AWAY IN RETREAT FROM THE CHAOS...
DONNER UND BLITZEN! EVEN THE OTHER ROADS ARE COVERED BY THOSE MACHINE GUNS. WE CANNOT GO ON IN THE VEHICLES, HERR COLONEL! THERE IS ONLY ONE ANSWER ...A FRONTAL ASSAULT ON THE BLOCKHOUSE TO DESTROY IT!
DUMKOPF! THE WHOLE FORCE WOULD BE MOWN DOWN BEFORE THEY GOT HALFWAY. NO... WE STAY HERE TO WAIT FOR OUR TANKS WHICH ARE COMING!

THE DAY WORE ON, WITH NO MOVEMENT BY THE GERMAN SOLDIERS...UNTIL THE DUSK OF EVENING A HEAVY METALLIC RUMBLING GREW FROM THE WEST...AND REACHED THE EARS OF THE BESIEGED RED DEVILS...
HERE THEY COME, SIR... JERRY'S CLANKING TIN LIZZIES... THE TANKS.
QUIET! SOMETHING'S COMING THROUGH ON THE WIRELESS ...IT'S ONE OF OUR UNIT HEADQUARTERS AT ARNHEM!

THE RADIO OPERATOR'S YOUNG FACE LENGTHENED AS HE LISTENED...
THEY CAN'T RECEIVE ME... BUT I CAN HEAR THE REPORTS COMING IN. OUR BOYS HAVE REACHED THE BRIDGE BUT THEY CAN'T CAPTURE IT AS THE JERRIES HAVE GOT IT UNDER VERY HEAVY FIRE!
KEEP LISTENING... WE'LL SEE WHAT THESE NEW ARRIVALS ARE UP TO!

THE TANKS PROVED TO BE FOUR "TIGERS" AND SOON THEIR LONG BARRELLED GUNS WERE PIN-POINTING THE BLOCKHOUSE. THEN THE BARRAGE STARTED...
...AND FOR A SPLIT-SECOND ANGRY BLOSSOMS OF VIVID ORANGE FLAME GREW ON THE MASSIVE STONE WALLS...

MEANWHILE TWENTY MILES TO THE EAST A GREAT BATTLE WAS BEGINNING AT ARNHEM. IT HAD BEEN PLANNED TO LAST FOR THREE DAYS...UNTIL THE ALLIED LAND ARMIES BROKE THROUGH AND JOINED THE PARACHUTE TROOPS. BUT THAT BREAK THROUGH DID NOT COME IN THE TIME ALLOWED... OR IN DOUBLE THAT TIME, OR TREBLE. IN FACT, FOR TEN DAYS OF FANTASTICALLY COURAGEOUS FIGHTING AGAINST VASTLY GREATER ENEMY NUMBERS, THE AIRBORNE DIVISION HELD OUT...WAITING FOR THE LINK UP WHICH NEVER CAME!

AND WHAT OF DICK NORTON AND HIS MEN DURING THOSE HISTORY MAKING DAYS? *INCREDIBLY, THEY TOO, HELD OUT!* TRUE, GERMAN UNITS HEADING FOR ARNHEM NOW USED A ROUTE TO THE NORTH... BUT A LARGE FORCE STILL HAD TO BESIEGE THE BLOCKHOUSE...
WELL, SIR, THIS IS THE LAST OF THE FOOD... RECKON THERE'S ENOUGH FOR ONE GOOD MEAL. THEN WE GO HUNGRY!
TEN DAYS AND WE'RE STILL HERE... AND FIGHTING! IT'S A WONDER THIS PLACE IS STILL STANDING... BUT IT CAN'T TAKE MUCH MORE POUNDING BEFORE IT COMES IN ON TOP OF US!

IN THE CORNER, THE WIRELESS OPERATOR GLARED DISGUSTEDLY AT THE SMALL WIRELESS SET HE HAD PARACHUTED WITH.
USELESS DARNED THING! HAVEN'T EVEN HAD A PEEP OUT OF IT SINCE WE LANDED ... AND I CAN ONLY RECEIVE ON THE JERRY SET!

SUDDENLY HIS EYES WIDENED... HIS HANDS LEAPED TO COVER HIS EARPHONES AS HE LISTENED INTENTLY...
IT'S HEADQUARTERS... VERY FAINT! THEY'RE CALLING ALL UNITS STILL IN CONTACT WITH THE ENEMY... *JUMPING JEHOSOPHAT! THAT WAS THE CODE WORD FOR WITHDRAWAL ... WHAT'S LEFT OF THE DIVISION MUST BE PULLING OUT OF ARNHEM!*

ALL EYES CENTRED ON DICK, SILENTLY QUESTIONING...
THEN OUR TASK IS FINISHED...WE'RE FREE TO GET OUT NOW...IF WE CAN!
BUT HOW, SIR? WE'RE COMPLETELY SURROUNDED!
BUT IF SOME OF THOSE JERRIES WERE DRAWN AWAY WITH A DIVERSION? I'VE GOT THE GLIMMERINGS OF AN IDEA... LISTEN...

THE GERMANS SHELLED THE BLOCKHOUSE AGAIN AS DUSK FELL...UNTIL DARKNESS BLOTTED OUT THE DAY'S SHAPES. THEN, JUST BEFORE MIDNIGHT...
WHO THE...? SERGEANT REED! YOUR ORDERS WERE TO LEAD THE MEN OUT WHEN I MADE THE DIVERSIONARY ATTACK! GET BACK TO IT!
SORRY, SIR... BUT I'M DISOBEYING ORDERS! CORPORAL SMITH IS TAKING THE MEN ON THEIR BREAKOUT... I'M GOING WITH YOU! BETWEEN US WE'LL MAKE ENOUGH NOISE FOR A BATTALION!

RELUCTANTLY THE YOUNG OFFICER HAD TO ADMIT THE SERGEANT WAS RIGHT. HE NODDED AND NOISELESSLY LED THE WAY DOWN THE HILL. MINUTES SLID BY...AND THEN THE SILENCE OF THE NIGHT WAS SHATTERED WITH MAN-MADE FURY...

GRENADES EXPLODED SHATTERINGLY IN THE MAIN GERMAN POSITION... AND SLIVERS OF STEEL SLICED VICIOUSLY THROUGH THE FLAME-LIT NIGHT.
EMERGENCY! REPORT FULL SCALE ENEMY ASSAULT ON HEADQUARTERS! ORDER ALL UNITS TO COUNTER ATTACK AT ONCE!

FOR TEN FLEETING MINUTES, DICK AND BILL REED KEPT UP THEIR DEATH-DEFYING ATTACK...DODGING THROUGH THE DARKNESS LIKE GHOSTS...AND POURING BULLETS AND HIGH EXPLOSIVE INTO THE GERMAN HEADQUARTERS. THEN, AT LAST...
STAND WHERE YOU ARE! DROP YOUR WEAPONS OR WE SHOOT!
THEY'VE GOT US, SERGEANT... DO AS HE SAYS! BUT FROM THE DIRECTION IN WHICH THEY'VE COME, THERE MUST BE A HECK OF A BIG HOLE IN THE RING AROUND THE BLOCKHOUSE!

CLOSELY GUARDED, THE PRISONERS WERE MARCHED BEFORE THE GERMAN COMMANDER, WHO ALMOST BURST WITH RAGE WHEN HE SAW HOW MANY MEN HAD WROUGHT SUCH CONFUSION.
TWO OF YOU! YET YOU ATTACKED US AS IF THERE WERE A HUNDRED! ACH... I UNDERSTAND! YOU ARE THE LEADERS TRYING TO BLAST YOUR WAY OUT OF OUR TRAP! NOW YOUR MEN UP THERE HAVE NO COMMANDER... IN THE MORNING WE WILL ATTACK, AND THEY WILL GIVE IN QUICKLY!
35

BY THE FIRST FAINT LIGHT OF DAWN, THE WHOLE GERMAN FORCE SWEPT UP THE HILL IN AN ALL-OUT ATTACK ON THE BLOCKHOUSE... AND NOT A SHOT MET THEM!
LOOK AT THEM, SIR... DEAD PUZZLED BECAUSE THEY CAN'T FIND A THING. SEEMS THE BIRDMEN HAVE FLOWN!
HEAR THAT RUMBLING FROM THE SOUTH? HEAVY GUNS... IT MUST BE OUR MAIN ARMY ADVANCING, AND THEY CAN'T BE MORE THAN TWENTY MILES AWAY! WITH ANY LUCK, CORPORAL SMITH AND THE LADS MUST BE DARNED NEARLY THERE BY NOW!

Chapter 4. FINAL ASSAULT

EVENTS MOVED SWIFTLY AFTER THAT. THE GERMANS BEGAN A FULL RETREAT EASTWARDS WHICH, THREE DAYS LATER, TOOK THEM TWENTY MILES BEYOND THE RHINE INTO GERMANY. THERE DICK NORTON AND BILL REED WERE TAKEN TO LUDINGHAUSEN PRISONER-OF-WAR CAMP.

BRITISH SCUM... INTO THE RAT TRAP WHERE YOU BELONG.

WELCOME TO THE 'APPY 'OME, CHUM... BE IT EVER SO 'UMBLE! JUST IN TIME TO ENJOY THE WINTER SPORTS... WHICH MAINLY CONSISTS OF TRYING TO KEEP FROM FREEZING NOW THE SNOW IS COMING!

ALTHOUGH LUDINGHAUSEN WAS NOT A LARGE PRISONER-OF-WAR CAMP IT WAS WELL GUARDED. FOR SEVERAL DAYS DICK STUDIED THE SECURITY ARRANGEMENTS... AND THEN REPORTED BEFORE THE PRISONERS' ESCAPE COMMITTEE...

SO DICK WAS FORCED TO WAIT THROUGH THE SHORT GLOOMY DAYS OF WORSENING WINTER WEATHER WHICH FOLLOWED. SNOW AND ICE COVERED THE CAMP ...AND THERE WAS LITTLE WARMTH FOR THE PRISONERS. THE WEEKS BECAME MONTHS...AND STILL THE ALLIES COULD NOT CROSS THE RHINE. RUMOURS WERE RIFE THAT THE GERMANS WERE DEFENDING THE LAST BARRIER TO THEIR FATHERLAND WITH INCREDIBLE FURY. CHRISTMAS CAME AND WENT...

AT NIGHT THE BARBED WIRE BARRIER AROUND THE CAMP WAS BRILLIANTLY LIT BY POWERFUL FLOOD LIGHTS... AND STRANGELY ENOUGH THEY FORMED THE KEY TO DICK'S SCHEME.
I LEARNED TO THROW A KNIFE IN BURMA... NOW WE'LL SEE IF I'VE FORGOTTEN HOW!
IT'S ONLY AN ISSUE EATING KNIFE... BUT IT'S AS SHARP AS I COULD HONE IT, SIR!

THE PROBING SEARCHLIGHT SWEPT ON ...AND A SILENT LITHE FIGURE DRIFTED TOWARDS THE WIRE. AN ARM DREW BACK... THERE WAS A FLASH OF FLYING STEEL...
...AND THEN FOR ONE SPLIT-SECOND AN EYE-SEARING BLUE FLASH LIT THE HEAVENS... THEN UTTER DARKNESS!

GUTTURAL GERMAN SHOUTS ECHOED URGENTLY THROUGH THE VELVET BLACKNESS... THE POWER FUSES HAD BLOWN... THE SEARCHLIGHTS TOO WERE USELESS. IT WOULD TAKE MINUTES TO GET EMERGENCY LIGHTS WORKING...
THE JERRIES NEVER MEANT THEIR BENCHES FOR THIS SORT OF LARK, SIR!
NOW THEY'LL KNOW BETTER! GO BACK AND GET READY FOR THE RUN UP!

A THICK WHITE CHALK LINE SHONE ALONG THE MIDDLE OF THE WOODEN SEATS TO GUIDE THE MEN AS THEY RACED THROUGH THE DARKNESS *STRAIGHT UP THE SLOPING BENCHES* ..
TEN SECONDS MORE ... THAT'S ALL WE WANT! AFTER THAT THE JERRIES WILL NEVER TAKE US AGAIN... **ALIVE!**

THE END OF THOSE PRECIOUS MOMENTS FOUND THE TWO MEN STUMBLING TOWARDS THE EDGE OF THE STEUBENHEM WALD... ONE OF THE THICKEST AND LARGEST FORESTS IN WEST GERMANY!
WOULDN'T WE HAVE A BETTER CHANCE BY STEERING CLEAR OF THE FOREST, SIR? WE'LL GET LOST DEAD EASY IN THERE!
THE GERMANS WILL BE HUNTING FOR US SOON... ALONG WITH ABOUT FIFTY OTHERS WHO PLANNED TO BREAK OUT WHEN I FUSED THE LIGHTS! THE MOST DIFFICULT PLACE TO SEARCH IS THIS FOREST... AND THAT'S WHY IT'S OUR BEST CHANCE.

SOON THE EERIE DEPTHS OF THE BLACK FOREST SHROUDED THEM. IMMEDIATELY DICK TOOK THE LEAD AND UNERRINGLY FOUND A WESTWARD PATH.
CAN YOU EASE UP A BIT, SIR? I CAN'T MATCH YOUR PACE.
ALL RIGHT, SERGEANT I'LL SLOW DOWN A LITTLE, BUT THERE'S ABOUT FIFTEEN MORE MILES OF THIS...AND WE MUST DO IT BY DAYBREAK TO ENSURE DODGING THE SEARCH PARTIES.

THAT MARCH SOON BECAME A LIVING NIGHTMARE TO BILL REED. HE GAVE UP TRYING TO FOCUS HIS RED-RIMMED EYES IN THE DARK AND JUST FOLLOWED DICK'S ARROW STRAIGHT STEPS. THEN MUSCLE-RACKING MILES PASSED WITH THE HOURS UNTIL...
WE'VE REACHED THE OTHER SIDE...AND BY DAYBREAK! HOW THE HECK DID YOU DO IT, SIR?
IT WAS WORSE THAN THIS IN BURMA, SERGEANT...OR HAVE YOU FORGOTTEN? IN THOSE MONTHS IN THE JUNGLE I FOUND A SENSE OF DIRECTION I COULD TRUST WITH MY EYES SHUT!

OTHER MEMORIES FLOWED BEFORE BILL REED'S EYES AS THEY REACHED THE FOREST'S EDGE. MEMORIES OF A YOUNGER BROTHER...AND A BATTLE ON A BURMESE HILL WHICH LEFT ONLY ONE SURVIVOR...DICK NORTON...
I REMEMBER IT, SIR...AND MY BROTHER! HE WAS YOUR PLATOON CORPORAL IN THAT LAST FIGHT AGAINST THE JAPS. HE DIED THERE... AND YOU LIVED! WHY, SIR? WHY?
YOUR BROTHER? WHY IN HEAVENS NAME DIDN'T YOU TELL ME BEFORE? IF ONLY I'D KNOWN...
...THEN DICK'S VOICE DIED AS HE SAW THE ACCUSATION BURNING IN BILL REED'S UNFLINCHING GAZE!

SO YOU THINK I SHOULD HAVE DIED WITH MY MEN...OR BROUGHT THEM ALL BACK ALIVE! WELL, IT WAS A LONG TIME BEFORE I COULD REMEMBER WHAT HAPPENED ON THAT HILL, BUT GRADUALLY IT ALL CAME BACK... AND NOW YOU'LL KNOW!

SLOWLY AND TIGHT VOICED, DICK BEGAN TO RELIVE THE FURY OF THAT ILL-FATED DAY...THROUGH THE NEVER ENDING ENEMY ATTACKS... THE HOURS OF MERCILESS MORTARING...THE BROKEN WIRELESS MESSAGE AND THEN THE FINAL CRUSHING ONSLAUGHT BY THE JAPS. BILL REED HEARD IT ALL... AND KNEW HE HAD FOUND THE ANSWER...
...IT WAS ONLY A MIRACLE THAT SAVED ME. YOUR BROTHER WAS A GALLANT SOLDIER AND HE WENT DOWN FIGHTING WITH HIS FACE TO THE ENEMY... LIKE A MAN! I'M PROUD TO HAVE FOUGHT BESIDE HIM!
YOU DOUBLED YOUR OWN DANGER GETTING ME OUT OF THE CAMP AND THROUGH THE FOREST... AND AFTER SEEING YOU IN ACTION, SIR, I SHOULD HAVE KNOWN YOU DIDN'T LEAVE THOSE MEN TO DIE!

THE BOND OF FRIENDSHIP SEALED IN A HANDCLASP NEEDED NO WORDS. TOGETHER THEY TURNED TOWARDS THE RHINE...AND BILL REED GASPED IN BREATH-TAKING AMAZEMENT...
BY GLORY... I'M DREAMING! LOOK, AIRBORNE TROOPS...AND THEY'RE DROPPING!
IT MUST BE THE ALLIED ASSAULT ACROSS THE RHINE, SERGEANT! THE DROPPING ZONE'S ABOUT A MILE AWAY... LET'S GO!

EXHAUSTION FORGOTTEN, THEY RACED OVER THE FIELDS TOWARDS THE DROPPING ZONE. ALREADY THE GERMAN DEFENCES WERE TAKING UP THE CHALLENGE...
GREAT GUNS... THOSE TANKS WILL MASSACRE THOSE BOYS AS THEY LAND!
BUT WE'RE NOT GOING TO LET 'EM, SERGEANT! WHEN I GIVE THE WORD, GO LIKE BLAZES FOR THAT NEAREST TANK. READY...NOW!

THE TANK'S GUN FLAMED ANGRILY AND A SCREECHING HIGH EXPLOSIVE SHELL STREAKED ACROSS THE OPEN COUNTRY. THE TANK COMMANDER BARKED A CORRECTION... AND THEN A CHOPPING, IRON-HARD FIST ALMOST SLAMMED HIM OUT OF THE TURRET...
HAUL HIM DOWN, SERGEANT... AND GRAB HIS LUGER! THEN INTO THIS OVERGROWN BULLY BEEF TIN AND SEE IF YOU CAN MAKE THE GUNNER BEHAVE!

GRASPING THE GERMAN OFFICER'S PISTOL, BILL DROPPED INTO THE TANK. SEVERAL DULL THUDS FOLLOWED... THEN THE SERGEANT'S CHEERFUL VOICE FLOATED UP.
ONE SORE-HEADED JERRY GUN CREW AWAITING ORDERS, SIR!
RIGHT! TRAVERSE THE GUN LEFT... RIGHT ON TO OUR NEXT DOOR NEIGHBOUR!

THE TURRET TURNED AND THE LONG BARRELLED 90 m.m. GUN SETTLED ON ITS NEW TARGET. DICK'S HAND DROPPED AND... CRAACK!
RELOAD! STAND BY FOR NEW TARGET!
21

SUDDENLY WARNED, THE THIRD TANK COMMANDER RE-ACTED SWIFTLY. HIS GUN SWUNG SMOOTHLY, SEEKING ITS NEW PREY... AND FIRED WITH DESPERATE HASTE!
THIS GAME'S FOR KEEPS, JERRY... NO SECOND CHANCES... FIRE!
21

BILL REED HAD RELOADED WITH ARMOUR PIERCING SHOT... IT PUNCHED A HOLE IN THE ENEMY TANK STEEL AS IF IT WERE CHEESE... AND THEN IT MUST HAVE HIT A PETROL TANK...
LOOKS AS IF WE CAN RELAX NOW, SERGEANT... THE RED BERET BOYS ARE HERE!
MAYBE THEY'VE GOT TEA FOR A BREW UP, SIR!
WELL I'LL BE DARNED! WHERE THE HECK DID YOU TWO CHAPS COME FROM? WHERE'S YOUR UNIT?

WE'RE A COUPLE OF LEFT OVERS' FROM ARNHEM ... THOUGHT WE'D BETTER GNE YOU A FRIENDLY WELCOME! WHICH OUTFIT IS ON THIS SHOW?
WE'RE SIXTH AIRBORNE DIVISION... AND YOU CERTAINLY HELPED US OUT! HEY, DID YOU SAY ARNHEM?
21

SHORTLY AFTERWARDS DICK AND BILL REED WERE IN THE UNIT'S MAKESHIFT HEADGUARTERS, ALREADY MANY FIERCE BATTLES WERE RAGING NEARBY AS THE PARACHUTISTS FOUGHT TO TAKE THEIR HEAVILY DEFENDED OBJECTIVES.
... A FANTASTIC STORY, CAPTAIN NORTON... AND IT FOLLOWS ON FROM THE REPORT YOUR SECTION CORPORAL MADE WHEN YOUR MEN REACHED THE ALLIED LINES AFTER ARNHEM. NOW I SUPPOSE YOU WANT A GOOD REST.
WELL, WE'VE JUST HAD SIX MONTHS HOLIDAY IN A P.O.W. CAMP, MAJOR... HOW ABOUT LETTING US JOIN IN YOUR OUTFIT'S PARTY?

THERE WAS NO DENYING THOSE TWO EAGER-EYED MEN. AND SO IT WAS THAT DICK NORTON AND BILL, OFFICER AND SERGEANT IN RANK, YET GALLANT BROTHERS-IN-ARMS, FOUGHT SIDE BY SIDE AGAIN, IN THAT EPIC BATTLE OF THE RHINE CROSSING. IT WAS THE GREAT COURAGE OF THOUSANDS OF MEN LIKE THEM THAT MADE IT A SPLENDID VICTORY... AND SMASHED THE GERMAN ARMY ANOTHER STEP DOWN THE ROAD TO TOTAL DEFEAT.
ROT TEUFELS!
RED DEVILS! NO WONDER THE GERMANS FEAR AND DREAD THAT NAME... AND THEY ALWAYS WILL, AS LONG AS THERE ARE SUCH MEN AS THOSE TWO WEARING THE RED BERET!

TASK FORCE

1944. BRITISH AND CANADIAN FORCES WERE HALTED ON THE THRESHOLD OF HOLLAND BY THAT GREAT WATER BARRIER, THE SCHELDT ESTUARY. ACROSS ITS SULLEN BREADTH LAY ENEMY-OCCUPIED WALCHEREN AND SOUTH BEVELAND, BLOCKING A SEAWAY TO COVETED ANTWERP.
ILOZ
NOY
TO R.A.F. BOMBER COMMAND FELL THE UNHAPPY TASK OF BREACHING THE DUTCH DYKES AND FLOODING THE FARMLANDS OF SOUTH BEVELAND... PRIOR TO THE ALLIED ASSAULT.

Chapter 1 IN THE BREACH
SCORNING THE SAVAGE REACTION FROM THE ENEMY'S FORMIDABLE DEFENCES, THE RAIDING LANCASTERS BORE STEADILY IN ...
BOMB DOORS OPEN, SKIPPER!

IN THE NOSE OF THE FOREMOST LANCASTER JN-Y, BOMB-AIMER SERGEANT CHRIS HARMER WAS GUIDING THE PLANE ON TO THE TARGET. HIMSELF A YOUNG FARMER IN PEACETIME, HE KNEW VERY WELL THE UTTER RUIN THAT THE INFLOODING SEA-WATER WOULD BRING TO THE FRIENDLY DUTCH.
STEADY, SIR..! THAT'S IT..! HOLD IT, SIR!

CLOSE BESIDE CHRIS HARMER WAS MAJOR BILL MILNER, D.S.M., ROYAL MARINE COMMANDOS, VETERAN BEACH-HEAD FIGHTER FROM NORTH AFRICA TO NORMANDY. HE WAS THERE TO OBSERVE FOR HIMSELF THE EFFECT OF DYKE-BREACHING ON A FORCE OF MARINE COMMANDOS, AT THAT MOMENT WAITING OFF-SHORE TO STORM THE GAP.
I WONDER IF THIS BREACHING WILL REALLY HELP JACK HALLAM'S LOT . . . PRETTY TRICKY WHICHEVER WAY YOU HIT THE SHORE.

SUDDENLY, THE PLANE LIFTED . . .
BOMBS GONE, SIR!
BELIEVE TARGET HIT, SIR!

THE GREAT AIRCRAFT CIRCLED THROUGH A MURDEROUS CURTAIN OF FIRE, ITS CREW COOLLY GAUGING THE EFFECTIVENESS OF THE ATTACK.
WE'VE CLOBBERED IT, ALL RIGHT.
THAT WATER'S GOING IN LIKE A WALL!

WITH STUPENDOUS FORCE, THE SEA BROKE THROUGH TO ADD ITS TERRIFYING ROAR TO THE THUNDER OF THE LANCASTERS AS THEY SWEPT LOW OVERHEAD TO STRAFE THE GUN POSITIONS.
LOOK, THE DYKE!
RUN-RUN FOR YOUR LIVES!

BILL MILNER SWITCHED HIS GAZE SWIFTLY SEAWARD TO WHERE THE ASSAULT BOATS WERE LUNGING SHOREWARD. SOON HE WAS TO LEAD A SIMILAR RAID ON NEIGHBOURING WALCHEREN ISLAND, AN EVEN TOUGHER PROPOSITION.
THERE ARE THE LANDING CRAFT! THEY'LL HIT THE GAPS IN A FEW MINUTES.

NEXT SECOND, HOWEVER, A VIOLENT EXPLOSION ROCKED THE LANCASTER... IT HAD DARED THE GERMAN A.A. FOR TOO LONG..
IOY

BY A FREAK OF BAD LUCK, THE ENEMY CANNON-SHELL HIT A RACK OF SIGNAL FLARES WHICH BURST INTO WHITE-HOT FLAME.
FIRE!

FANNED BY THE DRAUGHT, THE FLAMES SWEPT THROUGH THE FUSELAGE AND WITH THE HEAT CRACKING HIS CABIN WINDOWS, THE CAPTAIN GASPED THE ORDER TO ABANDON.
BALE OUT! EVERYBODY OUT!
JNOY

ONE AFTER THE OTHER, BILL MILNER AND THE CREW LEAPED FROM THAT BLAZING INFERNO INTO THE COOL NIGHT AIR.

CHRIS HARMER HESITATED IN THE DOORWAY, NOT QUITE SURE WHETHER EVERYONE HAD JUMPED BUT THE PLANE LURCHED AND HE, TOO, WAS FLUNG OUT.
THE OLD LANC'S HAD IT AND NO MISTAKE — HOPE THE SKIPPER HAD TIME TO GET OUT.

SOON, CHRIS SAW FLAT, FEATURELESS COUNTRY RUSHING UP TO MEET HIM AND AS HE NEARED THE GROUND, A SOLITARY FIGURE MOVED OUT FROM THE COVER OF SOME BUSHES.

THE AIRMAN'S HEART SANK FOR CAPTURE SEEMED IMMINENT, BUT THE MAN WAS A YOUNG DUTCHMAN – EAGER TO HELP. HE QUICKLY BUNDLED CHRIS' TELL-TALE PARACHUTE OUT OF SIGHT AND INTRODUCED HIMSELF...
I AM BERNHARD GROOT. I LEAD YOU TO FRIENDS. COME SWIFTLY!

GERMAN PATROLS HAD BEEN ALERTED BY THE COMMANDO ATTACK ON NEIGHBOURING BEVELAND AND THE YOUNG DUTCHMAN HAD TO USE EXTREME CAUTION AS HE LED CHRIS TO AN OLD SHED – THE MEETING PLACE OF THE LOCAL RESISTANCE GROUP. THERE, CHRIS TOLD HIS STORY...
A SAD THING, TO FLOOD OUR LAND – BUT IT IS WAR.
WE ARE SORRY TO HAVE TO DO IT BUT IT WAS NECESSARY FOR OUR ATTACK ON BEVELAND.
WE CAN HOPE THEN THAT SOON THEY WILL COME HERE TO WALCHEREN.

MEANWHILE, MAJOR BILL MILNER HAD PARACHUTED INTO THE COLD WATERS OF THE ESTUARY, BUT THANKS TO THE LITTLE RED LAMP AFFIXED TO HIS LIFE-JACKET, HE WAS EVENTUALLY FOUND, NUMBED BUT THANKFUL, BY A ROVING BRITISH M.T.B.
SOMEBODY IN THE WATER, SIR — ON THE STARBOARD BOW!
AHOY, THERE!
531

WARM CLOTHING AND A MUG OF STEAMING COCOA SOON REVIVED BILL — HIS FIRST QUESTIONS WERE OF THE OTHERS WHO HAD BALED OUT.
WATCHING THE COURSE OF YOUR BURNING PLANE, I'D SAY THE OTHERS MUST HAVE COME DOWN INLAND, BUT WE'LL KEEP LOOKING.
THANKS.

BILL ANSWERED EAGER QUESTIONS ABOUT THE ATTACK ON BEVELAND AND THEN . . .
WE'VE RADIOED YOUR RESCUE. WHERE DO YOU WANT TO BE PUT ASHORE?
AT FORT HAGEN, IF YOU CAN. I MUST GET BACK TO HELP ORGANISE THE NEXT STEP — A SEABORNE ATTACK ON WALCHEREN.

A FURTHER SEARCH PROVED FRUITLESS, AND THE M.T.B.'s SKIPPER RELUCTANTLY STEERED FOR FORT HAGEN, A PORT ON THE SOUTH SHORES OF THE ESTUARY. THERE, BILL WAS GREETED BY HIS COMMANDING OFFICER, BRIGADIER JACKSON.
WE HEARD YOU'D BEEN PICKED UP, MILNER—DARN GLAD TO SEE YOU. FEEL OKAY?
YES, SIR... THANKS TO THE NAVY!

BENEATH THE CHEERFUL GREETING, BILL SENSED THERE WAS SOMETHING WORRYING THE SENIOR MAN. IN THE OFFICE HE WAS SOON TOLD...
I HEAR OUR BOYS HAVE SECURED A BEACH-HEAD, SIR.
YES, WE HAVE A FIRM HOLD ON SOUTH BEVELAND—BUT AT A GRIEVOUS SACRIFICE OF LIVES—SOMETHING WHICH I EARNESTLY HOPE WILL NEVER BE REPEATED.
East Scheldt
Douburg
West Kapelle
Veere
NTH BEVELAND
WALCHEREN
Middelburg
SOUTH BEVELAND
ZEELAND
Flushing
Ft Hendrik
West Scheldt
Hoedekeskerke
Breskens
Cadzand
Knocke
NETHER
Waterv

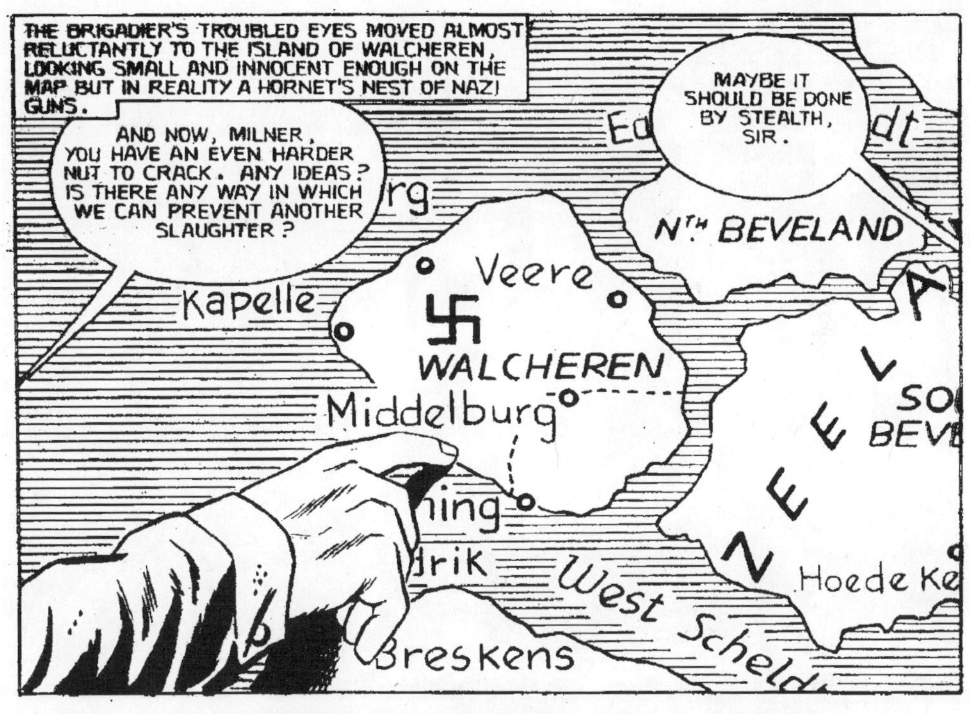
THE BRIGADIER'S TROUBLED EYES MOVED ALMOST RELUCTANTLY TO THE ISLAND OF WALCHEREN, LOOKING SMALL AND INNOCENT ENOUGH ON THE MAP BUT IN REALITY A HORNET'S NEST OF NAZI GUNS.
AND NOW, MILNER, YOU HAVE AN EVEN HARDER NUT TO CRACK. ANY IDEAS? IS THERE ANY WAY IN WHICH WE CAN PREVENT ANOTHER SLAUGHTER?
MAYBE IT SHOULD BE DONE BY STEALTH, SIR.
Nth BEVELAND
Veere
Kapelle
WALCHEREN
Middelburg
ZEELA
Breskens
West Scheld
Hoede Ke

BOMBING THE BEVELAND DYKES WAS FINE, SIR, BUT IT WAS LIKE BANGING ON THE FRONT DOOR! WHY DON'T WE TRY THROWING A FEINT ATTACK ON WALCHEREN WITH BAGS OF NOISE, WHILE THE REAL ATTACK GOES ASHORE QUIETLY AND SHINS OVER THE DYKES?
LET'S GO OVER IT WITH THE PLANNING STAFF.

AFTER A GOOD DEAL OF CONTROVERSY AT STAFF LEVEL, BILL MILNER'S PLAN WAS SCEPTICALLY ACCEPTED. THEN, THINGS MOVED FAST—IN A FEW DAYS A BRIEFING OF MIXED NAVAL AND COMMANDO LEADERS WAS CALLED. IT WAS TO BE A DAWN ATTACK.
DUTCH BOATS, CALLED HOOGAARS, WILL TAKE US AS NEAR WALCHEREN AS CONDITIONS PERMIT. WE THEN TAKE TO DINGHIES. BY THAT TIME THE FEINT ATTACK WILL BE BANGING AWAY TO OUR LEFT, GIVING US A CHANCE TO SNEAK ASHORE.

THERE WAS NO FEAR ON THE FACES BEFORE HIM—YET BILL MILNER KNEW HE WAS ASKING THESE MEN TO RISK THEIR LIVES ON A GAMBLE—HIS GAMBLE.
IT'S TRUE WE'RE A SMALL FORCE BUT IT'S NOT OUR JOB TO CAPTURE THE WHOLE DARN ISLAND. WE'VE GOT TO DESTROY THE COAST DEFENCES WHILE THE CANADIAN BOYS FOLLOW UP AND COME ASHORE IN FORCE.

Chapter 2 SILENT ASSAULT
THE PEACEFUL-LOOKING FLEET OF DUTCH MUSSEL-FISHING VESSELS PUT OUT FROM FORT HAGEN ONE DARK, MOONLESS NIGHT. ABOARD CROUCHED THE SET-FACED MEN OF THE RAIDING FORCE, PICKED FIGHTERS EVERY ONE.

THE FEINT ATTACK FORCE EMBARKED IN ITS ASSAULT BOATS LATER. IT WOULD APPROACH WALCHEREN A MILE TO THE LEFT OF THE REAL ATTACK, HOPING TO ATTRACT THE GERMAN DEFENCES TO THE WRONG SPOT.
THIRTY MINUTES TO ZERO...
LCA
LCA
LCA

MEANWHILE, ON WALCHEREN ITSELF, RESISTANCE MEN WERE ASSEMBLING AT THEIR LONELY RENDEZVOUS...

AND ON THEIR SECRET RADIO, THEY HEARD THE CODE WORD 'TULIP' — IT WAS THE SIGNAL WALCHEREN HAD LIVED AND PRAYED FOR. YOUNG BERNHARD GROOT COULD SCARCELY CONTROL THE QUIVER IN HIS VOICE AS HE BREATHED THE GOOD NEWS...
THEY COME! *THE BRITISH COME!*
AT LAST — AT LAST!
WE KNOW OUR TASKS...

ONE BY ONE THEY VANISHED INTO THE NIGHT UNTIL THE EXCITED CHRIS HARMER FOUND HIMSELF ALONE WITH BERNHARD AND JAN VEERT, A TOUGH YOUNG FARMER.
I'VE GOT TO HELP, BERNHARD. WHAT CAN I DO?
SURE YOU HELP. YOU COME WITH ME AND JAN. I SHOW YOU.

WITH QUICKENING PULSE, CHRIS FOLLOWED THE DUTCHMEN AS THEY MOVED CAUTIOUSLY TOWARDS THE DYKE WALL. SUDDENLY THEY HALTED AND BERNHARD POINTED...
SEE THOSE POLES AND NETS. THEY HIDE A VAN WHICH GIVES CURRENT TO THE SEARCHLIGHTS. WE MUST DESTROY IT!
BUT FIRST WE MUST WAIT FOR SOUND OF THE BATTLE.

STILL THE NIGHT WAS SILENT SAVE FOR THE SULLEN ROAR OF THE SEA AND THE LOW HUM OF THE POWER GENERATOR. THEY SHIVERED AND WAITED WHILE BERNHARD KEPT WATCH ON THE GERMAN AREA HEADQUARTERS.
A DESPATCH RIDER! I SEE BRUCKNER AND HIS LITTLE PLAYMATES.

BERNHARD WAS RIGHT. IT WAS BRUCKNER HIMSELF—OBERSTLEUTNANT ERNST BRUCKNER, DEFENCE COMMANDER FOR SOUTH WALCHEREN. HE QUESTIONED THE DESPATCH RIDER SHARPLY...
TELEPHONE WIRES CUT, EH? WHERE IS THIS ATTACK?
THREE KILOMETERS WEST, MEIN KOMMANDER... MANY SHIPS!

BRUCKNER'S EYES NARROWED—HIS WAS A HARD, SHREWD BRAIN.
WE MUST RUSH EVERY SPARE SOLDIER THERE AT ONCE, JA!
FOOL! NO MAN LEAVES HIS POST. FIRST WE INVESTIGATE. COME!

AS BERNHARD WATCHED THE GERMANS TURN AND MOVE AWAY, CHRIS HARMER TOUCHED HIM ON THE SHOULDER...
LISTEN! THERE'S FIRING! IT'S THE FEINT ATTACK!

CHRIS' EARS HAD NOT DECEIVED HIM. THE FEINT ATTACK FORCE SWEPT IN TOWARDS THE BEACH WITH GUNS BLAZING.
FIRE! MAKE AS MUCH NOISE AS YOU CAN!
LCA
LCA
LCA

ARRIVING BY FAST CAR, ERNST BRUCKNER SOUGHT TO ASSESS THE WEIGHT OF THE ATTACK AND WHAT HE SAW MADE HIM PAUSE. THE FATE OF THE ATTACK HUNG IN THE BALANCE...
SHALL WE NOT OPEN FIRE, MEIN KOMMANDER?
WAIT! OUR VISITORS MAKE MUCH NOISE...TOO SOON...THAT IS NOT THE USUAL WAY OF THE BRITISH.

ALONG THE COAST, THE SOUND OF FIRING HAD GALVANISED THE THREE HIDDEN WATCHERS INTO VIOLENT ACTION...
AAAGH!
ACH..!

CHRIS WAS THE FIRST TO SPRING INTO THE VAN. A QUICK LOOK ROUND AND HE RIPPED OUT THE SEARCHLIGHT CABLE...

THE EFFECT WAS INSTANTANEOUS...
HIMMEL— WHAT'S HAPPENED ?
CURRENT FAILURE !

THE SILENT ATTACK WAS ALREADY ON ITS WAY IN — WITH MAJOR BILL MILNER IN THE LEADING RAFT...

ASHORE, THE FAILURE OF THE SEARCHLIGHTS WAS REPORTED TO BRUCKNER . . .
MEIN KOMMANDER . . . ALL THE SEARCHLIGHTS IN THE NEXT SECTOR HAVE GONE OUT!

INSTANTLY, THE NAZI OFFICER KNEW WHAT HE MUST DO . . .
AS I SUSPECTED! GENTLEMEN, WE CAN IGNORE THIS ATTACK. DOUBLE THE DEFENCE IN THE NEXT SECTOR!

STEALTHILY, REINFORCEMENTS TOOK UP POSITIONS IN THE DARKENED SECTOR AND THEIR OMINOUS MOVEMENT WAS NOT LOST ON THE THREE DISMAYED WATCHERS. SOMETHING HAD GONE WRONG . . .

THE MARINE COMMANDOS WERE ALREADY LEAPING ASHORE—SCRAMBLING UP THE SLIPPERY STONEWORK OF THE DYKE WALL.

THE FIRST RANKS CRAWLED OVER THE PARAPET—AND A BLAZING INFERNO OF MACHINE-GUN FIRE RIPPED INTO THEM.

AGAIN AND AGAIN THEY STORMED THE PARAPET, NOT COUNTING THE COST, BUT SUDDEN DEATH MET THEM EVERY TIME. BRUCKNER'S EYES GLINTED IN EVIL SATISFACTION.
AHA..! YOU SEE, GENTLEMEN — THE STUPID ENGLANDERS COULD NOT HOODWINK ME!

THE RAIDING FORCE HAD BEEN DECIMATED BUT BILL MILNER HAD NOT YET ADMITTED DEFEAT...
TELL 'EM BEHIND THE WALL TO THROW EVERYTHING THEY'VE GOT. THE REST OF US WILL RUSH THE NEAREST JERRIES.

THE CHARGE WAS DESPERATE—SUICIDAL— AND FOR A WHILE IT LOOKED AS IF IT MIGHT SUCCEED.

A SECOND WAVE FROM THE DYKE WALL SWEPT IN TO REINFORCE THE OTHERS—IT WAS HAND TO HAND, STEEL TO STEEL...
UP THE MARINES!

AGAINST THE NORMAL DEFENCES THEY MIGHT HAVE WON THE DAY — *BUT THE DEFENCES HAD BEEN DOUBLED.*

FROM A SAFE DISTANCE, BRUCKNER'S SELF-SATISFACTION TURNED TO CONTEMPT.
THE STUPID BRITISH! WILL THEY NEVER LEARN THAT THE GERMAN SOLDIER HAS NO EQUAL! DO THEY THINK THEY CAN STOP THE BULLETS WITH THEIR BARE HANDS?

AT LAST BILL MILNER WAS FORCED TO A BITTER DECISION...
ALL RIGHT! BACK, EVERYBODY! BACK TO THE BOATS!

RELUCTANTLY THE MARINES OBEYED . . .
AAAGH!

BILL AND A FEW PICKED MEN KEPT THE ENEMY AT BAY WHILE THEIR COMRADES LAUNCHED THE DINGHIES.

THEN IT WAS EVERY MAN FOR HIMSELF WITH GERMAN BULLETS PICKING OFF THE EXHAUSTED SWIMMERS IN THE ICY WATER.

A MOTOR GUN BOAT OFF SHORE PICKED UP THE SURVIVORS — THEY WERE PITIFULLY FEW.
HOW'S THE TALLY, SIR?
BAD. WE'VE LEFT A LOT OF GOOD MEN BEHIND, I'M AFRAID.

HAD BILL MILNER'S BITTER THOUGHTS BEEN ABLE TO CARRY HIM BACK TO WALCHEREN HE WOULD HAVE SEEN THE HUMILIATION HEAPED UPON THE GALLANT MEN WHO HAD BEEN LEFT ASHORE.
A SPELL IN THE CELLAR PRISONS WILL COOL THEIR SPIRIT!
KEEP MOVING!
LAY OFF, YOU SWAB — HE'S WOUNDED!

THE PRISONERS WERE HERDED INTO COLD, DAMP UNDERGROUND CELLARS WHERE THE ONLY AIR AND LIGHT CAME FROM OPEN GRATINGS AT GROUND LEVEL.

THE FAILURE OF THE RAID HAD FLUNG THE DUTCH RESISTANCE INTO A SORRY PLIGHT. THEY HAD BOLDLY SHOWN THEIR HAND AND MANY WERE CORNERED AND DIED FIGHTING.

OTHERS, INCLUDING THE BRITISH AIRMAN, CHRIS HARMER, SLIPPED AWAY INTO HIDING, BUT THE ENEMY WERE HUNTING THEM VENGEFULLY.
WILL THE BRITISH TRY AGAIN?
OF COURSE. SOMEHOW WE MUST GET TO THE RADIO SET AND FIND OUT.
YES, MAYBE WE HEAR A MESSAGE.

CHRIS HARMER'S FAITH IN THE MARINE COMMANDOS WAS TO BE AMPLY ANSWERED. DEFEAT HAD NO PLACE IN THEIR TRADITIONS. MAJOR BILL MILNER KNEW BUT ONE ALL-CONSUMING PURPOSE — TO WHIP THE ENEMY ON WALCHEREN ISLAND.
BETWEEN THE DYKE AND BRUCKNER'S H.Q. THERE'S HALF A MILE OF DEFENCE POSTS. IF WE COULD SMASH THOSE...
...YOU'D GAIN A FOOTING. BUT YOU CAN'T DEPEND ON SURPRISE ANY MORE.

YOU'RE RIGHT, SIR. NO MORE SURPRISES. THIS TIME WE'LL GO IN AT THE FRONT DOOR — AND A BATCH OF LANCASTER BOMBERS CAN DO THE KNOCKING!

Chapter 3 ROCKET SHIPS
SENIOR OFFICERS, RESPONSIBLE FOR THE CLEARANCE OF THE NETHERLANDS, GATHERED IN CRITICAL CONFERENCE. THEY AGREED IN PRINCIPLE TO A FULL-SCALE FRONTAL ATTACK, BUT...
OUR LOSSES AT THE BEVELAND ATTACK WERE FAR TOO HEAVY. HOW ARE YOU GOING TO AVOID A REPETITION OF THAT?
BY ELIMINATING THEIR GROUND DEFENCES, SIR—WITH FLOODING AND FIRE POWER—PROBABLY ROCKET MISSILES.

ROCKETS, EH? I SUPPOSE YOU HAVE SOME IDEA HOW YOU'RE GOING TO GET THEM WHERE YOU WANT THEM?
YES, SIR, WE'VE BEEN WORKING ON THAT!

THE OPERATION WAS APPROVED AND BILL LOST NO TIME IN GETTING THE NAVY TO GIVE HIM ANOTHER LOOK AT A SPECIALLY EQUIPPED TANK LANDING CRAFT.
HERE SHE IS, MAJOR. A FLOATING GUY FAWKES NIGHT.

IT WAS A LANDING CRAFT ROCKETS. CLIMBING ABOARD, BILL STOOD FASCINATED BY THE SERRIED ARRAY OF ROCKETS. HE HAD SEEN THEM IN ACTION BEFORE AND FOR SHOCK BOMBARDMENT HE KNEW FEW THINGS THAT COULD EQUAL THEIR DEVASTATING FIRE-POWER.
THIS LITTLE LOT IS ABOUT EQUAL TO THIRTY CRUISERS MOUNTED WITH A DOZEN SIX-INCH GUNS!
THIS CRAFT'S TOO BIG FOR MY PURPOSE. NOW SUPPOSING...

WHAT'S THE CHANCES OF GETTING A BATTERY OF THESE ROCKETS ON A BUFFALO AMPHIBIOUS TANK?
MM! I DON'T SEE WHY NOT! LET'S SEE THE BACK-ROOM BOYS!

A BRIEF CONSULTATION WITH THE NAVAL DRAWING OFFICE AND IN TWENTY-FOUR HOURS...
WE HAD SOME DIFFICULTY WITH THE MOUNTINGS BUT THIS ARRANGEMENT SEEMS SATISFACTORY.
IT LOOKS JUST THE JOB TO ME!
COMMANDO

BUT AN IDEA WAS ONE THING AND ITS REALISATION ANOTHER—AS BILL FOUND OUT WHEN HE WENT TO SEE THE RESULTS A FEW DAYS LATER.
ONLY HALF-A-DOZEN! BUT I ASKED FOR...
SORRY, MILNER, BUT THESE ARE ALL THE BUFFALOES THEY CAN SPARE YOU.
29

THE BULK OF BUFFALOES ARE WANTED FOR THE JOB AT WESTKAPELLE. ONE THING, YOURS WILL BE A BIT MORE LETHAL THAN THEIRS — EVEN THIS SMALL BATTERY PACKS A HECK OF A PUNCH.
THE TOWN OF WESTKAPELLE, ON THE SOUTH WEST CORNER OF WALCHEREN, WAS TO BE THE TARGET FOR THE MAIN ATTACK BY ANOTHER FORCE OF MARINE COMMANDOS. BILL SIGHED RESIGNEDLY.

ON THE WAY OUT FOR A TRIAL WITH THE ROCKETS, THE BUFFALO PASSED A SHERMAN "SWIMMING TANK."
BY THE WAY, I HEAR YOU'RE GETTING SOME OF THESE CRAZY SHERMANS, TOO.
IS THAT SO? NOW I FEEL I'M GETTING SOMEWHERE!
35

THE RESULT OF THE ROCKET TEST PLEASED BILL EVEN MORE. THIS WAS THE FIERY SPEARHEAD WHICH MIGHT BLAST A GAP IN THE WALCHEREN DEFENCES.
WOW!

MEANWHILE, PREPARATIONS WERE MOUNTING TO A FEVERISH CLIMAX. BILL MILNER FELT UNUSUALLY STRAINED AS TIME BEGAN RUNNING OUT. YET HE WAS CONFIDENT THAT ALL WAS WELL...
EVERYTHING CLEAR IN YOUR MIND NOW, BILL?
QUITE, SIR. THE LANCASTERS BREACH THE DYKE JUST BEFORE DAWN ...MY ROCKET BUFFALOES GO IN WITH THE FLOOD AND SMASH A WAY THROUGH THE FIRST DEFENCES...

...NEXT FOLLOW THE SWIMMING TANKS, AND FINALLY THE ASSAULT BARGES. WE ESTABLISH A BRIDGEHEAD AND HOLD IT UNTIL RELIEVED BY THE MAIN WAVE OF CANADIANS.

ON THE NIGHT BEFORE THE ATTACK, BILL MILNER WAS PRESENT AT THE BRIEFING OF THE LANCASTER CREWS ON DYKE CONSTRUCTION.
THE OUTSIDE SLOPE OF THE DYKE IS MADE IMMENSELY STRONG BY HONEYCOMBED CONCRETE BLOCKS. YOU'LL MOVE NOTHING UNTIL YOU'VE MOVED THEM. IT'S A WASTE OF EFFORT TO JUST BOMB ALONG THE TOP.
PATH
HEXAGONAL CONCRETE SLABS
SEA LEVEL

THE WING COMMANDER PUT IN A WORD...
WE AIM TO DROP OUR BOMBS IN THE SEA CLOSE BESIDE THE DYKE— THAT'LL SET UP A TERRIFIC WATER PRESSURE.
YES, IT'S YOUR ONLY CHANCE. IT'LL BE HIGH-TIDE, SO YOU'LL HAVE THE DEPTH OF WATER, ALL RIGHT.
PATH
GRASS SLOPE
HEXAGONAL CONCRETE SLABS
SEA LEVEL
MUD AND SILT

THEN FOLLOWED THE CODE WORD "TULIP" TO ALERT THE DUTCH RESISTANCE, AND A MORE DETAILED WARNING. RISKING THEIR NECKS, CHRIS HARMER AND BERNHARD HAD REACHED THEIR HIDDEN SET JUST IN TIME, FEELING THAT SOMEONE HAD TO KEEP IN TOUCH WITH THE ALLIES.

AT DAWN, THEY BOMB THE DYKES!

WHERE?

HERE . . . OPPOSITE THE GERMAN HEADQUARTERS!

CHRIS COULD UNDERSTAND HIS FRIEND'S TWISTED FEELINGS. HIS LAND MIGHT BE FREED BUT IT WOULD BE RUINED, LOST TO THEIR EVER HUNGRY ENEMY – THE SEA!

THERE WAS NO TIME TO LOSE FOR AT DAWN THE ATTACK WOULD COME. A MESSAGE WAS SMUGGLED TO THE BURGOMASTER WHO AT ONCE WENT TO SEE OBERSTLEUTNANT BRUCKNER SURELY HE WOULD MOVE THE PRISONERS. BUT ONE LOOK AT THAT CYNICALLY SMILING GERMAN WAS ANSWER ENOUGH...
MY DEAR BURGOMASTER – IF THE STUPID BRITISH, BY THEIR WANTON DESTRUCTION OF YOUR DYKES AND LAND, DESTROY THEIR OWN COMRADES, THAT IS NO CONCERN OF MINE.

I WILL NOT PRESS HOW YOU CAME BY THIS DETAILED INTELLIGENCE. I AM GRATEFUL TO LEARN JUST WHERE THE BRITISH WILL STRIKE! GOOT NIGHT, MEIN BURGOMASTER!

NEWS OF THE BURGOMASTER'S FAILURE REACHED THE ANXIOUSLY-WAITING BRITISH R.A.F. SERGEANT. DESPERATELY, HE CAST ABOUT IN HIS MIND...
...WE MIGHT'VE RUSHED THE PLACE BY FORCE BUT WE'RE ALL SCATTERED NOW. WE MUST WARN THEM OVER THE OTHER SIDE! THEY MUSTN'T BOMB THE DYKES!
BUT HOW, MY FRIEND? OUR RADIO TRANSMITTER HAS BEEN DISCOVERED BY THE GERMANS.

NO MORE SIGNALS CAME THROUGH ON THE LITTLE RECEIVER AND AS CHRIS REPLACED THE EARPHONES, HE CAME TO A SUDDEN DECISION. IT WAS CRAZY BUT IT WAS BETTER THAN SITTING... WAITING...
I'VE GOT TO GET BACK...BACK ACROSS THE WATER...MAYBE THERE'S STILL TIME...
I HAVE A BOAT HIDDEN. I COME WITH YOU.

SUDDENLY, THE DOOR OF THE SHED CRASHED OPEN. BROAD, STEEL-HELMETED FIGURES BLOCKED THE WAY AND A HARSH VOICE RANG OUT.
WHO ARE YOU? WHAT ARE YOU DOING HERE?

INSTANTLY, CHRIS LAUNCHED HIMSELF FORWARD...
UUUGH!

NEXT MOMENT, HE AND BERNHARD WERE RACING THROUGH THE NIGHT, WHIPPED ON BY SHOUTS AND BULLETS THAT RIPPED ABOUT THEM.

IT WAS AN HOUR BEFORE BERNHARD COULD LEAD CHRIS SAFELY TO THE LITTLE BOAT ON A REMOTE SECTION OF THE COAST.

THEY STRAINED AT THE OARS UNTIL THEY WERE CLEAR OF LAND AND THEN BERNHARD STEPPED THE LITTLE MAST AND SET THE SAIL. BUT THE ELEMENTS WERE AGAINST THEM ...
SLOW HEADWAY, MY FRIEND... AGAINST THE WIND.
WE MIGHT DO BETTER ON THE OTHER TACK. DO YOUR BEST, BERNHARD, FOR HEAVENS' SAKE!

AFTER SEEMING HOURS OF TEDIOUS TACKING, IT LOOKED TO THE SPRAY-DRENCHED PAIR THAT THEIR OBJECTIVE WAS AS FAR AWAY AS EVER. THEN THE WIND SUDDENLY DIED, LEAVING THEM MOTIONLESS IN A CHILL EARLY MIST.
THERE'S NOTHING FOR IT NOW BUT TO ROW.
BEATING DOWN A MOUNTING DESPAIR, CHRIS SEIZED THE OARS. HE DARE NOT LOOK FOR THE FIRST GLIMMER THAT WOULD HERALD THE DAWN.

Chapter 4 STORMING THE DYKES
MEANWHILE, MAJOR BILL MILNER'S FORCE HAD SLIPPED OUT OF FORT HAGEN. BILL HIMSELF WAS IN THE LEADING ROCKET SHIP. NOW THE TIME HAD COME FOR ACTION, HE FELT ALL HIS OLD CONFIDENCE RETURNING. IT WAS ALWAYS THE WAITING THAT DAUNTED...
63
63
WELL TO THE WEST, THE MAIN ASSAULT FORCE WOULD ALSO BE POUNDING TOWARDS THEIR TOUGHEST ASSIGNMENT— WESTKAPELLE.

AT THE SAME MOMENT, EIGHT LANCASTER AIRCRAFT OF BOMBER COMMAND STOOD WARMING UP. STARKLY SINISTER IN THAT DARK HOUR BEFORE DAWN, THEIR GIANT FRAMES CRADLED THE AWESOME WEIGHT OF 12,000 lb. "EARTHQUAKE" BOMBS.

AS THE FIRST FAINT STREAKS OF LIGHT APPEARED IN THE EAST, THE GROUND SHOOK WITH THE THUNDEROUS TAKE-OFF. OPERATION "FLOODGATES" WAS AIRBORNE!

TO CHRIS HARMER AND BERNHARD, THE FIRST FAINT GLIMMERINGS OF DAWN SPELT A NUMBING DEFEAT. THEY HAD LOST THE RACE AGAINST TIME.

THE YOUNG SERGEANT'S HEAD LIFTED AS A FAR-OFF STEADY RUMBLING SOUNDED LOW IN THE SKY. HE RECOGNISED THE OMINOUS SOUND ONLY TOO WELL...
LANCASTERS!

IN THAT SAME DESPAIRING MOMENT, BERNHARD ROSE TO HIS FEET. HE, TOO, HAD HEARD A SOUND... BUT A SOUND THAT CAME FROM AHEAD AND ON THE WATER ITSELF. SUDDENLY HE BROKE THE GLUM SILENCE WITH A SHOUT...
LOOK... SHIPS! IT IS THE ATTACK FORCE!
YOU'RE RIGHT! SHOUT... WAVE!

IT WAS BILL MILNER'S FORCE CHURNING STEADILY TOWARDS ITS TARGET. A SHARP-EYED LOOK-OUT SPOTTED THE PAIR WAVING FRANTICALLY.
IT SEEMS URGENT, MAJOR. ONE'S AN AIRMAN BY THE LOOK OF HIS JACKET.
OKAY, GEORGE. SLOW ALONGSIDE AND HAUL 'EM IN ... BUT WE CAN'T STOP.

BILL MILNER RECOGNISED CHRIS INSTANTLY...
WELL, BLOW ME ... IT'S THE YOUNG BOMB-AIMER! SO YOU BALED OUT OKAY, AFTER ALL!
THAT'S RIGHT. BUT THERE'S SOMETHING URGENT, SIR ... MUST TELL YOU.

SOBERED BY THE OTHER'S DISTRACTED LOOK, BILL LISTENED INTENTLY WHILE CHRIS POURED OUT HIS FEARS.
YOU REMEMBER THAT PLACE, SIR. THOSE CELLARS ARE BELOW SEA-LEVEL ... EVERYTHING IS. WHEN THOSE LANCS SMASH THAT DYKE ...
SO BRUCKNER WOULD LET MY LADS DROWN LIKE RATS, EH?

SUDDENLY ANGRY, BILL'S NATURAL IMPULSE WAS TO CONTACT BASE AND CALL OFF THE BOMBERS. BUT OTHER FORCES BEYOND HIMSELF WERE IN MOTION—DEMANDING—INSISTENT—FORCES GREATER THAN EVEN THE HUMANE PROMPTING TO SAVE A FEW DOOMED MEN.
MY OWN LADS IN THOSE CELLARS! BUT—BUT THIS IS A FULL-SCALE ATTACK—COMMITTED—WITH MANY LIVES DEPENDING ON IT—I CAN'T TURN BACK NOW!

HE KNEW HE HAD NO CHOICE BUT TO GO ON. HE WRACKED HIS BRAINS FOR SOME SOLUTION, SOME WAY TO PRESS HOME THE ATTACK AND YET SAVE THE IMPRISONED MEN. SUDDENLY, HE SAW A SLIM RAY OF HOPE...
WE WEREN'T GOING THROUGH THE GAP BEFORE THE WATER LEVELLED OFF A BIT. BUT NOW WE'LL HAVE TO RIDE IN WITH THE FLOOD... AND GET TO THE CELLARS BEFORE THE SEA DOES!

NEW ORDERS WERE FLASHED TO THE SMALL FLEET. THE SKY WAS ALREADY LIGHTENING AND FOREWARNED BY RADAR, THE ENEMY GUNS WERE PROBING FOR THE APPROACHING INVASION FORCE.

THE DRUMMING OF THE BOMBERS' ENGINES BECAME A MIGHTY ROAR IN THE SKY. IN CLOSE FORMATION THEY SWEPT OVERHEAD...
THE LANCS! WE'RE GOING TO BE TOO LATE!

THE BOMBERS' FLIGHT LEADER GAVE A TERSE ORDER . . .
OKAY — WE'LL DO A DUMMY RUN.

CHRIS HARMER WATCHED BLEAKLY AS THE LEADING LANCASTER WENT INTO ITS BOMB RUN — THEN AN EXCLAMATION OF RELIEF BURST FROM HIS LIPS . . .
BY GOLLY! THEY'RE MAKING A DUMMY RUN . . .
THANK HEAVENS! IT MAY JUST ABOUT GIVE US TIME!

IN LINE AHEAD, THE LANCASTERS CIRCLED SEAWARDS — THEN ROARED IN AGAIN . . .
BOMB DOORS OPEN!
IT'S ALL YOURS, BOMB-AIMER — AND MAKE IT GOOD!
AR G

NEVER WAVERING, EVEN THOUGH THE SKY WAS POCK-MARKED WITH SHELL-BURSTS ALL ABOUT THEM, THE GIANT BOMBERS THUNDERED OVER BILL MILNER'S STRIKE FORCE TOWARDS THEIR TARGET...
AR G

FROM A DEFENSIVE POSITION NEAR TO HIS HEADQUARTERS, OBERSTLEUTNANT ERNST BRUCKNER TRIED TO ASSESS THE STRENGTH OF THE ATTACK...
IS THIS ANOTHER FEINT, I WONDER, WHILE THE REAL ATTACK GOES IN AT WESTKAPELLE ?

THE CONTINUOUS THUNDER OF AIRCRAFT REACHED THE EARS OF THE COMMANDOS IMPRISONED IN THE CELLAR. HARSHLY TREATED THOUGH THEY HAD BEEN, THEIR SPIRITS LIFTED IMMEDIATELY...
SOUNDS LIKE FOUR-ENGINED STUFF.. MUST BE OURS!
YUS... COME TO PLASTER JERRY. UP THE RAFF!

THE ROCKET BUFFALOES WERE CLOSING WITH THE DYKE AS THE LEADING LANCASTER BEGAN ITS RUN...
A SHADE MORE RIGHT ...HOLD IT ...HOLD IT...

SECONDS LATER THE SEA ERUPTED TO THE TERRIBLE BLAST OF FIVE TONS OF HIGH EXPLOSIVE.

THE TORTURED SEA HAD BARELY SUBSIDED WHEN IT WAS TORN AFRESH BY THE SECOND PLANE'S DEVASTATING LOAD.
BANG ON THE TARGET—*BUT THE WALL'S STILL HOLDING!*

GERMAN MACHINE-GUNNERS CLOSE TO THE INSIDE WALL OF THE DYKE WERE THE FIRST TO NOTICE THE EFFECT OF THE PRECISION BOMBING.
HIMMEL! THE DYKE...

FROM WHERE THE GERMAN COMMANDER STOOD, THE DAMAGE WAS NOT APPARENT AND A COLD SMILE TWITCHED HIS LIPS AS A LANCASTER WAS HIT . . .

THE LAST "EARTHQUAKE" BOMB HAD BEEN DROPPED – THE DYKE STILL HELD – BUT ONLY FOR SECONDS.
IT'S GOING, SIR. THE DYKE'S GOING!
ANY MOMENT NOW!

BILL'S FINGERS CLOSED ABOUT THE VEREY PISTOL THAT WOULD SIGNAL THE ASSAULT. SUDDENLY A SHOUT WENT UP. THE DYKE CAVED IN AND BILL'S HAND FLEW UPWARD . . .
FORWAAAARD!

Chapter 5 A RACE WITH DEATH

THE LITTLE ARMADA SURGED FORWARD TOWARDS THE EVER-WIDENING GAP IN THE STONE WALL...

THE TERRIBLE, RELENTLESS PRESSURE OF THE SEA BEGAN TO WIDEN THE CRACKS IN THE WALL STARTED BY THE BOMBS. SUDDENLY IT BEGAN TO CRUMBLE...
HIMMEL! THE DYKE IS BREAKING!

BRUCKNER'S EYES NARROWED. FOR THE FIRST TIME HE FELT A TWINGE OF ANXIETY AND HE ISSUED IMMEDIATE ORDERS TO WITHDRAW TO PREPARED POSITIONS ON HIGHER GROUND.

IN THE CELLARS BELOW THE GERMAN H.Q., A STAB OF APPREHENSION RAN THROUGH THE PRISONERS...
THAT RUMBLING WASN'T THUNDER, MATE.
THEN WHAT WAS IT?

MAJOR BILL MILNER WAS ALREADY AIMING HIS CRAFT TOWARDS THE CRUMBLING GAP IN THE DYKE AND A SALVO OF ROCKETS SOARED INLAND . . .
FIRE!

INSTANTLY ANOTHER BUFFALO FOLLOWED SUIT . . . AND ANOTHER.

THE DEADLY MISSILES STREAKED OVER THE TEMPESTUOUS WATERS AND SMASHED INTO THE ENEMY GUN EMPLACEMENTS WITH PULVERISING FORCE.

RIDING ON THE FIRST GREAT SURGE OF IN-RUSHING WATER WAS THE COMMANDO LEADER'S BUFFALO . . .
HOLD ON TIGHT, EVERYONE!
67
67

THE HEAVY AMPHIBIOUS VEHICLES WERE TOSSED ABOUT ALMOST HELPLESSLY IN THE TORRENT AND A COLLISION WAS ONLY NARROWLY AVOIDED . . .

THEN THEY WERE ON EVEN KEEL, PLOUGHING THROUGH THE WATER TOWARDS THE ENEMY WITH GUNS CRASHING DEAFENINGLY.
67

THE TIDAL WAVE OF DESTRUCTION SWEPT DOWN ON THE GERMANS' FORWARD DEFENCES — OVERWHELMING THEM IN THOUSANDS OF TONS OF FOAMING WATER . . .
AAAGH!

ERNST BRUCKNER AND HIS OFFICERS SCUTTLED BACK TOWARDS THE H.Q. BUILDING AS THE SEA BORE DOWN UPON THEM . . .
QUICK, QUICK! INTO HEADQUARTERS — WE WILL FIGHT FROM THERE!

THE SHERMAN "SWIMMING TANKS" HAD TOUCHED GROUND AND THE CREWS PROMPTLY DROPPED THEIR CANVAS SCREENS AND ENGAGED ENEMY STRONGPOINTS AT POINT-BLANK RANGE. THE THUNDER OF BATTLE WAS INCREASING...
21

BUT MORE TERRIBLE THAN ANY GUNS, THE UNBRIDLED SEA BEGAN TO BURY EVERYTHING IN ITS PATH. INDIFFERENT TO FRIEND OR FOE, IT BEGAN TO POUR THROUGH THE GROUND-LEVEL WINDOWS OF THE CELLAR PRISON.
GUARD! LET US OUT!
WE'LL DROWN!
THEY'VE SMASHED THE DYKE!

EVEN THE DIN OF BATTLE COULD NOT HIDE FROM BILL'S EARS THE CRIES OF THE TRAPPED MEN. THE BUILDING WAS A VERITABLE FORTRESS, ITS GUNS TAKING SAVAGE TOLL OF MEN AND BOATS.

BILL MILNER HAD BEEN RELUCTANT TO USE HIS FULL FIRE-POWER ON THE BUILDING THAT HELD THE PRISONERS BUT SOMETHING HAD TO BE DONE... SOMETHING SWIFT, FORCEFUL AND DECISIVE.
ROCKETS!

THE SALVO SLAMMED INTO THE BUILDING WITH A FORCE THAT WIPED OUT GUNS AND MEN AND STUPEFIED THE SURVIVORS. BILL'S COMMANDOS STORMED FORWARD...
IN WE GO, LADS— DOWN TO THE CELLARS!

THE PLIGHT OF THE PRISONERS WAS SERIOUS—THE LEVEL OF THE WATER CREPT REMORSELESSY HIGHER AND THEIR DESPAIRING YELLS BROUGHT NO ANSWER...
LET US OUT OF HERE!
HOLD UP, MATEY.
IT'S CRAMP ...MY...MY LEG.

THE GERMANS WERE FIGHTING WITH THE FEROCITY OF CORNERED RATS, DISPUTING EVERY INCH OF THE ADVANCE.
BUT EVERY LOST MOMENT SPURRED BILL'S MEN TO FIERCER EFFORTS.

BY SHEER PHYSICAL FORCE, THE COMMANDO LEADER BEAT HIS WAY THROUGH THE ENEMY AND DRAWN BY THE SHOUTS OF THE PRISONERS, HE LEAPED DOWN A FLIGHT OF STONE STEPS. FOR A MOMENT, A GUARD BARRED HIS WAY...
HURRY!
COMING, LADS!
AAGH!

SNATCHING THE KEYS FROM A HOOK ON THE WALL, BILL WRENCHED OPEN THE CELLAR DOOR TO FACE A SIGHT THAT, TOUGH AS HE WAS, WOULD HAUNT HIM EVERMORE... THE FACES OF DOOMED MEN SUDDENLY REPRIEVED.
IT'S THE MAJOR!
ARE WE GLAD TO SEE YOU, SIR!

MEANWHILE, YOUNG BERNHARD GROOT WAS HAVING HIS OWN PERSONAL MOMENT OF SATISFACTION. ALL THE MISERY AND PRIVATION SUFFERED BY HIS PEOPLE UNDER THE HATED NAZI RULE WENT INTO A CRASHING UPPERCUT TO BRUCKNER'S JAW.
UUUUGH!

THE FIRING IN THE H. Q. BUILDING HAD BEGUN TO DIE DOWN — THE BRUTAL GERMAN DEFENDERS HAD AT LAST BEEN OVERPOWERED. WHEN BILL LED THE SOAKED BUT HAPPY PRISONERS OUT OF THE CELLARS, HE FOUND MORE GOOD NEWS AWAITING HIM...
THE ENEMY'S ON THE RUN, SIR!
GREAT WORK, BOYS!

STUBBORN TO THE LAST, THE RETREATING GERMANS ON WALCHEREN CONTINUED TO GIVE STRONG RESISTANCE TO CANADIAN TROOPS ATTACKING FROM THE EAST. BUT WITH VICTORY AT WESTKAPELLE TO SPEED THE ENEMY'S EXIT, THE ISLAND WAS FINALLY CLEARED. WHEN IT WAS ALL OVER, BILL HAD A WORD OF SYMPATHY FOR YOUNG BERNHARD...
SORRY WE HAD TO FLOOD YOUR GOOD LAND, MY FRIEND, THERE WAS NO OTHER WAY.
BETTER THAT THAN GERMANS, MAJOR. NEVER FEAR, WE SHALL RECLAIM IT ONCE AGAIN.

MEANWHILE, CHRIS HARMER, FLYING ONCE AGAIN WITH HIS SQUADRON, WAS ABLE TO GAZE DOWN UPON A TRULY SATISFYING SIGHT . . . THAT OF ALLIED SHIPS STEAMING UNMOLESTED PAST WALCHEREN TO ANTWERP —GATEWAY TO THE RUHR.
THE CLEARING OF WALCHEREN AND BEVELAND MEANT AN ALLIED DEATH-BLOW AT NORTHERN GERMANY AND EVEN AT BERLIN ITSELF. IT WAS JUST ONE MORE TRIUMPH FOR THOSE TOUGH, BEACH-STORMING WARRIORS OF LAND AND SEA — THE ROYAL MARINE COMMANDOS!